triumphlearning™

Common Core Coach
Geometry

Common Core Coach, Geometry, First Edition   T210NA   ISBN-13: 978-1-61997-993-2
Contributing Writer: Colleen O'Donnell Oppenzato   **Cover Illustration:** John Schreiner/Deborah Wolfe LTD

Triumph Learning® 136 Madison Avenue, 7th Floor, New York, NY 10016

Contents

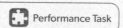

⚙️ Problem Solving   🧩 Performance Task

Functions

Building Functions

Build new functions from existing functions.

Linear, Quadratic, and Exponential Models

Construct and compare linear, quadratic, and exponential models and solve problems.

Grade 7 Geometry

Draw, construct, and describe geometrical figures and describe the relationships between them.

Grade 8 Geometry

Understand congruence and similarity using physical models, transparencies, or geometry software.

Understand and apply the Pythagorean Theorem.

Geometry

Congruence

Experiment with transformations in the plane.

Understand congruence in terms of rigid motions.

Prove geometric theorems.

Make geometric constructions.

Functions

Building Functions

Build new functions from existing functions.

Linear, Quadratic, and Exponential Models

Construct and compare linear, quadratic, and exponential models and solve problems.

Trigonometric Functions

Model periodic phenomena with trigonometric functions.

Unit 1
Congruence, Proof, and Constructions

1 Transformations and Congruence

Rigid Motions

UNDERSTAND A **transformation** involves moving all of the points that make up a geometric figure according to the same rule. The original figure is called the **preimage**, and the transformed figure is called the **image**. Transformations that change the position of a figure without changing its shape or size are known as **rigid motions**.

A translation is a rigid motion that slides a figure to a new location. In a translation, all points are moved the same distance in the same direction. A figure may be translated any distance and in any direction.

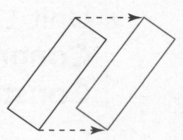

In the example on the right, the blue rectangle is the preimage and the green rectangle is the image. The dashed-line arrows illustrate how two of the points move during the translation. Notice that the arrows are the same length because the points move the same distance. The arrows are also parallel, because the points move in the same direction.

A reflection is a rigid motion that flips a figure over a line, called the line of reflection. After a reflection, each point on the image lies the same distance from the line of reflection as its corresponding point on the preimage, but on the opposite side. A reflection over a line produces a mirror image of the original preimage.

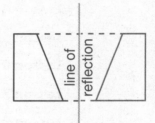

A rotation is a rigid motion that turns a figure about a point, called the center of rotation. A rotation moves the points in a figure along curved paths around the center of rotation. Each point is moved the same number of degrees around the center. After a rotation, each point on the image lies the same distance from the center of rotation as its corresponding point on the preimage.

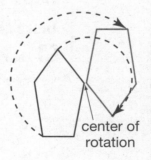

center of rotation

⌐€ Connect

Sketch the images formed when △ABC is transformed in three different ways. Rotate △ABC 90° clockwise around point C, translate △ABC to the right, and reflect △ABC across a vertical line.

1 Perform the rotation.

Imagine placing one finger on vertex C and using another finger to turn the rest of the triangle about that point. The shape that results from this is the image.

Name the new vertices using the ' mark. The vertex A′ is read as *A prime*.

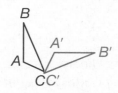

2 Perform the translation.

Imagine pushing on the figure and sliding it to the right. This action is a translation. Name the vertices of this figure using the ″ mark, to differentiate it from the image produced in Step 1. The vertex A″ is read as *A double prime*.

3 Perform the reflection.

Imagine picking the triangle up and flipping it over, like a pancake. Or, think of placing a mirror to the right of the figure and looking at its image in the mirror. The triangle you would observe in either case would be the result of a reflection. The vertex A‴ is read as *A triple prime*.

DISCUSS

Compare the three images formed. How are they similar? How do they differ?

Congruence and Coordinates

UNDERSTAND A polygon is a closed figure made up of straight-line sides connected by vertices. The side between two vertices is the **line segment** that has those vertices as endpoints. The length of a side is equal to the distance between its two endpoints, or between the vertices. Whenever two line segments share a common endpoint, they form an **angle**.

Two polygons are **congruent** if all of the following are true: they have the same number of sides and angles, corresponding sides have the same length, and corresponding angles have the same measure. Sides or angles are corresponding if they are in the same location in a figure. For example, quadrilaterals *ABCD* and *WXYZ* are congruent. Angle *W* corresponds to angle *A*, so these two angles are congruent, or have the same measure. Side $\overline{XY}$ corresponds to side $\overline{BC}$ so these two sides are congruent, or have the same length.

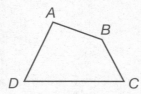 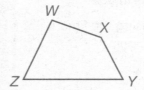

UNDERSTAND Rigid motions preserve angle measures and lengths of line segments. This means that when a rigid motion is performed on a figure, the corresponding sides and angles of the image and the preimage are congruent. In other words, after a rigid motion, the image is congruent to the preimage, though often in a different location and sometimes having a different orientation, meaning it is turned or flipped.

You can prove two figures are congruent by finding a rigid motion (or series of rigid motions) that produces one figure from the other. When the figures graphed on a coordinate plane undergo rigid motions, the coordinates of the points that make up the figure change in predictable ways.

On the first coordinate plane on the right, the blue triangle was translated 6 units to the right. The vertex (2, 3) on the preimage maps to the point (2 + 6, 3), or (8, 3), on the green image. For each point on the preimage, the corresponding point on the image can be found by adding 6 to the *x*-coordinate. By showing that each point of the image is a result of the same transformation of a point from the preimage, you can prove that the triangles are congruent.

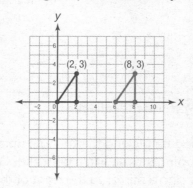

On the second coordinate plane, the blue triangle was reflected over the *y*-axis. The vertex (2, 3) on the preimage maps to the point (−2, 3) on the image. For each point on the preimage, the corresponding point on the image can be found by changing the sign of the *x*-coordinate.

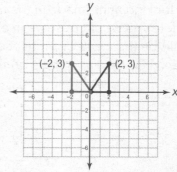

⊏ Connect

Figure *ABCDEF* was put through a series of transformations. Identify each transformation.

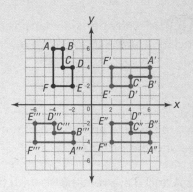

1

Identify the transformation from *ABCDEF* to *A'B'C'D'E'F'*.

The figure has been turned on its side. Vertex *A* is in the upper left corner of *ABCDEF*, but *A'* is in the upper right corner of *A'B'C'D'E'F'*. However, the vertex names are in the same order when read clockwise. The figure appears to have been rotated. Notice that each point on *A'B'C'D'E'F'* is the same distance from the origin as its corresponding point on *ABCDEF*. Figure *ABCDEF* was rotated around the origin.

2

Identify the transformation from *A'B'C'D'E'F'* to *A"B"C"D"E"F"*.

Figure *A"B"C"D"E"F"* is a mirror image of figure *A'B'C'D'E'F'*. Vertex *A'* is in the upper right corner of *A'B'C'D'E'F'*, but *A"* is in the lower right corner of *A"B"C"D"E"F"*. The vertex names are in a different order when read clockwise. The figure appears to have been reflected. Each point on *A"B"C"D"E"F"* is the same distance from the x-axis as its corresponding point on *A'B'C'D'E'F'*. Figure *A'B'C'D'E'F'* was reflected across the x-axis.

3

Identify the transformation from *A"B"C"D"E"F"* to *A'''B'''C'''D'''E'''F'''*.

Figure *A'''B'''C'''D'''E'''F'''* is oriented the same way as figure *A"B"C"D"E"F"*, but it was shifted to a different location on the graph. Vertex *A"* is in the lower right corner of *A"B"C"D"E"F"*, and *A'''* is in the lower right corner of *A'''B'''C'''D'''E'''F'''*.

Since the orientation did not change, figure *A'''B'''C'''D'''E'''F'''* is the result of a translation, 8 units to the left.

DISCUSS

Compare the figures. Did the size or shape of the figure change as it was transformed? How could you confirm this?

EXAMPLE A Identify transformations that could be applied to figure A to form figure B.

```
        3                          3
   ┌───────────┐              ┌───────────┐
 1 │  Figure A │ 1          1 │  Figure B │ 1
   └───────────┘              └───────────┘
        3                          3
```

1

Compare the size and shape of the image and the preimage.

Figures A and B are rectangles with the same height and width, so they have the same size and shape. This means that figure B could be the result of one or more rigid transformations of figure A.

2

Determine if figure A can form figure B through a translation.

The two figures have the same orientation, but figure B is about 1 unit to the right of figure A. The upper left corner of figure B is 4 units to the right of the upper left corner of figure A. In fact, this is true about all corresponding points on the two figures.

▶ A translation 4 units to the right will transform figure A into figure B.

3

Determine if figure A can form figure B through a reflection.

Figure B is a mirror image of figure A. A vertical line drawn half-way between the figures could serve as a line of reflection.

▶ A horizontal reflection will transform figure A into figure B.

4

Determine if figure A can form figure B through a rotation.

If you were to turn this page upside down, the figures would look the same. Turning the figures upside down is a way of rotating them. The center of rotation lies halfway between the figures.

▶ A half-turn rotation, or a rotation of 180°, will transform figure A into figure B.

DISCUSS

What transformations can be applied to MNOP to form M′N′O′P′?

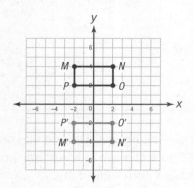

EXAMPLE B Determine if the two pentagons are congruent.

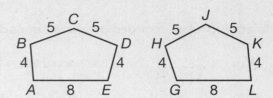

1

Compare the side lengths.

Beginning at vertices A and G and moving clockwise, we can see that corresponding sides are congruent.

$AB = GH = 4$ $BC = HJ = 5$

$CD = JK = 5$ $DE = KL = 4$

$AE = GL = 8$

2

Align one pair of vertices.

Vertices J and C both lie opposite to sides measuring 8 units. Translate pentagon $GHJKL$ left so that vertex J lies on top of vertex C.

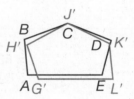

The image produced by the translation does not appear to cover $ABCDE$.

3

Try another rigid motion.

Notice that $BC = HJ = CD = JK = 5$ and $AB = GH = DE = KL = 4$. This means that the sides closest to each other will still be congruent after a horizontal reflection of one of the figures. Try reflecting $G'H'J'K'L'$ across a vertical line through J' to see if this causes the sides to line up.

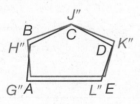

The image produced by the reflection does not appear to cover $ABCDE$.

▶ Rigid motions will not carry $GHJKL$ onto $ABCDE$, so the figures are not congruent.

MODEL

Suppose you were given two other pentagons. If all of the corresponding angle measures were congruent, can the pentagons be proven congruent? Create a sketch to support your answer.

Practice

Write an appropriate word or phrase in each blank.

1. A(n) _____ is the part of a line that falls between two points, called endpoints.

2. A(n) _____ is formed by two line segments or rays that have a common endpoint

3. A(n) _____ is a slide of a figure to a new location.

4. Two figures are congruent if their corresponding sides have equal _____ and their corresponding _____ have equal measure.

Identify a transformation that could be applied to △ABC to form △A'B'C'.

5.

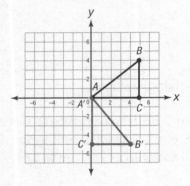

_____

6.

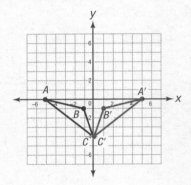

_____

> **REMEMBER** A reflection is a flip, a rotation is a turn, and a translation is a slide.

For questions 7 and 8, determine if each pair of figures are congruent. If so, describe rigid motions that would carry one figure on to the other.

7.

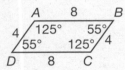

_____

_____

8.

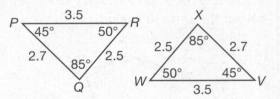

_____

_____

> **REMEMBER** Congruent figures have all corresponding sides and angles congruent.

Choose the best answer.

9. Which rigid motions could be used to transform △*JKL* into △*J'K'L'*?

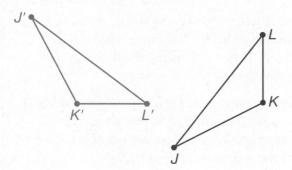

A. translation of △*JKL* up and to the left

B. translation of △*JKL* down and to the right

C. 90° clockwise rotation of △*JKL* about point *K* followed by a translation to the left

D. 90° counterclockwise rotation of △*JKL* about point *K* followed by a translation to the right

10. Across which line was trapezoid *MNPQ* reflected to form trapezoid *M'N'P'Q'*?

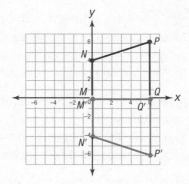

A. the *x*-axis

B. the *y*-axis

C. the line $y = x$

D. the line $y = -x$

Solve.

11. **ROTATE** Rotate quadrilateral *FGHJ* 180° about the origin to form quadrilateral *F'G'H'J'*. Draw the image *F'G'H'J'* on the coordinate plane.

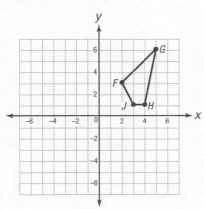

12. **PREDICT** Mei-Lin uses a computer drawing program to draw a polygon. She then uses the program to copy the polygon, to rotate the copy 90°, and then to flip it horizontally. How will her original drawing compare to the final image? Will the length of the sides be the same in both drawings? Will the angle measures be the same? Explain how you know.

_____

_____

_____

_____

_____

2 Translations

UNDERSTAND A **translation** is an operation that slides a geometric figure in the plane. You can think of a translation of a geometric figure as a function in which the input is not a single value, x, but rather a point on the coordinate plane, (x, y). When you apply the function to a point, the output will be the coordinates of the translated image of that point.

You can translate not only individual points but also entire graphs and figures. When you apply a translation function to every point on a figure, the resulting points will form the translated figure. For each **line segment** on the original figure, the translated image will contain either a corresponding **parallel line segment** or a **collinear line segment** of equal length.

In a **horizontal translation,** the x-coordinate changes, but the y-coordinate stays the same. A horizontal translation of a units can be represented by the function $T(x, y) = (x + a, y)$. If $a > 0$, the figure slides to the right. If $a < 0$, the figure slides to the left.

The transformation shown on the right is the result of applying the function $T(x, y) = (x + 7, y)$ to $\triangle JKL$. In this example, a is a positive number, 7, so the figure slides to the right.

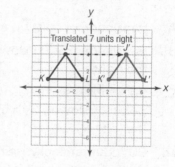

In a **vertical translation**, the y-coordinate changes, but the x-coordinate stays the same. A vertical translation of b units can be represented by the function $T(x, y) = (x, y + b)$. If $b > 0$, the figure slides up. If $b < 0$, the figure slides down.

The transformation shown on the right is the result of applying the function $T(x, y) = (x, y + 5)$ to $\triangle DFG$. In this example, b is a positive number, 5, so the figure slides up.

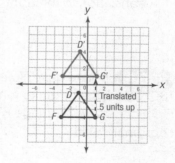

In a slant translation, both the x- and y-coordinates change. Slant translations can be described by the function $T(x, y) = (x + a, y + b)$.

The transformation shown on the right is the result of applying the function $T(x, y) = (x - 8, y - 6)$ to $\triangle ABC$. In this example, a and b are both negative, so the figure slides to the left and down.

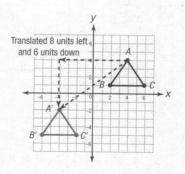

⟜◖ Connect

Translate trapezoid *WXYZ* 4 units to the left and 2 units up to form trapezoid *W′X′Y′Z′*. Identify the coordinates of the vertices of the translated image.

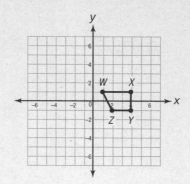

1

Starting at point *W*, count 4 units to the left and 2 units up.

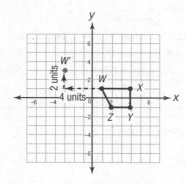

Plot point *W′* there. Notice that its coordinates are (−3, 3).

2

Translate every other point in the same way—by sliding it 4 units to the left and 2 units up. Then connect the points to form trapezoid *W′X′Y′Z′*.

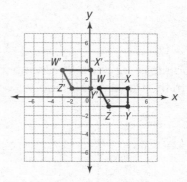

▶ The coordinates of the vertices of the translated image, *W′X′Y′Z′*, are *W′*(−3, 3), *X′*(0, 3), *Y′*(0, 1), and *Z′*(−2, 1).

◣DISCUSS

What function represents the translation that you performed? How do you know?

$T(x, y) = $ _____

EXAMPLE A Translate △*PQR* according to the rule below:

$T(x, y) = (x + 6, y - 1)$

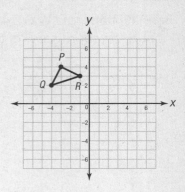

1

Identify the coordinates of the vertices of △*PQR*.

The vertices are $P(-3, 4)$, $Q(-4, 2)$, and $R(-1, 3)$.

2

Treat each point as an input and substitute it into the rule above to find the coordinates of the translated image.

$T(-3, 4) = (-3 + 6, 4 - 1) = (3, 3)$

$T(-4, 2) = (-4 + 6, 2 - 1) = (2, 1)$

$T(-1, 3) = (-1 + 6, 3 - 1) = (5, 2)$

3

Plot points P', Q', and R'. Connect them to form the translated image.

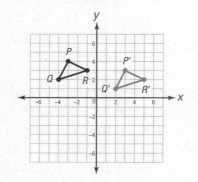

DISCUSS

On the diagram in Step 3, trace the path of each vertex of △*PQR* to its translated image on △*P'Q'R'*. Compare how each point moves from the preimage (or original figure) to the image. Explain what this means about the relationship between the sides of the preimage and the sides of the image.

EXAMPLE B Use a function to describe how parallelogram *ABCD* could be translated so it covers parallelogram *WXYZ* exactly.

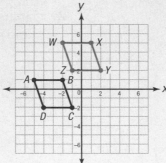

1

Describe the slide needed to move vertex *C* of parallelogram *ABCD* onto point *Y*, the corresponding point on parallelogram *WXYZ*.

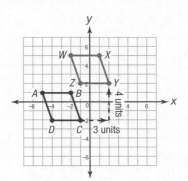

The diagram shows that point *C* must slide 3 units to the right and 4 units up to move onto point *Y*. Every other point in *ABCD* must slide in the same way.

2

Use a function to describe the translation.

A horizontal translation of 3 units to the right is in the positive direction. It can be represented by the expression $x + 3$.

A vertical translation of 4 units up is also in the positive direction. It can be represented by the expression $y + 4$.

▶ The rule for the translation is:
$T(x, y) = (x + 3, y + 4)$.

CHECK

Substitute the coordinates of the vertices of parallelogram *ABCD* into the rule $T(x, y) = (x + 3, y + 4)$. Check that the resulting coordinates match those of the vertices of parallelogram *WXYZ*.

Practice

Draw the image for each translation of the given preimage. Use prime (′) symbols to name points on each image.

1. Translate $\overleftrightarrow{AB}$ 3 units to the right.

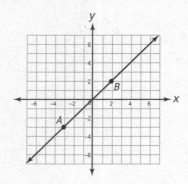

HINT
A translation to the right affects the *x*-coordinate.

2. Translate trapezoid *PQRS* 7 units to the left and 4 units down.

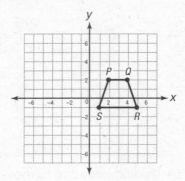

3. $T(x, y) = (x, y - 4)$

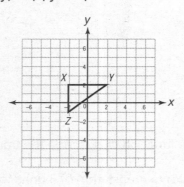

4. $T(x, y) = (x - 8, y + 3)$

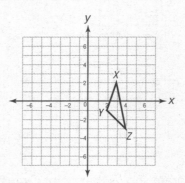

REMEMBER The preimage and the image should be the same size and same shape.

Write a function to describe how the quadrilateral *ABCD* was translated to form *A′B′C′D′* in each graph.

5.

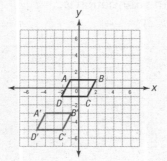

$T(x, y) = $ _____

6.

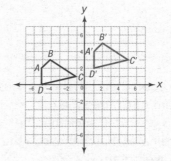

$T(x, y) = $ _____

Use the graph on the right for questions 7–9.

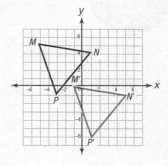

7. Name the line segment that is parallel to $\overline{MN}$. _____

8. Name a line segment that is parallel to $\overline{MP}$. _____

9. How does $\overline{NP}$ compare to $\overline{N'P'}$?

_____

Solve.

10. A triangle with vertices $A(1, -3)$, $B(-7, 12)$, and $C(5, 0)$ is translated according to the rule $T(x, y) = (x - 3, y + 9)$. What are the coordinates of the vertices of the translated image?

_____

_____

_____

11. Point P at $(-4, 3)$ is translated to form its image, point P', at $(6, 1)$. Write a function to represent the translation. If point $R(-5, -6)$ and point $S(1, 2)$ are also translated using that rule, what will be the coordinates of their images?

_____

_____

_____

12. **DESCRIBE** A librarian wants to move the bookcase shown in the diagram from its current location to the "New" location. Describe a series of translations that could be used to move the bookcase to its new location, keeping in mind that it cannot be moved through a wall.

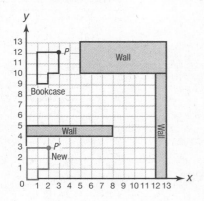

_____

_____

_____

13. **EXPLAIN** Use a function to describe the translation that moves pentagon *ABCDF* so it covers pentagon *KLMNP* exactly. Then write the function that moves pentagon *KLMNP* so it covers pentagon *ABCDF* exactly. Compare the two functions and explain any differences between them.

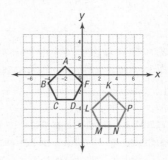

_____

_____

_____

_____

Reflections

LESSON 3

UNDERSTAND A **reflection** is a transformation that flips a figure across a line called a **line of reflection**. Each reflected point is the same distance from the line of reflection as its corresponding point on the preimage, but it is on the opposite side of the line. The resulting image and the preimage are mirror images of one another. The line of reflection can be the *x*-axis, the *y*-axis, or any other line in the coordinate plane.

You can think of a reflection of a figure as a function in which the input is not a single value, *x*, but rather a point on the coordinate plane, (x, y). When you apply the function to a point on a figure, the output will be the coordinates of the reflected image of that point.

When a point is reflected across the *y*-axis, the sign of its *x*-coordinate changes. The function for a reflection across the *y*-axis is:

$$R_{y\text{-axis}}(x, y) = (-x, y)$$

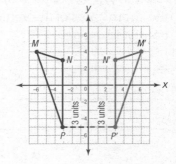

When a point is reflected across the *x*-axis, the sign of its *y*-coordinate changes. The function for a reflection across the *x*-axis is:

$$R_{x\text{-axis}}(x, y) = (x, -y)$$

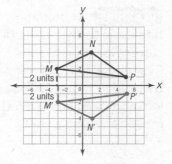

Another common line of reflection is the diagonal line $y = x$. To reflect over this line, swap the *x*- and *y*-coordinates. The function for a reflection across line $y = x$ is:

$$R_{y = x}(x, y) = (y, x)$$

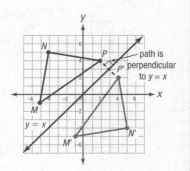

The path that a point takes across the line of reflection is always **perpendicular** to the line of reflection. Perpendicular lines form right angles when they cross one another. As shown in the diagram on the right, the path from point *P* to point *P′* forms right angles with the line of reflection, $y = x$.

⊶ Connect

Reflect △ABC across the x-axis. Then reflect △ABC across the y-axis.

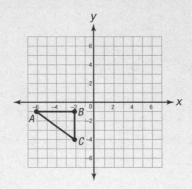

1
Identify the coordinates of the vertices of △ABC.

The vertices of the triangle are A(−6, −1), B(−2, −1), and C(−2, −4).

2
To reflect the vertices of △ABC across the x-axis, change the signs of the y-coordinates. Then draw the image.

$A(−6, −1) \longrightarrow A'(−6, 1)$

$B(−2, −1) \longrightarrow B'(−2, 1)$

$C(−2, −4) \longrightarrow C'(−2, 4)$

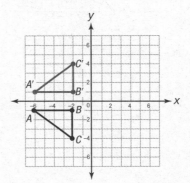

3
To reflect the vertices of △ABC across the y-axis, change the signs of the x-coordinates. Then draw the image.

$A(−6, −1) \longrightarrow A''(6, −1)$

$B(−2, −1) \longrightarrow B''(2, −1)$

$C(−2, −4) \longrightarrow C''(2, −4)$

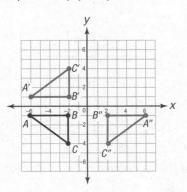

TRY
Use function notation to describe how △ABC is transformed to △A'B'C' and how △ABC is transformed to △A''B''C''.

EXAMPLE A Graph the image of quadrilateral *JKLM* after the reflection described below.

$$F(x, y) = (y, x).$$

Then describe the reflection in words.

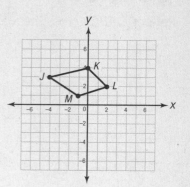

1

Identify the coordinates of the vertices of quadrilateral *JKLM*.

The quadrilateral has vertices $J(-4, 3)$, $K(0, 4)$, $L(2, 2)$, and $M(-1, 1)$.

2

Apply the function to the vertices.

$F(-4, 3) = (3, -4)$

$F(0, 4) = (4, 0)$

$F(2, 2) = (2, 2)$

$F(-1, 1) = (1, -1)$

3

Graph the image.

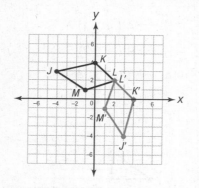

4

Describe the reflection in words.

Find the line that lies halfway between corresponding points of the figure.

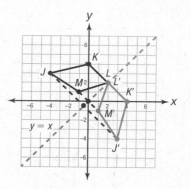

Each of these halfway marks lies on the line $y = x$.

▶ The function performs a reflection across the line $y = x$.

TRY

Apply the same function, $F(x, y) = (y, x)$, to $J'K'L'M'$. What image results?

Figures can be reflected over horizontal or vertical lines that are not the *x*- or *y*-axis as well.

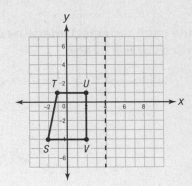

EXAMPLE B Trapezoid *STUV* is graphed on the right. Reflect this trapezoid over the line $x = 4$.

1

Reflect vertices *U* and *V*.

Point *U*, at (2, 1), is 2 units to the left of $x = 4$. So, its reflection will be 2 units to the right of $x = 4$. So, plot a point at (6, 1) and name it *U'*.

Use the same strategy to plot point *V'*.

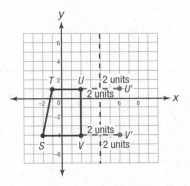

2

Find and plot the other two points of the image.

Point *T* at (−1, 1) is 5 units to the left of $x = 4$. So, plot point *T'* 5 units to the right of $x = 4$ at (9, 1).

Point *S* is 6 units to the left of $x = 4$. So, plot point *S'* at (10, −4), which is 6 units to the right of $x = 4$.

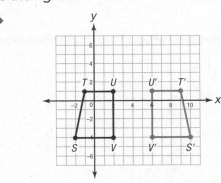

DISCUSS

How could you describe the reflection of trapezoid *STUV* over the line $x = 4$ using function notation?

Practice

Draw each reflected image as described and name its vertices. Identify the coordinates of the vertices of the image.

1. Reflect △ABC across the x-axis.

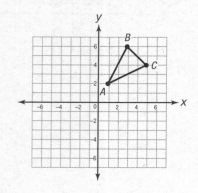

A′(___, ___) B′(___, ___) C′(___, ___)

> **REMEMBER** When a point is reflected across the x-axis, the sign of its y-coordinate changes.

2. Reflect pentagon GHJKL across the line y = 3.

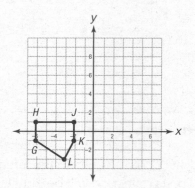

G′(___, ___) H′(___, ___) J′(___, ___)

K′(___, ___) L′(___, ___)

Fill in each blank with an appropriate word or phrase.

3. A reflection results in two figures that look like _____ of each other.

4. Lines that meet and form right angles are called _____ lines.

5. A point and its reflection are each the same distance from _____.

6. The path that a point takes across the line of reflection is _____ to the line of reflection.

Use the given function to transform △DEF. Then describe the transformation in words.

7. R(x, y) = (−x, y)

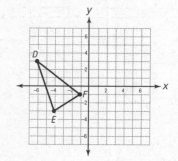

_____

8. R(x, y) = (y, x)

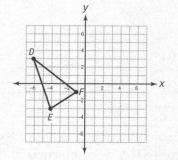

_____

Identify the coordinates of the image for each reflection as described.

9. Reflect $M(3, 4)$ across the x-axis.

$M'($_____, _____$)$

10. Reflect $N(-2, -8)$ across the y-axis.

$N'($_____, _____$)$

11. Reflect $P(-2, 0)$ across the line $y = x$.

$P'($_____, _____$)$

12. Reflect $Q(5, 10)$ across the line $y = x$.

$Q'($_____, _____$)$

Describe how quadrilateral *ABCD* was reflected to form quadrilateral *A′B′C′D′*, using both words and function notation.

13.

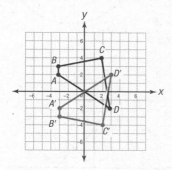

Words: _____

Function: _____

14.

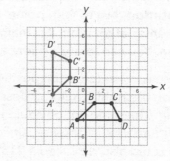

Words: _____

Function: _____

Solve.

15. **JUSTIFY** Camille drew the square below on a coordinate plane. She says that if she reflects the square over the x-axis it will look exactly the same as if she reflects it over the y-axis. Is she correct or incorrect? Use words, numbers and/or drawings to justify your answer.

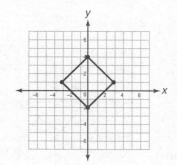

_____

_____

16. **DRAW** Patrick reflected a figure in two steps. The result was that each point (x, y) was transformed to the point $(-y, x)$. Draw a triangle (any triangle) on the plane below and transform it as described. Then describe what two reflections Patrick performed.

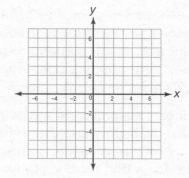

_____

_____

Rotations

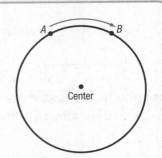

UNDERSTAND A **circle** is the set of all points that are the same distance from a point called the center. Visualize turning the circle shown on the right so that point *A* moves onto point *B*. If you did that, the points would remain the same distance from the center, but they would each be in a different location.

A **rotation** is a transformation that turns a figure around a point, called the **center of rotation**. Just as with points on a circle, when you rotate a point around a center of rotation, it remains the same distance from the center of rotation. You can rotate a figure any number of degrees.

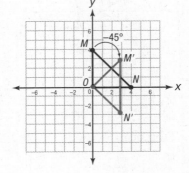

Counterclockwise is considered the positive direction, so the rotation shown on the right would be described as −45° rotation around the origin. The same image could be obtained, however, by rotating the figure 315° clockwise, since 360 − 45 = 315. So, this rotation could also be called a 315° rotation around the origin.

You can represent a rotation as a function for which the input is a coordinate pair. The output of that function is the image produced by the rotation.

A 90° rotation is equivalent to a −270° rotation and has this function:

$$R_{90°}(x, y) = (-y, x)$$

A 180° rotation is equivalent to a −180° rotation and has this function:

$$R_{180°}(x, y) = (-x, -y)$$

A 270° rotation is equivalent to a −90° rotation and has this function:

$$R_{270°}(x, y) = (y, -x)$$

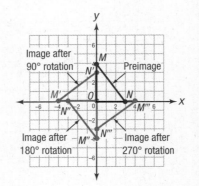

Compare the preimage on the right and its image after a 90° rotation or a 270° rotation. Notice that the hypotenuse of each of these images is perpendicular to the hypotenuse of the preimage. Corresponding sides of a figure and its image after a 90° or 270° rotation lie on perpendicular lines.

Now compare the preimage and its image after a 180° rotation. Notice that the hypotenuse of the image is parallel to the hypotenuse of the preimage. Corresponding sides of a figure and its image after a 180° rotation always lie on parallel lines or on the same line.

⟜ Connect

Triangle *GHJ* is graphed on the coordinate plane. Draw the image of this triangle after counterclockwise rotations of 90°, 180°, and 270° about the origin.

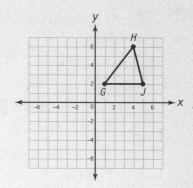

1

Apply the functions for the given counterclockwise rotations to the vertices of the triangle.

The vertices of △*GHJ* are *G*(1, 2), *H*(4, 6), and *J*(5, 2).

The function that represents a 90° rotation around the origin is $R_{90°}(x, y) = (-y, x)$.

$R_{90°}(1, 2) = (-2, 1)$

$R_{90°}(4, 6) = (-6, 4)$

$R_{90°}(5, 2) = (-2, 5)$

The function that represents a 180° rotation around the origin is $R_{180°}(x, y) = (-x, -y)$.

$R_{180°}(1, 2) = (-1, -2)$

$R_{180°}(4, 6) = (-4, -6)$

$R_{180°}(5, 2) = (-5, -2)$

The function that represents a 270° rotation around the origin is $R_{270°}(x, y) = (y, -x)$.

$R_{270°}(1, 2) = (2, -1)$

$R_{270°}(4, 6) = (6, -4)$

$R_{270°}(5, 2) = (2, -5)$

2

Graph and label each image.

Plot the vertices of each image, label them, and connect them.

▶

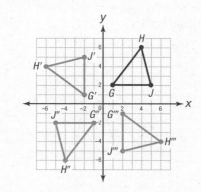

TRY

Identify the coordinates of the vertices of the images if the rotations had been in a clockwise direction.

EXAMPLE A Quadrilateral *STUV* is graphed on the coordinate plane. Transform quadrilateral *STUV* using this function:

$$R_\theta(x, y) = (-y, x)$$

Identify the degree measure of the rotation that the function performs. (Note: The Greek letter theta (θ) is often used to represent unknown angle measures.)

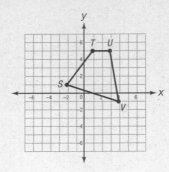

1

Identify the coordinates of the vertices of quadrilateral *STUV*.

The figure has vertices $S(-2, 1)$, $T(1, 5)$, $U(3, 5)$, and $V(4, -1)$.

2

Identify the coordinates of the rotated image and the degree measure of the rotation.

$R_\theta(x, y) = (-y, x)$, so:

$S(-2, 1) \rightarrow S'(-1, -2)$

$T(1, 5) \rightarrow T'(-5, 1)$

$U(3, 5) \rightarrow U'(-5, 3)$

$V(4, -1) \rightarrow V'(1, 4)$

When the opposite value of *y* is taken and the values of *x* and −*y* are switched, this indicates a 90° rotation.

3

Graph the rotated image and identify the transformation. Check your answer visually.

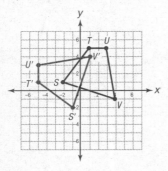

Eyeballing the graph confirms that this is a 90° rotation.

▶ $S'T'U'V'$ is the result of a 90° rotation.

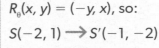

What is the relationship between the corresponding sides of the preimage and its image?

EXAMPLE B Triangle *BCD* was rotated to form its image, triangle *B'C'D'*. Identify the transformation and write a function to describe it.

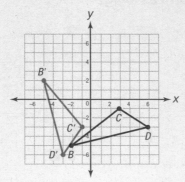

1

Identify the coordinates of the vertices of both triangles.

The vertices of the preimage, △*BCD*, are *B*(−2, −5), *C*(3, −1), and *D*(6, −3).

The vertices of the image, △*B'C'D'*, are *B'*(−5, 2), *C'*(−1, −3), and *D'*(−3, −6).

2

Compare the triangles visually to identify the transformation.

From eyeballing the figures, it looks like △*BCD* was turned about $\frac{1}{4}$ clockwise around the origin to form △*B'C'D'*. That is a −90° rotation, which is the same as a 270° rotation.

3

Use the function for a 270° rotation to confirm your guess.

The function for a 270° rotation is $R_{270°}(x, y) = (y, -x)$. Apply this function to the vertices of △*BCD*.

$R_{270°}(-2, -5) = (-5, 2)$ This is *B'*.

$R_{270°}(3, -1) = (-1, -3)$ This is *C'*.

$R_{270°}(6, -3) = (-3, -6)$ This is *D'*.

Each point (*x*, *y*) on △*BCD* has a corresponding point (*y*, −*x*) on its image, so △*B'C'D'* is the result of a 270° rotation.

▶ The transformation is a 270° rotation, which can be represented by the function $R_{270°}(x, y) = (y, -x)$.

TRY

Identify and write a function to describe the rotation needed to move △*B'C'D'* back onto △*BCD*. How does this notation compare to the notation for the 270° rotation?

Practice

Identify the number of degrees (45°, 90°, 180°, or 270°) by which each quadrilateral *ABCD* has been rotated about the origin to form its image.

1.

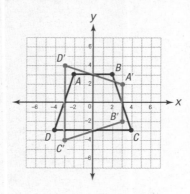

_____

2.

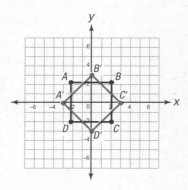

_____

> REMEMBER A −90° rotation is equal to a 270° rotation.

Describe how △*DEF* was rotated to form △*D′E′F′* both in words and in function notation.

3.

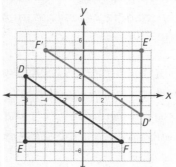

Words: _____

Function: _____

4.

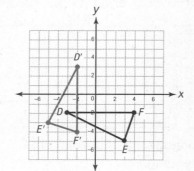

Words: _____

Function: _____

Write *true* or *false* for each statement. If false, rewrite the statement to make it true.

5.   A circle is the set of all points that are equidistant from a point called the center.

_____

6.   A quarter-turn in the counterclockwise direction is equivalent to a −90° rotation.

_____

7.   Corresponding sides of a preimage and an image after a 270° rotation are parallel.

_____

Use the given function to rotate △KLM to form △K′L′M′. Identify the coordinates of the vertices of the image. Then identify the degree measure of the rotation.

8. $R_\theta(x, y) = (-x, -y)$

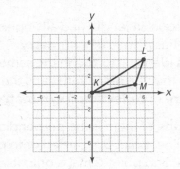

$K'(\underline{\quad}, \underline{\quad})\ L'(\underline{\quad}, \underline{\quad})\ M'(\underline{\quad}, \underline{\quad})$

_____

9. $R_\theta(x, y) = (-y, x)$

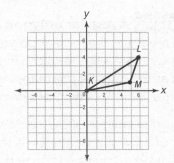

$K'(\underline{\quad}, \underline{\quad})\ L'(\underline{\quad}, \underline{\quad})\ M'(\underline{\quad}, \underline{\quad})$

_____

Solve.

10. **EXPLAIN** Sal drew a rectangle on a coordinate plane. He then rotated it 90° as shown below. Is there another way he could have rotated the rectangle that would have yielded the same image? Explain your reasoning.

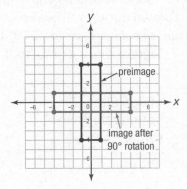

_____
_____
_____

11. **DRAW** An artist drew a blue and white trapezoid on a computer. She wants to copy and rotate this image three times about the origin to create a figure that looks like a pinwheel. Describe three rotations she could use. Draw the pinwheel that would result from those three rotations.

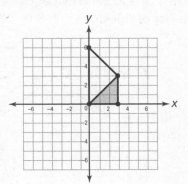

_____
_____
_____

Symmetry and Sequences of Transformations

Types of Symmetry

UNDERSTAND A **regular polygon** is a polygon with all sides equal in length and all angles equal in measure. If a regular polygon has *n* sides, then it also has *n* **lines of symmetry**. When you reflect a figure over a line of symmetry, the image is identical to and in the same location as the original preimage. When this happens, we say that the reflection maps the figure onto itself. This type of symmetry is called **line symmetry** or **reflectional symmetry**.

The regular pentagon shown below has 5 lines of symmetry. One of them is the perpendicular bisector of $\overline{AE}$. If this pentagon is reflected across the dashed line, point *B* is carried onto point *D* and vice versa, point *A* is carried onto point *E* and vice versa, and point *C* maps onto itself because it is on the line of reflection. The image is identical to its preimage.

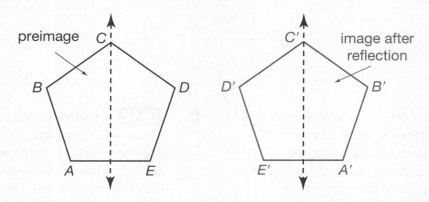

The pentagon also has **rotational symmetry**. A figure that has rotational symmetry will map onto itself more than once during a 360° turn. Notice that if a circle is drawn through all five vertices, the circle is divided into five equal-length arcs. To find the measure of each arc, divide 360° by the number of sides. 360° ÷ 5 = 72°. Rotating the pentagon 72 degrees maps it onto itself.

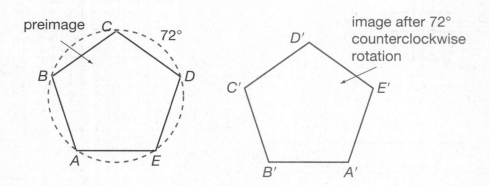

If you were to rotate the pentagon another 72°, which is a 144° rotation from the original preimage, you would produce the same figure again. You can do this 3 more times. In general, a regular polygon with *n* sides will map onto itself *n* times during a 360° turn.

⌐E Connect

Describe two ways in which the rectangle graphed below could be mapped back onto itself.

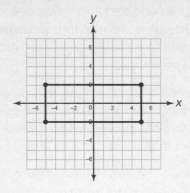

1

Look for line symmetry.

If you reflect the rectangle over the *x*-axis, then the top half maps onto the bottom half and vice versa.

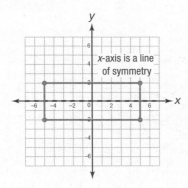

x-axis is a line of symmetry

▶ A reflection across the *x*-axis maps the rectangle back onto itself.

2

Look for rotational symmetry.

If you rotate the rectangle 180°, the upper left corner maps onto the lower right corner and vice versa. The resulting figure is identical to the original rectangle.

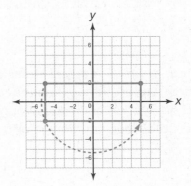

▶ A rotation of 180° around the origin will map the rectangle back onto itself.

DISCUSS

Is there a third way to map the rectangle onto itself in one step? If so, describe it. If not, explain why not.

Transformations in Sequence

UNDERSTAND Sometimes, more than one transformation is needed to produce a particular image from a given preimage. There are often multiple sequences that can produce a given image. Whether a single rigid motion or a sequence of rigid motions is used, the final image is always congruent to the original preimage.

To determine the necessary sequence of transformations, compare the preimage to the image much as you have done for individual transformations. If the orientation of the figure has changed, then a reflection or rotation has probably taken place. Once the figures have the same orientation, apply translations in the sequence to align the figures.

Consider △*TVW* and △*T′V′W′* below. The image has a different orientation than the preimage. Examining the shape and the placement of the vertices shows that the image appears to be a 180° rotation of the preimage. Try rotating △*TVW* by 180° around the origin and comparing the image to △*T′V′W′*.

After the rotation, the orientation of the image matches the orientation of △*T′V′W′*, but each point on the image is 3 units below △*T′V′W′*. Apply a translation to align the figures.

So, a 180° rotation of △*TVW* about the origin followed by a translation of 3 units up will produce △*T′V′W′*.

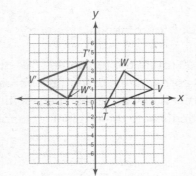

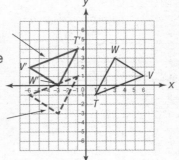

image after translation of rotated image 3 units up

image after 180° rotation around the origin

The order in which you apply transformations does not always matter, but in this case, it does. If you translate △*TVW* up 3 units and *then* rotate, you end up with a congruent figure with the correct orientation but in the wrong place. You would still need to perform another translation (6 units up) to map your image onto △*T′V′W′*.

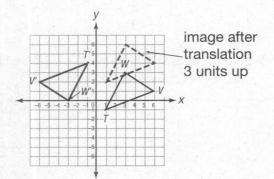

image after translation 3 units up

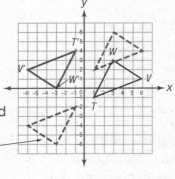

image of translated image after 180° rotation about the origin

⊏ Connect

Describe a sequence of transformations that could be used to map trapezoid *ABCD* onto trapezoid *A'B'C'D'*.

1

Compare the size, shape, and orientation of the image and the preimage.

The trapezoids appear to have the same size and shape, so a series of rigid motions should produce one from the other.

ABCD is taller than it is wide, and *A'B'C'D'* is wider than it is tall, so the two figures have different orientations. The sequence may include a rotation.

2

Rotate the preimage and compare to *A'B'C'D'*.

In the image, side *A'B'* is on the bottom and *C'D'* is on top, so rotate *ABCD* 90° counterclockwise around point *A*.

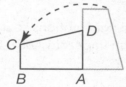

On the blue image, begin at vertex *A* and read the vertices clockwise around the figure: *A - B - C - D*.

Do the same with the green image, beginning at vertex *A'*: *A' - D' - C' - B'*.

The corresponding vertices are not in the same order. This means that a reflection must be part of the sequence.

3

Reflect the rotated image and compare to *A'B'C'D'*.

Place a vertical line of reflection halfway between points *D* and *D'*. Reflect the rotated image over this line.

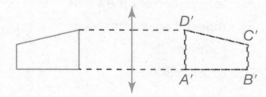

▶ A rotation of 90° counterclockwise followed by a horizontal reflection produces *A'B'C'D'* from *ABCD*.

TRY

Find other sequences that map trapezoid *ABCD* onto trapezoid *A'B'C'D'*.

Practice

Determine if the given figure has _rotational symmetry, line symmetry, both,_ or _neither._

1.   isosceles trapezoid

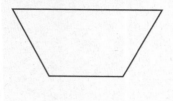

_____

2.   equilateral triangle

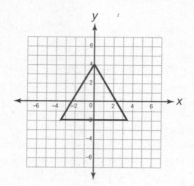

_____

3.   parallelogram

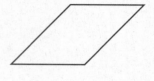

_____

> **HINT**   A figure has rotational symmetry if some turn of less than 360° maps it back onto itself.

Choose the best answer.

4.   Which sequence of rigid motions could be used to transform trapezoid _ABCD_ to trapezoid _A″B″C″D″_?

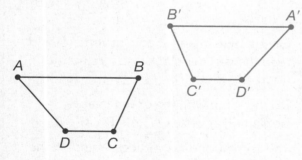

- **A.**   translation of trapezoid _ABCD_ up and to the left
- **B.**   translation of trapezoid _ABCD_ up and to the right
- **C.**   a 180° rotation of trapezoid _ABCD_ followed by a horizontal reflection
- **D.**   a horizontal reflection of trapezoid _ABCD_ followed by a translation up

5.   Which does **not** describe a way to map regular hexagon _PQRSTU_ back onto itself?

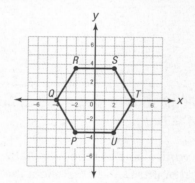

- **A.**   reflect it across the x-axis
- **B.**   reflect it across the y-axis
- **C.**   rotate it 60°
- **D.**   rotate it 90°

Write *true* or *false* for each statement.

6. Any figure will map back onto itself after a 360° turn about its center. _____

7. Any figure that has line symmetry must also have rotational symmetry. _____

Solve.

8. **SHOW** Describe a sequence of two transformations that could map △FGH onto △F′G′H′.

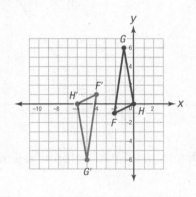

_____

_____

_____

9. **EXPLAIN** Reverse the order of the transformations in your sequence from question 8 and draw the image on the plane below. Does this affect the final image produced? Explain.

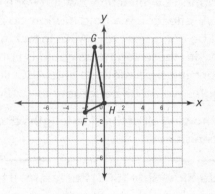

_____

_____

10. **DRAW** A certain quadrilateral can be mapped onto itself after 90°, 180°, and 270° rotations about its center. It can also be mapped onto itself by a horizontal reflection and a vertical reflection. Name the quadrilateral that fits that description and draw it below.

_____

Congruent Triangles

UNDERSTAND Two triangles are congruent if all of their corresponding angles are congruent and all of their corresponding sides are congruent. However, you do not need to know the measures of every side and angle to show that two triangles are congruent.

△ABC is formed from three line segments: $\overline{AB}$, $\overline{BC}$, and $\overline{AC}$. Suppose those segments were pulled apart and used to build another triangle, such as △A′B′C′ shown. This new triangle could be formed by reflecting △ABC over a vertical line. A reflection is a rigid motion, so △A′B′C′ must be congruent to △ABC. In fact, any triangle built with these segments could be produced by performing rigid motions on △ABC, so all such triangles would be congruent to △ABC.

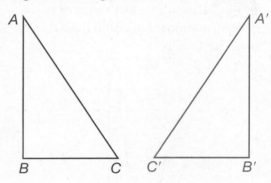

So, knowing all of the side lengths of two triangles is enough information to determine if they are congruent.

> **Side-Side-Side (SSS) Postulate:** If three sides of one triangle are congruent to three sides of another triangle, then the triangles are congruent.

UNDERSTAND You can also use the Side-Angle-Side (SAS) Postulate to prove that two triangles are congruent.

> **Side-Angle-Side (SAS) Postulate:** If two sides and the included angle of one triangle are congruent to two sides and the included angle of another triangle, then the triangles are congruent.

Look at △DEF on the coordinate plane. Applying rigid motions to two of its sides produced new line segments. Sides $\overline{DE}$ and $\overline{EF}$ were translated 7 units to the right to form $\overline{GH}$ and $\overline{HI}$. $\overline{DE}$ and $\overline{EF}$ were rotated 180° about the origin to form $\overline{JK}$ and $\overline{KL}$. $\overline{DE}$ and $\overline{EF}$ were reflected over the x-axis to form $\overline{MN}$ and $\overline{NO}$.

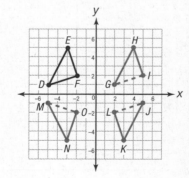

Each rigid motion preserved the lengths of the segments as well as the angle between them. In all three images, only one segment can be drawn to complete each triangle. Those line segments, shown as dotted lines, are congruent to $\overline{DF}$. So, △DEF ≅ △GHI ≅ △JKL ≅ △MNO. The symbol ≅ means "is congruent to."

⊏ Connect

The coordinate plane on the right shows △ABC and △DEF.

Use the SAS Postulate to show that the triangles are congruent. Then, identify rigid motions that could transform △ABC into △DEF.

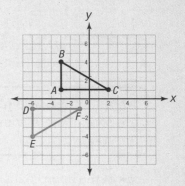

1

Make a plan.

Each triangle has one horizontal side and one vertical side that intersect, so both are right triangles. Since all right angles are congruent, the triangles have at least one pair of corresponding congruent angles. To prove the triangles congruent by the SAS Postulate, find the lengths of the adjacent sides (legs) that form the right angles.

2

Find and compare the lengths of the corresponding legs.

Count the units to find the length of each leg.

$AB = 3$ $DE = 3$

$AC = 5$ $DF = 5$

$\overline{AB} \cong \overline{DE}$ and $\overline{AC} \cong \overline{DF}$

▶ The triangles have two pairs of corresponding congruent sides, and their included angles are congruent right angles. So, according to the SAS Postulate, △ABC ≅ △DEF.

3

Identify rigid motions that can transform △ABC to △DEF.

Study the shapes of the triangles.

▶ $\overline{AC}$ corresponds to $\overline{DF}$ and is parallel to it. Vertex B is above $\overline{AC}$ on the left, while vertex E lies below $\overline{DF}$ and is also on the left. △ABC could be reflected over the x-axis. After such a reflection, △A′B′C′ would have vertices A′(−3, −1), B′(−3, −4), and C′(2, −1). To transform this image to △DEF, translate it 3 units to the left.

DISCUSS

If △ABC had instead been rotated 90° and then translated down 1 unit, would the resulting image be congruent to △ABC? How could you prove your answer?

Congruence with Multiple Angles

UNDERSTAND A third method for proving that triangles are congruent is the Angle-Side-Angle Theorem.

> **Angle-Side-Angle (ASA) Theorem:** If two angles and the included side of one triangle are congruent to two angles and the included side of another triangle, then the triangles are congruent.

Look at the coordinate planes below. Triangle GHJ is shown on the left. On the right, sides $\overline{HJ}$ and $\overline{GJ}$ of the triangle have been replaced by rays.

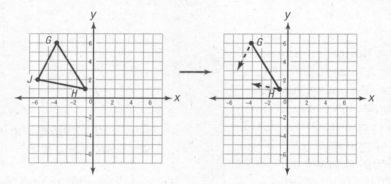

The coordinate plane on the right of this paragraph shows three transformations of $\overline{GH}$ and the rays extending from points G and H. $\overline{KL}$ is a translation of $\overline{GH}$ 6 units to the right. $\overline{ON}$ is a 180° rotation of $\overline{GH}$. $\overline{RQ}$ is a reflection of $\overline{GH}$ over the x-axis.

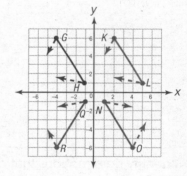

Each of those rigid motions has carried the angle-side-angle combination to a new location. The segments $\overline{KL}$, $\overline{ON}$, and $\overline{RQ}$ are congruent to $\overline{GH}$. Rigid motions also preserved the angles formed by the segment and each ray.

The coordinate plane on the lower right shows the triangles formed by extending the rays until they intersect.

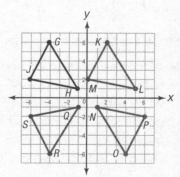

In each case, the rays can only intersect at one point and thus can form only one triangle. Each of these triangles is congruent to △GHJ.

⊏ Connect

Triangles *PQR* and *STU* are shown on the coordinate plane on the right.

Given that $\angle P \cong \angle S$ and $\angle R \cong \angle U$, prove that the triangles are congruent. Then identify rigid motions that can transform $\triangle PQR$ into $\triangle STU$.

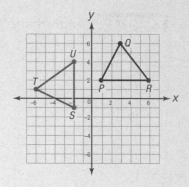

1

Make a plan.

You already know that two pairs of corresponding angles are congruent. If you can show that the included sides are the same length, then the triangles are congruent by the ASA Theorem.

2

Find the lengths of the included sides.

In $\triangle PQR$, the included side of $\angle P$ and $\angle R$ is $\overline{PR}$. Find the length of $\overline{PR}$ by counting units.

> $PR = 5$

In $\triangle STU$, the included side for $\angle S$ and $\angle U$ is $\overline{SU}$. Find the length of $\overline{SU}$ by counting units.

> $SU = 5$

▶ Since two pairs of corresponding angles and the included sides are congruent, $\triangle PQR \cong \triangle STU$ by the ASA Theorem.

3

Identify rigid motions that could transform $\triangle PQR$ into $\triangle STU$.

Study the shapes of the triangles.

Side $\overline{PR}$ is horizontal, and corresponding side $\overline{SU}$ is vertical. It appears that $\triangle PQR$ was rotated 90° counterclockwise. If that rotation were around the origin, $\triangle P'Q'R'$ would have vertices at $P'(-2, 1)$, $Q'(-6, 3)$, and $R'(-2, 6)$. To transform this image to $\triangle STU$, translate it 2 units down.

▶ Triangle *STU* can be produced by rotating $\triangle PQR$ 90° counterclockwise and then translating the image down 2 units.

In triangles *ABC* and *DEF*, $\angle A = \angle D = 20°$, $\angle B = \angle E = 60°$, and $\angle C = \angle F = 100°$. Are triangles *ABC* and *DEF* congruent?

EXAMPLE A Show that △*TUV* is congruent to △*XYZ*.

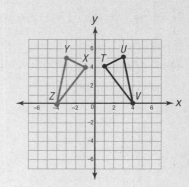

1

Make a plan.

To use the SSS Postulate, you need to show that each side on △*XYZ* has a corresponding congruent side on △*TUV*. To do so, show that each side of △*XYZ* is a rigid-motion transformation of a side of △*TUV*.

2

Compare the endpoints of $\overline{XY}$ and $\overline{TU}$.

Points *T* and *X* have the same *y*-coordinates but opposite *x*-coordinates. The same is true for points *U* and *Y*. This indicates that $\overline{TU}$ can be reflected over the *y*-axis to form $\overline{XY}$. As a result, you know that $\overline{XY} \cong \overline{TU}$.

3

Follow the same process for the other two pairs of corresponding sides.

The endpoints of $\overline{YZ}$ and $\overline{UV}$ have the same *y*-coordinates but opposite *x*-coordinates.

The endpoints of $\overline{XZ}$ and $\overline{TV}$ also have the same *y*-coordinates but opposite *x*-coordinates.

So, $\overline{YZ}$ is a reflection of $\overline{UV}$ over the *y*-axis, and $\overline{XZ}$ is a reflection of $\overline{TV}$ over the *y*-axis.

4

Draw a conclusion.

▶ Since each side of △*XYZ* is a reflection of the corresponding side of △*TUV*, the corresponding sides of the triangles are congruent. According to the SSS Postulate, △*TUV* ≅ △*XYZ*.

DISCUSS

How does ∠*Z* compare to ∠*V*? Could one angle have a greater measure than the other?

42 Unit 1: Congruence, Proof, and Constructions

EXAMPLE B Ian is studying wing designs for airplanes. He compares two wings whose triangular cross sections both contain one 20° angle, an adjacent side that measures 6 feet, and a non-adjacent side that measures 3 feet. Determine if the triangular cross sections are identical.

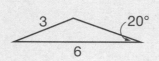 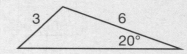

1

Make a plan.

Identical triangles are congruent, so rigid motions should carry one of the figures onto the other. Transform one of the figures so that known congruent parts line up, and compare the other parts.

2

Attempt to align the angle and adjacent side.

The angles are already aligned, but the 6-foot sides are not. Rotate the second triangle 20° counterclockwise so that its 6-foot side is also horizontal.

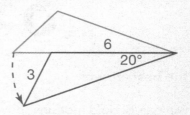

3

Re-align the angles.

The angles are no longer aligned, so reflect the image vertically to bring them back into alignment.

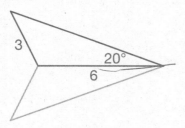

4

Translate the image onto the other triangle.

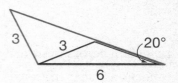

The angle and adjacent side are aligned, but the remaining sides and angles do not match.

▶ The cross sections are not congruent.

DISCUSS

If two triangles have two pairs of congruent sides and one pair of congruent angles, can you prove that the triangles are congruent?

Practice

Use the coordinate plane below for questions 1–4.

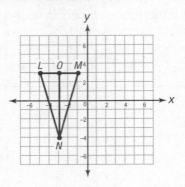

1. $\angle LON$ and $\angle MON$ both measure _____ degrees.

2. $LO = OM =$ _____ units

3. $\triangle LON$ and $\triangle MON$ share side _____.

4. Triangles *LON* and *MON* are congruent by the _____ Postulate.

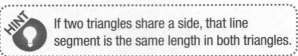

HINT If two triangles share a side, that line segment is the same length in both triangles.

Choose the best answer.

5. Which pair of rigid motions shows that $\triangle ABC$ and $\triangle A'B'C'$ are congruent?

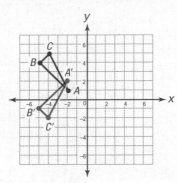

   A. reflection across the *x*-axis followed by a translation of 3 units up

   B. reflection across the *x*-axis followed by a translation of 3 units down

   C. rotation of 180° about the origin followed by a reflection over the *y*-axis

   D. rotation of 90° counterclockwise about the origin followed by a translation of 4 units down

6. The coordinate plane on the right shows isosceles right triangles *HIJ* and *KLM*.

Use the ASA Postulate to prove that △*HIJ* and △*KLM* are congruent. Identify rigid motions that could transform △*HIJ* into △*KLM*.

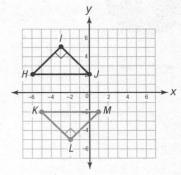

_____

_____

_____

_____

_____

7. Triangle *ABC* was reflected horizontally, reflected vertically, and then translated to form triangle *A'B'C'*. Identify the lengths and angle measures below.

A'B' = _____

AC = _____

m∠*B'* = _____

m∠*A* = _____

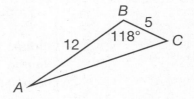

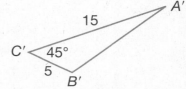

Use the following information for questions 8 and 9.

Right triangle *NOP* has vertices *N*(1, 1), *O*(1, 5), and *P*(4, 1).
Right triangle *QRS* has vertices *Q*(−4, −1), *R*(−4, −5), and *S*(−1, −1).

8. SKETCH Sketch both triangles on the coordinate plane.

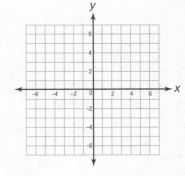

9. PROVE Prove that △*NOP* and △*QRS* are congruent.

_____

_____

_____

_____

_____

Using Congruence to Prove Theorems

EXAMPLE A Prove that the sum of the measures of the interior angles of a triangle is 180°.

1

Draw a triangle.

Draw a triangle and label its vertices *A*, *B*, and *C*.

2

Produce an image and join two angles.

Rotate △*ABC* 180° to produce congruent image △*A'B'C'*. If necessary, translate the image so that point *B'* lies on point *C*.

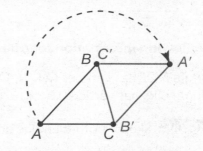

3

Produce another image and join all three angles.

Rotate △*A'B'C'* 180° to produce another congruent image, △*A"B"C"*. This image can also be created by translating △*ABC* to the right. Translate the image so that point *A"* lies on points *C* and *B'*.

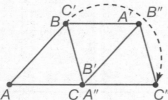
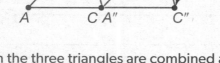

When the three triangles are combined as shown, $\overline{AC}$ and $\overline{A''C''}$ are collinear, so

m∠*A"* + m∠*B'* + m∠*C* = 180°

Since all three triangles are congruent,
m∠*B'* = m∠*B* and m∠*A"* = m∠*A*.

▶ m∠*A* + m∠*B* + m∠*C* = 180°

Would this proof also work for a right triangle? An obtuse triangle?

EXAMPLE B Non-adjacent angles formed by two intersecting lines are called vertical angles. Angles 1 and 3 are vertical angles. Use a 180° rotation of a triangle to prove that vertical angles are congruent.

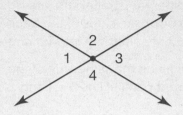

1

Draw a triangle.

Draw △MNP. Let x represent the measure of ∠P.

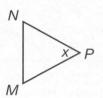

2

Rotate △MNP 180° about point P.

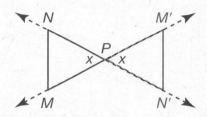

Recall that after a rotation of 180°, corresponding line segments are either parallel or collinear. Corresponding segments $\overline{MP}$ and $\overline{M'P}$ both contain point P, so they must be collinear. Similarly, segments $\overline{NP}$ and $\overline{N'P}$ must be collinear. So, ∠MPN and ∠M'PN' are vertical angles.

∠MPN and ∠M'PN' are corresponding parts of congruent triangles MPN and M'PN'. Corresponding parts of congruent triangles are congruent (CPCTC).

▶ Vertical angles ∠MPN and ∠M'PN' are congruent.

TRY

Are angles 2 and 4 also congruent? How could you prove this?

EXAMPLE C The diagram on the right shows two parallel lines cut by a transversal. Alternate interior angles are angles that lie between two parallel lines, are each adjacent to a different parallel line, are both adjacent to the transversal, and lie on opposite sides of the transversal. In the diagram on the right, ∠1 and ∠2 are alternate interior angles.

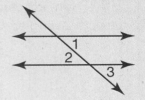

Corresponding angles are angles that lie on the same side of the transversal and the same side of different parallel lines. ∠1 and ∠3 are corresponding angles.

On △ABC below, point M is the midpoint of $\overline{AC}$. Use this triangle to prove that alternate interior angles are congruent and corresponding angles are congruent.

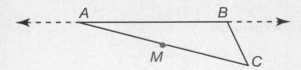

1

Rotate △ABC 180° around point M.

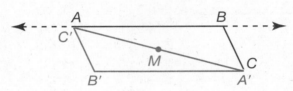

Rotating $\overline{AB}$ from the preimage produces corresponding side $\overline{A'B'}$ in the image. Corresponding sides are parallel after a rotation of 180°, so $\overline{AB} \parallel \overline{A'B'}$.

2

Extend $\overline{A'B'}$ and $\overline{AC}$ into lines.

Because $\overline{AB}$ is parallel to $\overline{A'B'}$, $\overleftrightarrow{AB}$ must be parallel $\overleftrightarrow{A'B'}$.

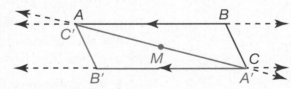

$\overleftrightarrow{AC}$ is a transversal that cuts across parallel lines $\overleftrightarrow{AB}$ and $\overleftrightarrow{A'B'}$.

3

Compare alternate interior angles.

Angles *BAC* and *B'A'C'* are alternate interior angles.

Rotation is a rigid motion, and rotating ∠*BAC* produced ∠*B'A'C'*, so these two angles must be congruent.

▶ ∠*BAC* ≅ ∠*B'A'C'*

4

Rotate ∠*A'B'C'* 180° around point *A'*.

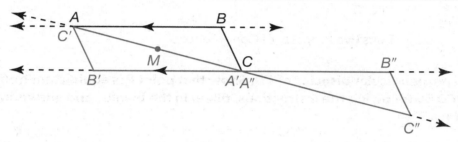

$\overline{A''B''}$ is collinear with $\overline{A'B'}$, so it is part of $\overleftrightarrow{A'B'}$. $\overline{A''C''}$ is collinear with $\overline{A'C'}$, so it is part of the transversal.

5

Compare alternate interior angles.

Angles *BAC* and *B''A''C''* are corresponding angles.

Rotating ∠*B'A'C'* produced ∠*B''A''C''*, so ∠*B'A'C'* must be congruent to ∠*B''A''C''*.

Angle *B'A'C'* is congruent to angle *BAC*, so angle *B''A''C''* must also be congruent to angle *BAC*.

▶ ∠*B''A''C''* ≅ ∠*BAC*

CHECK

How could knowing about vertical angles help you determine that ∠1 and ∠3 are congruent?

Practice

Show that in parallelogram *QRST*, opposite angles ∠*Q* and ∠*S* are congruent by following the instructions and filling in the blanks.

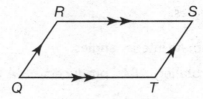

1. Draw diagonal $\overline{RT}$ on the figure.

2. Rotating △*RQT* _____° around the midpoint of _____ will produce an image that covers △*TSR*.

3. ∠*Q* ≅ ∠*Q'*   Corresponding angles are _____.

   ∠*Q'* ≅ ∠*S*   CPCTC

   ∠*Q* ≅ _____   Transitive Property of Congruence

Line *PM* is the perpendicular bisector of $\overline{CD}$. Show that point *P* is equidistant from the endpoints of $\overline{CD}$ by following the instructions, filling in the blanks, and answering the questions below.

4. $\overleftrightarrow{PM}$ is the perpendicular bisector of $\overline{CD}$, so ∠*PMC* and ∠*PMD* are both _____ angles and $\overline{CM}$ is congruent to _____.

5. Draw line segments $\overline{CP}$ and $\overline{DP}$ on the figure. Triangles *CMP* and *DMP* share side _____.

6. Which theorem or postulate can be used to prove that △*CMP* ≅ △*DMP*?

   _____

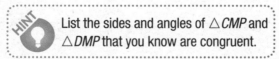

List the sides and angles of △*CMP* and △*DMP* that you know are congruent.

7. Corresponding sides of congruent triangles have equal lengths, so *PC* = _____. This means that point *P* is equidistant from points _____ and _____.

Use isosceles triangle *DEF* to prove that the base angles of an isosceles triangle are congruent. Follow the directions and fill in the blanks below.

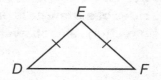

8. On the figure above, draw the median from angle *E* to side $\overline{DF}$.

9. By definition, a median connects a vertex to the _____ of the opposite side. So, point *M* divides $\overline{DF}$ into two congruent segments, $\overline{DM}$ and _____. Mark these segments as congruent on the figure.

10. The marks on the diagram show that the triangles have two pairs of congruent _____. Median $\overline{EM}$ is shared by both triangles, so by the reflexive property, $\overline{EM} \cong \overline{EM}$.

11. Three sides of $\triangle DME$ are congruent to three sides of _____, so those triangles are congruent by _____.

12. Corresponding parts of congruent triangles are _____, so $\angle D \cong$ _____.

Use parallelogram *QRST* to prove that opposite sides of a parallelogram are congruent. Follow the directions, fill in the blanks, and answer the questions below.

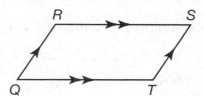

13. Draw diagonal $\overline{QS}$ on the figure above to cut the parallelogram into two triangles.

14. Because *QRST* is a parallelogram, $\overleftrightarrow{RS}$ and _____ are parallel lines. $\overleftrightarrow{QS}$ can be seen as a transversal. Angles *RSQ* and _____ are alternate interior angles, so they must be congruent.

15. $\overleftrightarrow{QR}$ and _____ are also parallel lines, and _____ is also a transversal cutting across these lines. Angles *RQS* and *TSQ* are _____, so they must be congruent.

16. Triangles *RQS* and *TSQ* share side _____, so they have at least one congruent side.

17. So, $\triangle RQS \cong \triangle TSQ$ by _____ Theorem.

18. $\overline{RS}$ must be congruent to $\overline{TQ}$ and $\overline{RQ}$ must be congruent to $\overline{TS}$ because _____ parts of congruent triangles are _____.

Use △ABC and its top half, △MBN, to show that the segment connecting the midpoints of two sides of a triangle is parallel to the third side and half the length of the third side. Follow the directions and answer the questions below.

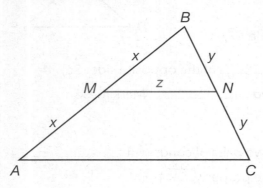
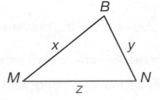

19. Using △MBN on the right, draw the rotated image △M'B'N' after a 180° rotation of △MBN around the midpoint of $\overline{MN}$. Label the lengths of the sides using x, y, and z.

Then, draw the rotated image △M"B"N" after a 180° rotation of △M'B'N' around the midpoint of $\overline{B'N'}$. Label the lengths of the sides using x, y, and z.

Finally, draw the rotated image △M'''B'''N''' after a 180° rotation of △M'B'N' around the midpoint of $\overline{B'M'}$. Label the lengths of the sides using x, y, and z.

20. Find the lengths of the following segments in terms of x, y, and z:

AB = _____   M"B = _____   CB = _____   N'''B = _____

How does ∠ABC compare to ∠MBN?

_____

Use a postulate or theorem to prove that △ABC is congruent to △M"BN''', which you drew.

_____

21. $\overline{M"N"}$ and $\overline{M'''N'''}$ can be combined to form $\overline{M"N'''}$. Compare $\overline{MN}$ to $\overline{M"N'''}$. Are the segments parallel, perpendicular, collinear, or none of these? Why?

_____

_____

How does the length of $\overline{M"N'''}$ compare to the length of $\overline{MN}$?

_____

_____

Complete the proofs.

22. **PROVE** Parallelogram *ABCD* has diagonals $\overline{AC}$ and $\overline{BD}$. The diagonals intersect at point *P*.

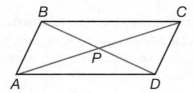

Prove that the diagonals of a parallelogram bisect each other by filling the two-column proof below.

Statements	Reasons
1. $\overline{AC}$ and $\overline{BD}$ are diagonals of parallelogram *ABCD*.	Given
2. $\overline{BC} \parallel \overline{AD}$	Opposite sides of a _____ are parallel.
3. $\angle BCA \cong \angle DAC$	_____ angles are congruent.
4. $\angle CBD \cong \angle ADB$	_____ angles are congruent.
5. $\overline{BC} \cong \overline{AD}$	Opposite sides of a _____ are congruent.
6. $\triangle BPC \cong \triangle DPA$	_____
7. $BP = DP$ and $AP = CP$	_____

23. **PROVE** Rectangle *ABCD* has diagonals $\overline{AC}$ and $\overline{BD}$. Prove that the diagonals are congruent.

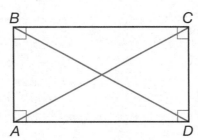

_____

_____

_____

_____

LESSON 8 Constructions of Lines and Angles

An important part of studying geometry is learning how to **construct** certain basic geometric figures. Some of the figures you can construct are line segments, angles, parallel lines, and perpendicular lines. Some of the tools you may use are a compass and a straightedge.

EXAMPLE A Construct a line segment that is congruent to $\overline{AB}$.

1
Using your straightedge, draw a ray that is longer than $\overline{AB}$. Label the endpoint as point C.

2
Place the compass point on point A. Place the pencil tip on point B. Then draw a curve.

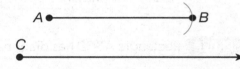

3
Without adjusting the compass span, place the compass point on point C. Draw a curve through the ray.

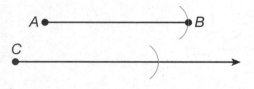

4
Label the point where the curve intersects the ray as point D.

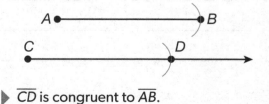

▶ $\overline{CD}$ is congruent to $\overline{AB}$.

DISCUSS

How could you construct a line segment that is twice as long as $\overline{AB}$?

EXAMPLE B Construct an angle that is congruent to ∠B.

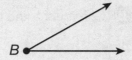

1

Using a straightedge, draw a ray. Label the endpoint as point E.

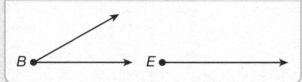

2

Place the compass point on point B and draw a curve. Label the points of intersection A and C. Then, without changing the compass span, place the compass point on point E. Draw a curve through the ray. Be sure that the curve extends well above the ray. Label the point of intersection as point F.

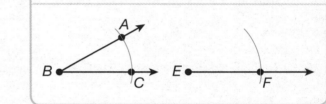

3

Place the compass point on point C and the pencil tip on point A. Draw a curve through point A. Then, without changing the compass span, place the compass point on point F. Draw a curve that intersects the curve you drew earlier. Label the point where the two curves intersect as point D.

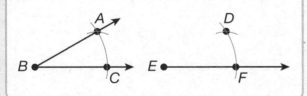

4

Draw a ray from point E through point D.

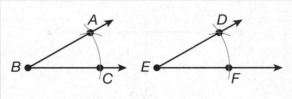

▶ ∠E is congruent to ∠B.

DISCUSS

How could you construct an angle with twice the measure of ∠B?

EXAMPLE C Construct a line that bisects $\overline{XY}$.

X •————————————————————• Y

1 Place the compass point on point X. Adjust the compass span so that it is more than half the length of XY. Draw a curve that intersects $\overline{XY}$.

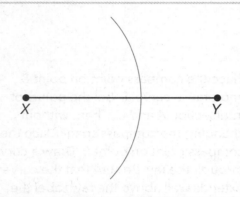

2 Without adjusting the compass span, place the compass point on point Y. Draw a second curve that intersects the first curve in two places. Label the points of intersection as points A and B.

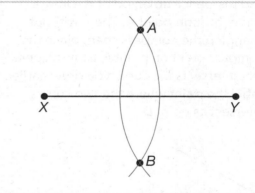

3 Use a straightedge to draw a line through points A and B. Label the intersection of $\overline{XY}$ and $\overleftrightarrow{AB}$ as point M.

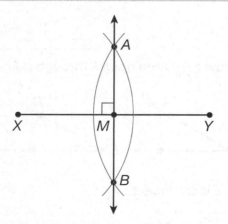

▶ Point M is the midpoint of $\overline{XY}$, and $\overleftrightarrow{AB}$ bisects $\overline{XY}$.

What can be said about the lengths of $\overline{AM}$ and $\overline{BM}$?

EXAMPLE D Construct the bisector of ∠DEF.

D

E *F*

1

Place the compass point on the vertex of the angle, point *E*. Draw a curve that intersects both $\overrightarrow{ED}$ and $\overrightarrow{EF}$.

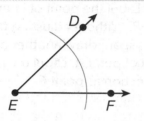

2

Place the compass point at the intersection of the curve and $\overrightarrow{ED}$. Draw a small curve inside the angle. Without changing the compass span, place the compass point at the intersection of the first curve and $\overrightarrow{EF}$. Draw another small curve inside the angle so that it intersects the small curve you drew earlier. Label the intersection of the curves as point *G*.

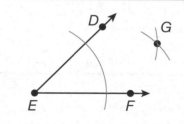

3

Use the straightedge to draw a ray from point *E* through point *G*.

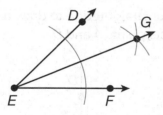

▶ Ray *EG* is the **angle bisector** of ∠DEF.

TRY

On a separate sheet of paper, draw a line segment and construct its bisector. Then bisect one of the angles formed by the line segment and its bisector.

EXAMPLE E Construct a perpendicular line from a point on a line.

1

Draw a line. Then draw point *A* on the line.

A

2

Place the compass point on point *A*. Set the compass span to any width. Draw a curve that intersects the line to the left of point *A*. Label the point of intersection as point *B*. Without adjusting the compass span, draw another curve to the right of point *A*. Label the point of intersection as point *C*.

B   *A*   *C*

3

Place the compass on point *B*. Set the compass span to any width greater than the length of $\overline{AB}$. Draw a curve above point *A*. Without adjusting the compass span, place the compass point on point *C*, then draw a curve that intersects the arc you just drew. Label the point of intersection as point *D*.

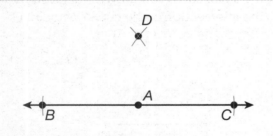

4

Use your straightedge to draw a line that connects points *A* and *D*.

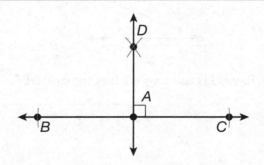

▶ $\overleftrightarrow{AD}$ is perpendicular to $\overleftrightarrow{BC}$ at point *A*.

DISCUSS

How could you construct a perpendicular line from point *B*?

EXAMPLE F Construct a perpendicular line from a point off a line.

1

Draw a line. Then draw point *E* above the line.

•*E*

2

Place the compass point on point *E*. Set the compass span to a width greater than the distance from point *E* to the line. Draw a curve that intersects the line to the left of point *E*. Label the point of intersection as point *F*. Without adjusting the compass span, draw another curve that intersects the line to the right of point *E*. Label the point of intersection as point *G*.

•*E*

F   *G*

3

Place the compass point on point *F*. Without adjusting the compass span, draw a curve below the line. Now place the compass point on point *G*. Then again without adjusting the compass span, draw a curve that intersects the curve below the line. Label the point of intersection as point *H*.

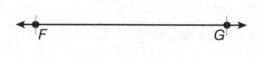

•*E*

F   *G*

✕*H*

4

Use a straightedge to draw a line connecting points *E* and *H*.

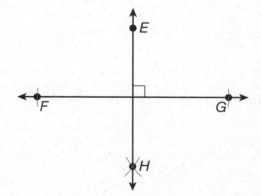

E

F   *G*

✕*H*

▶ $\overleftrightarrow{EH}$ is perpendicular to $\overleftrightarrow{FG}$.

TRY

In this example, if point *E* were below the original line, how would that change the process you use to construct a perpendicular line from point *E*?

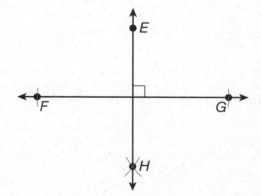

EXAMPLE G In Example C, you constructed $\overleftrightarrow{AB}$, the bisector of $\overline{XY}$. Prove that $\overleftrightarrow{AB}$ is perpendicular to $\overline{XY}$.

1

Draw triangles *AMX* and *AMY*. Use the SSS Postulate to prove the triangles are congruent.

Draw segments *AX* and *AY* to form triangles *AMX* and *AMY*.

Use the relationship between corresponding sides of the triangles to show that △*AMX* ≅ △*AMY*.

The two triangles share side $\overline{AM}$.

$\overline{XM} \cong \overline{YM}$ because $\overleftrightarrow{AB}$ bisects $\overline{XY}$ at point *M*.

$\overline{AX} \cong \overline{AY}$ because these distances were drawn with the same compass span.

So, △*AMX* ≅ △*AMY* by the SSS Postulate.

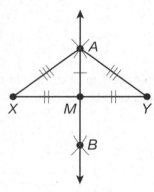

2

Show that $\overleftrightarrow{AB}$ is perpendicular to $\overline{XY}$.

∠*AMX* ≅ ∠*AMY* because corresponding angles of congruent triangles are congruent.

m∠*AMX* = m∠*AMY*

Angles *AMX* and *AMY* are a linear pair, so they are supplementary. The sum of their measures is 180°.

180° = m∠*AMX* + m∠*AMY*

Substitute m∠*AMX* for m∠*AMY*.

180° = m∠*AMX* + m∠*AMX* = 2 · m∠*AMX*

90° = m∠*AMX*

m∠*AMY* = m∠*AMX* = 90°

The angles formed by the intersection of $\overline{XY}$ and $\overleftrightarrow{AB}$ are right angles.

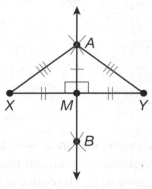

▸ $\overleftrightarrow{AB}$ is the **perpendicular bisector** of $\overline{XY}$.

DISCUSS

Does a line have a perpendicular bisector?

EXAMPLE H Construct a line parallel to $\overleftrightarrow{GH}$ through point J.

1

Use a straightedge to draw $\overleftrightarrow{GJ}$. Place the compass point on point G. Draw a small curve that intersects $\overleftrightarrow{GH}$ and $\overleftrightarrow{GJ}$. Label the points of intersection as points K and L. Then, without adjusting the compass span, place the compass point on point J. Draw a curve that intersects $\overleftrightarrow{GJ}$ above point J. Label that point of intersection as point M.

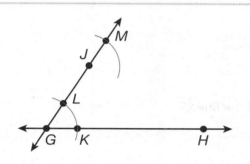

2

Place the compass point on point L. Adjust the compass span to draw a curve through point K. Then, without adjusting the compass span, place the compass point on point M. Draw a small curve in the interior of the angle that intersects the curve you drew earlier from point J. Label the point where those curves intersect as point N.

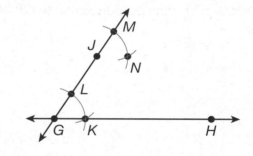

3

Use a straightedge to draw a line through points J and N.

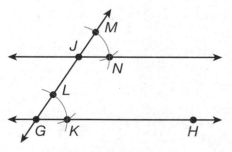

▶ Line JN is parallel to $\overleftrightarrow{GH}$.

How does the construction above relate to Example B, in which you copied an angle?

Practice

1. Construct a line segment congruent to $\overline{LM}$. Label the new segment $\overline{NP}$.

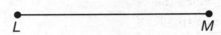

2. Construct the bisector of $\angle N$. Label the bisector $\overrightarrow{NQ}$.

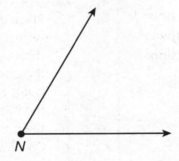

3. Construct a line perpendicular to $\overleftrightarrow{QP}$ at point P. Label the line $\overleftrightarrow{RS}$.

4. Construct a line parallel to $\overleftrightarrow{TV}$. Label the line $\overleftrightarrow{WZ}$.

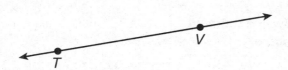

5. Bisect segment *LM*. Label the bisector $\overleftrightarrow{AB}$. Label the point where $\overleftrightarrow{AB}$ intersects $\overline{LM}$ as point *N*.

6. **THINK CRITICALLY** Think about the steps used to construct an angle congruent to a given angle.

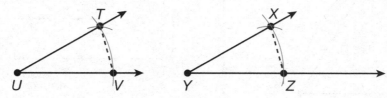

How can you use the steps for copying an angle and the triangle congruence postulates and theorems to prove that the angles are congruent?

_____

_____

_____

_____

_____

9 Constructions of Polygons

You can also use tools such as a compass and a straightedge to construct various polygons.

EXAMPLE A Construct an equilateral triangle.

1 Use a straightedge to draw line segment QP for the base of the triangle.

Q ————————— P

2 Set the span of your compass so that the compass point is on point Q and the pencil is on point P. Make a curve above the line. Without changing the compass span, move the compass point to point P. Then make another curve to intersect the first one. Label the intersection as point R.

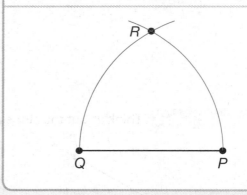

3 Use your straightedge to draw $\overline{QR}$ and $\overline{PR}$.

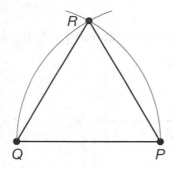

The same compass span was used to set the distance from point Q to point R and the distance from point P to point R. So, $\overline{QR}$ and $\overline{PR}$ must have the same length. Since the compass span you used to create point R matches the distance from point Q to point P, $\overline{QP}$ must have the same length as $\overline{QR}$ and $\overline{PR}$.

▶ Triangle PQR is an equilateral triangle.

CHECK

Using a ruler and a protractor, check that all sides and angles are congruent.

EXAMPLE B Construct a regular hexagon inscribed in a circle.

1 Draw a point and label it as point *A*. Then use your compass to construct a circle with point *A* as the center.

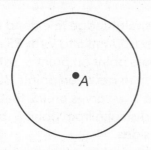

2 When a regular hexagon is inscribed in a circle, the length of each side of the hexagon is equal to the radius of the circle. So, begin by marking point *B* anywhere on the circle. Set the span of the compass by placing the compass point on point *B* and the pencil tip on point *A*. Now, with the compass point still on point *B*, draw a curve that intersects the circle. Label the point of intersection as point *C*.

3 Place the compass point on point *C*. Without adjusting the span of the compass, draw another curve that intersects the circle. Repeat this process three more times, going around the circle. Label the points of intersection as points *D*, *E*, *F*, and *G*.

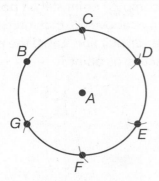

4 Use your straightedge to draw lines to connect adjacent points.

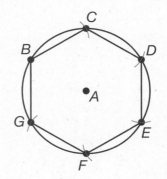

▶ Regular hexagon *BCDEFG* is inscribed in circle *A*.

TRY

On a separate sheet of paper, construct a regular hexagon inscribed in a circle.

EXAMPLE C Construct a square.

1

Use a straightedge to construct $\overline{RS}$ as the base of the square.

R •————————————• S

2

Use your straightedge to extend the segment past point S to form $\overrightarrow{RS}$. With the compass point on point S, set the compass span between points R and S. Then draw two curves on $\overrightarrow{RS}$ that are the same distance from point S, but on opposite sides.

3

Construct a line perpendicular to $\overrightarrow{RS}$ at point S.

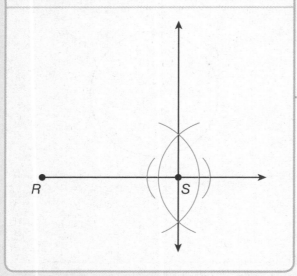

4

Set the compass span to the length of $\overline{RS}$ by placing the compass point on point S and the pencil on point R. Then, with the compass point still on point S, draw a curve above $\overrightarrow{RS}$ that intersects the perpendicular line. Label the point of intersection as point T.

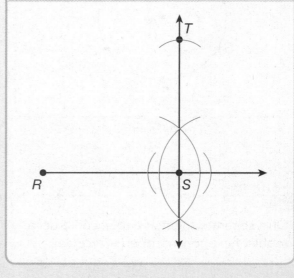

5

Without changing the compass span, set the compass point on point *T*. Draw a curve above point *R*. Then, again without changing the compass span, place the compass point on point *R*. Draw a curve that intersects the curve you just drew from point *T*. Label the point of intersection as point *U*.

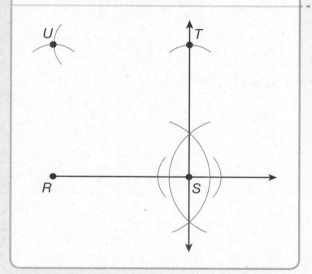

6

Use your straightedge to draw lines that connect points *R* and *U* and *points T* and *U*

▶ Figure *RSTU* is a square.

TRY

Once you have found point *T* in the construction above, you can try a different approach to constructing a square. Construct a line perpendicular to $\overleftrightarrow{ST}$ at point *T*, then construct a line perpendicular to $\overrightarrow{RS}$ at point *R*. How will you find point *U*?

Practice

1. Construct square *PQRS*, using $\overline{PQ}$ as the base of the square.

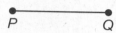

2. Construct equilateral triangle *FGH*, using $\overline{FG}$ as the base of the triangle.

3. Inscribe regular hexagon *RSTUVW* inside circle *Q*.

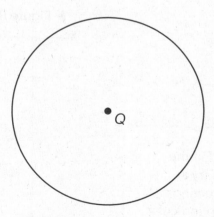

4. Construct equilateral triangle *ABC*, using $\overline{AB}$ as the base of the triangle.

A   B

5. Construct a circle, using point *J* as the center and $\overline{JK}$ as the radius. Then inscribe regular hexagon *KLMNOP* inside circle *J*.

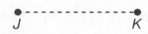

J   K

6. **THINK CRITICALLY** In Example C, you constructed square *RSTU*. Once you found point *T*, how could you have used the construction of parallel lines to complete the figure? Describe the steps you would use.

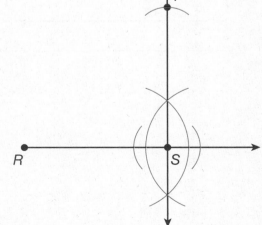

1 Review

Perform the transformation.

1. Transform parallelogram *MNOP* by rotating it 180° around the point (1, 1).

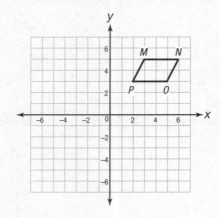

2. Transform △*DEF* by performing a reflection across the *x*-axis followed by a translation of 2 units right.

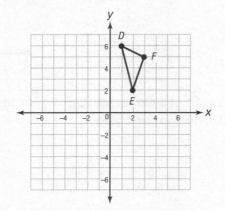

Prove the following.

3. Prove that vertical angles 1 and 3 are congruent.

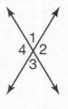

_____

_____

_____

4. In △*ABC* below, $\overline{CD}$ is a perpendicular bisector of $\overline{AB}$. Prove that △*ADC* ≅ △*BDC* using a triangle congruence postulate or theorem. Then, describe a transformation that could carry △*ADC* onto △*BDC*.

_____

_____

_____

Use a compass and straightedge for questions 5–7.

5.   Construct the bisector of ∠*LMN*. Label the bisector $\overrightarrow{MP}$.

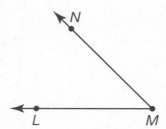

6.   Construct a line perpendicular to $\overleftrightarrow{AB}$ that passes through point *C*. Label it $\overleftrightarrow{CD}$.

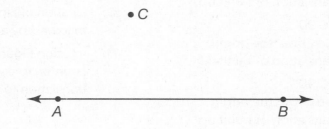

7.   Construct equilateral triangle *XYZ*, using $\overline{YZ}$ as the base of the triangle.

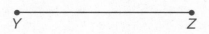

Choose the best answer.

8. Which pair of rigid motions could be used to show that △ABC and △A′B′C′ are congruent?

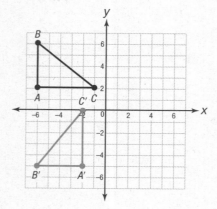

A. reflection of △ABC across the x-axis followed by a translation of 1 unit left

B. reflection of △ABC across the x-axis followed by a translation of 1 unit up

C. rotation of △ABC 90° counterclockwise about the origin followed by a translation of 1 unit left

D. rotation of △ABC 90° counterclockwise about the origin followed by a translation of 1 unit up

9. Which pair of rigid motions could be used to show that figure 1 is congruent to figure 2?

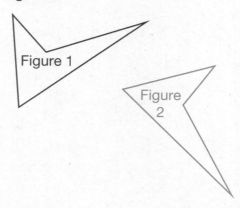

A. horizontal reflection of Figure 1 followed by a translation to the right

B. vertical reflection of Figure 1 followed by a translation to the right

C. rotation of Figure 1 of 90° clockwise followed by a translation to the right

D. rotation Figure 1 of 90° counterclockwise followed by a translation to the left

Describe a reflection or a rotation (of less than 360°) that can be used to map each figure onto itself.

10. parallelogram

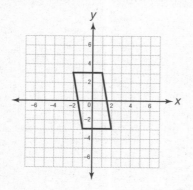

11. kite

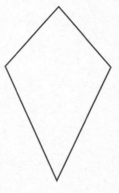

12. Quadrilateral *JKLM* and its reflected image are shown. Which statement is true of these two quadrilaterals?

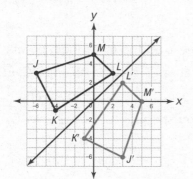

A. The image shows the result of a reflection across the *x*-axis.

B. The path that point *L* takes across the line of reflection is perpendicular to the line of reflection.

C. Each point (*x, y*) on quadrilateral *JKLM* maps to a point (−*y, x*) on its image.

D. Corresponding sides of quadrilateral *JKLM* and its image are parallel.

13. Triangle *DEF* is transformed to triangle *D′E′F′*. Which statement is **not** true of these two figures?

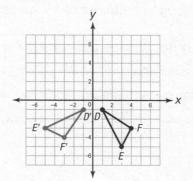

A. This transformation shows the image of △*DEF* after a 270° counterclockwise rotation about the origin.

B. This transformation preserved the side lengths and angle measures of the original figure.

C. Sides $\overline{DE}$ and $\overline{D′E′}$ lie on lines that are parallel to one another.

D. Sides $\overline{EF}$ and $\overline{E′F′}$ lie on lines that are perpendicular to one another.

Fill in each blank with an appropriate word or phrase.

14. Two lines are _____ if they intersect to form right angles.

15. A(n) _____ is a part of a line that falls between two points called endpoints.

16. A(n) _____ is created by two distinct rays or line segments that meet at a common endpoint.

Fill in the blanks to complete the proof.

PROVE The medians of a triangle meet at a single point.

In △ABC, E is the midpoint of $\overline{AB}$, and D is the midpoint of $\overline{BC}$.

17. In △ABC, $\overline{EC}$ and $\overline{AD}$ are medians that intersect at point P. AE = BE and CD = BD because medians extend from a vertex to the _____ of the opposite side.

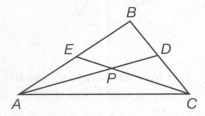

18. A line is added to connect points E and D. Because $\overleftrightarrow{ED}$ bisects $\overline{AB}$ and $\overline{BC}$, $\overline{ED}$ must be _____ to $\overline{AC}$ and ED must equal _____ · AC.

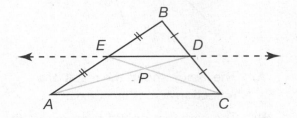

19. $\overleftrightarrow{ED}$ and $\overleftrightarrow{AC}$ are _____ lines cut by transversal $\overleftrightarrow{EC}$. Angles ∠DEC and ∠ACE are _____ angles, so ∠DEC ≅ ∠ACE.

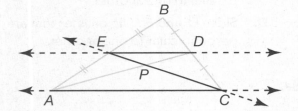

20. ∠EPD and ∠CPA are _____ angles, so ∠EPD ≅ ∠CPA. Triangles PED and PCA are similar according to _____.

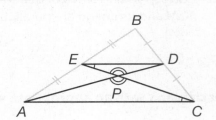

21. $\frac{ED}{AC}$ = _____ so $\frac{EP}{CP}$ = _____ and $\frac{DP}{AP}$ = _____. So, point P is $\frac{2}{3}$ of the way from point C to point E and $\frac{2}{3}$ of the way from point A to point D. Any two medians could have been chosen for this proof, so this is true for all three medians. All three medians meet at the single point that is $\frac{2}{3}$ of the way down each median.

**Use the given function to transform the given figure and graph the image. Use prime (')
symbols to name the vertices. Then, describe each transformation in words.**

22. $T(x, y) = (x - 4, y + 2)$

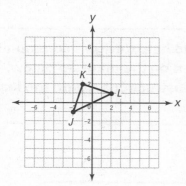

23. $R(x, y) = (x, -y)$

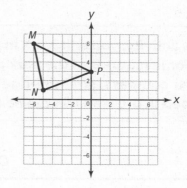

_____

_____

Solve.

24. **EXTEND** Triangle *RST* is shown. Sarah
reflects only side $\overline{RT}$ and angles *RTS* and
TRS across the *y*-axis. How many different
triangles can be formed if she extends
the rays of her reflected image until they
intersect? Which congruence postulate
does this illustrate?

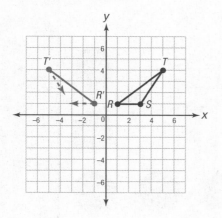

_____

_____

25. **PROVE** Prove that opposite angles of a
parallelogram are congruent. Draw on
the figure below to help explain your
reasoning.

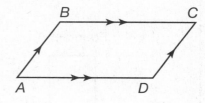

_____

_____

_____

_____

Park Design

For this activity, you will work in pairs or small groups to help design a community park. Some features of the park are already represented on the diagram below. Use your compass, straightedge, and knowledge of constructions to add the features described in the steps on the next page.

Community Park

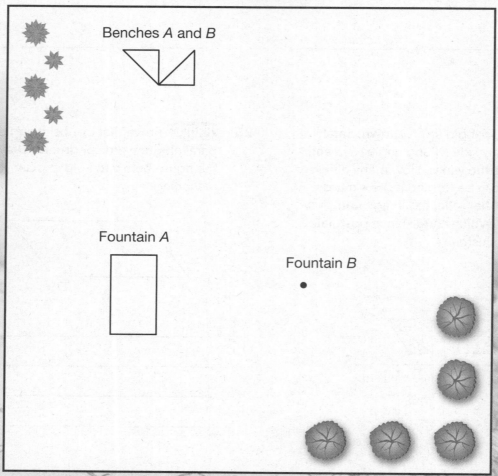

1. The landscaper wants to design a set of right triangular benches. Bench A and Bench B are shown on the diagram. He wants there to be 4 benches, arranged like petals of a flower. Draw Bench C, which is a rotation of Bench A 180° about its southern vertex (the point it shares with Bench B). Draw Bench D by rotating Bench B 180° about the same point.

2. Are the benches congruent figures? How do you know?

_____

_____

3. The landscaper wants to set aside two rectangular patches of land for fountains. The first, Fountain A, is shown. Fountain B will be the same size and shape as Fountain A. Construct Fountain B on the diagram, placing its northwest corner on the point shown. (Hint: Recall how to construct a line through a point and parallel to another line.)

4. Describe a transformation that could be used to produce the model of Fountain B from the model of Fountain A.

_____

_____

5. Next, the landscaper wants to place a sandbox in the northeast portion of the park for children to play in. His plans call for the sandbox to be hexagonal in shape. Construct a regular hexagon on the diagram to represent the sandbox.

6. Last, the landscaper wants to construct two identical triangular flowerbeds from wooden planks. He has placed three wooden planks—one 5-meter plank, one 12-meter plank, and one 13-meter plank—by each fountain. He begins to assemble the flowerbed near Fountain A and sends you to assemble the other flowerbed, but does not tell you how to arrange the sides of the triangle. Will the two flowerbeds be congruent? How do you know?

_____

_____

_____

Geometry

Number and Quantity

Quantities

Reason quantitatively and use units to solve problems.

Functions

Building Functions

Build a function that models a relationship between two quantities.

Build new functions from existing functions.

Linear, Quadratic, and Exponential Models

Construct and compare linear, quadratic, and exponential models and solve problems.

Interpret expressions for functions in terms of the situation they model.

Grade 7 Geometry

Draw, construct, and describe geometrical figures and describe the relationships between them.

Grade 8 Geometry

Understand congruence and similarity using physical models, transparencies, or geometry software.

Understand and apply the Pythagorean Theorem.

Geometry

Similarity, Right Triangles, and Trigonometry

Understand similarity in terms of similarity transformations.

Prove theorems involving similarity.

Define trigonometric ratios and solve problems involving right triangles.

Apply trigonometry to general triangles.

Modeling with Geometry

Apply geometric concepts in modeling situations.

Functions

Building Functions

Build new functions from existing functions.

Trigonometric Functions

Extend the domain of trigonometric functions using the unit circle.

Model periodic phenomena with trigonometric functions.

Prove and apply trigonometric identities.

Unit 2
Similarity, Proof, and Trigonometry

LESSON 10 Dilations and Similarity

Defining Dilation and Similarity

UNDERSTAND A **dilation** is a transformation that moves the points of a line, line segment, or figure either toward or away from a point called the **center of dilation**. The center of dilation can be any point inside the figure, on the figure, or outside the figure.

In the diagram on the right, blue triangle ABC was dilated to produce green triangle $A'B'C'$. The figures have the same shape, but $\triangle A'B'C'$ is twice the size of $\triangle ABC$.

If the center of dilation lies on a line or line segment, the dilated image of the line will be collinear with its preimage. So $\overline{A'B'}$ is collinear with its corresponding side, $\overline{AB}$. If a line or line segment does not pass through the center of dilation, the dilated image will be parallel to the preimage. So, $\overline{B'C'} \parallel \overline{BC}$ and $\overline{A'C'} \parallel \overline{AC}$. (The symbol $\parallel$ means "is parallel to.")

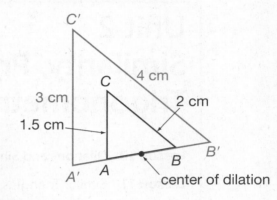

When a dilation is applied to a line segment or closed figure, it changes the size of the image according to a **scale factor**, k. If $k > 1$, the figure is enlarged. If $0 < k < 1$, the figure is reduced. In the figure above, $\triangle ABC$ was dilated by a scale factor of 2, so it was enlarged. Each side of $\triangle A'B'C'$ is twice as long as its corresponding side on $\triangle ABC$.

UNDERSTAND Dilating a figure produces a figure that is the same shape as the original figure, but a different size. Like rigid motions, dilations preserve angle measures. Unlike rigid motions, dilations do not preserve the lengths of line segments. Instead, they produce a figure with sides that are proportional to the sides of the preimage. So, the original figure and its dilated image are **similar** figures.

Trapezoid $ABCD$ was dilated by a scale factor of $\frac{3}{2}$ to form trapezoid $FGHJ$ on the right. The angle marks show that corresponding angles are congruent. Corresponding side lengths are proportional. So, $ABCD \sim FGHJ$. (The symbol $\sim$ means "is similar to.")

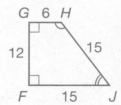

$\angle F \cong \angle A \quad \angle G \cong \angle B \quad \angle H \cong \angle C \quad \angle J \cong \angle D$

$\dfrac{FG}{AB} = \dfrac{12}{8} = \dfrac{3}{2} \qquad \dfrac{GH}{BC} = \dfrac{6}{4} = \dfrac{3}{2} \qquad \dfrac{HJ}{CD} = \dfrac{15}{10} = \dfrac{3}{2} \qquad \dfrac{FJ}{AD} = \dfrac{15}{10} = \dfrac{3}{2}$

A **regular polygon** is a polygon in which all sides have the same length and all angles have the same measure. Any two regular polygons of the same type—having the same number of sides—are similar to each other.

⚡ Connect

Is parallelogram *MNPQ* ~ parallelogram *STUV*? Explain how you know.

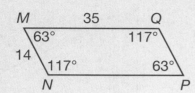

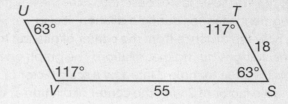

1

Compare corresponding angle measures.

Recall that the order of the letters in the names of the figures identifies corresponding vertices. So, vertex *M* corresponds to vertex *S*, vertex *N* corresponds to vertex *T*, and so on.

m∠*M* = m∠*S* = 63°

m∠*N* = m∠*T* = 117°

m∠*P* = m∠*U* = 63°

m∠*Q* = m∠*V* = 117°

Corresponding angles are equal in measure, or congruent.

2

Determine if corresponding sides have proportional lengths.

Opposite sides of parallelograms are congruent.

MQ = *NP* = 35   *TU* = *SV* = 55

MN = *PQ* = 14   *ST* = *UV* = 18

Compare corresponding sides to determine if they are proportional.

$$\frac{MQ}{SV} = \frac{35}{55} = \frac{7}{11}$$

$$\frac{MN}{ST} = \frac{14}{18} = \frac{7}{9}$$

$$\frac{NP}{TU} = \frac{MQ}{SV} = \frac{35}{55} = \frac{7}{11}$$

$$\frac{PQ}{UV} = \frac{MN}{ST} = \frac{14}{18} = \frac{7}{9}$$

▶ Not all corresponding sides are in the same ratio, so parallelogram *MNPQ* is not similar to parallelogram *STUV*.

DISCUSS

How could you change parallelogram *STUV* to make it similar to parallelogram *MNPQ*? Is that the only way to make the two parallelograms similar?

Dilations as Functions

UNDERSTAND The scale factor describes how the length of a line segment changes during a dilation. It also describes how the distance from the center of dilation to a given point changes during that dilation. The graph on the right shows the blue triangle dilated by a scale factor of 0.5 and a scale factor of 2 with the center of dilation at the origin. Notice that each vertex of the larger green triangle is twice as far from the origin as the corresponding vertex on the blue triangle, and each vertex of the smaller green triangle is half as far from the origin.

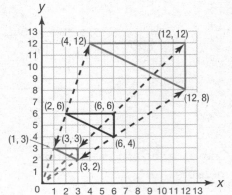

A dilation on the coordinate plane can be written as a function. The input of this function is a point on the coordinate plane, (x, y). When you apply the function to a point, the output of the function will be the coordinates of the dilated image of that point.

To dilate a point on a figure (x, y) by a scale factor k with the center of dilation at (a, b), use the following rule:

$$D_k(x, y) = (a + k(x - a), b + k(y - b))$$

When the center of dilation is the origin, $a = 0$ and $b = 0$, so this rule simplifies to:

$$D_k(x, y) = (kx, ky)$$

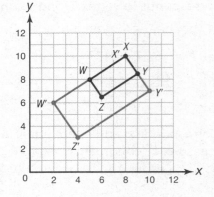

The graph to the right shows a dilation of rectangle $WXYZ$ with the center of dilation at $X(8, 10)$ and a scale factor of 2. The function that represents this transformation is

$$D_2(x, y) = (8 + 2(x - 8), 10 + 2(y - 10)) = (8 + 2x - 16, 10 + 2y - 20) = (2x - 8, 2y - 10)$$

Point W has coordinates $(5, 8)$. Substitute these coordinates into the function to find W'.

$$D_2(5, 8) = (8 + 2(5 - 8), 10 + 2(8 - 10)) = (8 + 2(-3), 10 + 2(-2)) = (8 - 6, 10 - 4) = (2, 6)$$

UNDERSTAND When the size of a figure changes in only one dimension, the transformation is called a stretch or a shrink. A vertical stretch pulls the points of a figure away from a horizontal line, such as the x-axis, and a vertical shrink pushes the points of the figure toward a horizontal line. A horizontal stretch pulls the points of a figure away from a vertical line, such as the y-axis, and a horizontal shrink pushes the points of the figure toward a vertical line. The lengths of line segments and the measure of angles usually change during a stretch or a shrink.

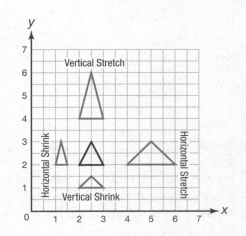

⊷ Connect

Dilate the line $y = 2x - 2$ using the rule $D_3(x, y) = (1 + 3(x - 1), 2 + 3(y - 2))$. Identify the scale factor and the center of dilation.

1

Dilate one point from the preimage.

The point (2, 2) is on the preimage. In the function, let $x = 2$ and $y = 2$.

$D_3(2, 2) = (1 + 3(2 - 1), 2 + 3(2 - 2))$

$D_3(2, 2) = (1 + 3(1), 2 + 3(0))$

$D_3(2, 2) = (4, 2)$

Plot (4, 2) as the image of point (2, 2).

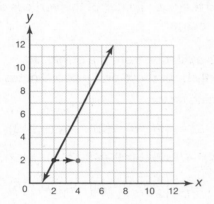

2

Dilate a second point and graph the image.

The point (3, 4) is also on the preimage.

$D_3(3, 4) = (1 + 3(3 - 1), 2 + 3(4 - 2))$

$D_3(3, 4) = (7, 8)$

Plot (7, 8) as the dilated image of (3, 4).

Two points is enough to determine a line, so draw a line through the two dilated points to graph the image.

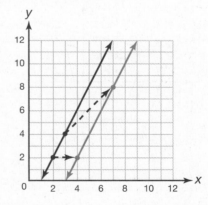

3

Identify the scale factor and the center of dilation.

Compare the general rule for dilations with scale factor k and center of dilation (a, b) to the given rule.

General rule:
$D_k(x, y) = (a + k(x - a), b + k(y - b))$

Given rule:
$D_k(x, y) = (1 + 3(x - 1), 2 + 3(y - 2))$

By comparing the formulas, we see that $k = 3$, $a = 1$, and $b = 2$.

▶ The scale factor is 3, and the center of dilation is (1, 2).

TRY ▷

Dilate the same line given the function $D_k(x, y) = (1 + 3(x - 1), 3y)$. Identify the scale factor and center of dilation, and compare the image and preimage.

EXAMPLE A Quadrilateral *ABCZ* is shown. Draw quadrilateral *A'B'C'Z'*, which is the result of a dilation centered at the origin by a scale factor of $\frac{3}{2}$. Then write a function to describe the dilation.

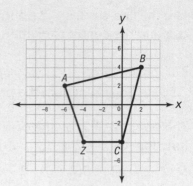

1 Identify the coordinates of the vertices of quadrilateral *ABCZ*.

The quadrilateral has vertices $A(-6, 2)$, $B(2, 4)$, $C(0, -4)$, and $Z(-4, -4)$.

2 Find the coordinates of the vertices of the image.

This is a dilation from the origin, so multiply both the *x*- and *y*-coordinates by the scale factor, $\frac{3}{2}$.

$A(-6, 2) \rightarrow \left(\frac{3}{2}(-6), \frac{3}{2}(2)\right) \rightarrow A'(-9, 3)$

$B(2, 4) \rightarrow \left(\frac{3}{2}(2), \frac{3}{2}(4)\right) \rightarrow B'(3, 6)$

$C(0, -4) \rightarrow \left(\frac{3}{2}(0), \frac{3}{2}(-4)\right) \rightarrow C'(0, -6)$

$Z(-4, -4) \rightarrow \left(\frac{3}{2}(-4), \frac{3}{2}(-4)\right) \rightarrow Z'(-6, -6)$

3 Graph the image.

Plot the vertices and connect them.

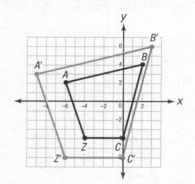

4 Use function notation to describe the dilation.

The function notation must show that each *x*-coordinate and each *y*-coordinate are multiplied by $\frac{3}{2}$.

▶ The function $D_{\frac{3}{2}}(x, y) = \left(\frac{3}{2}x, \frac{3}{2}y\right)$ represents the transformation.

DISCUSS

Compare the lengths of $\overline{ZC}$ and $\overline{Z'C'}$. How do you think the lengths of the other corresponding segments compare?

EXAMPLE B Triangles *MNP* and *ABC* are similar. Describe in words the dilation that would transform △*MNP* into △*ABC*.

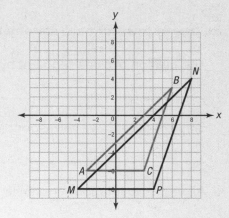

1

Determine the scale factor of the dilation.

After dilation, corresponding sides of an image and its preimage are parallel. So, $\overline{AB}$ corresponds to $\overline{MN}$, $\overline{BC}$ corresponds to $\overline{NP}$, and $\overline{AC}$ corresponds to $\overline{MP}$.

Since $\overline{AC}$ and $\overline{MP}$ are horizontal, they can be measured simply by counting units. $AC = 6$ units and $MP = 8$ units. The scale factor of the dilation is equal to the ratio of the corresponding sides: $\frac{AC}{MP} = \frac{6}{8} = \frac{3}{4}$.

2

Locate the center of dilation.

The triangles do not share any vertices in common, so the center of dilation cannot be one of the vertices.

In order to locate the center of dilation, draw lines connecting corresponding vertices. The point at which they intersect is the center of dilation.

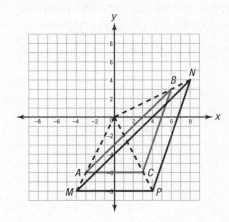

The lines appear to intersect at the origin.

3

Check your solution.

If the origin is the center of dilation, then each point (x, y) on △*MNP* will be dilated to form a corresponding point $\left(\frac{3}{4}x, \frac{3}{4}y\right)$ on △*ABC*.

$M(-4, -8) \longrightarrow \left(\frac{3}{4}(-4), \frac{3}{4}(-8)\right) \rightarrow (-3, -6)$

$N(8, 4) \longrightarrow \left(\frac{3}{4}(8), \frac{3}{4}(4)\right) \rightarrow (6, 3)$

$P(4, -8) \longrightarrow \left(\frac{3}{4}(4), \frac{3}{4}(-8)\right) \rightarrow (3, -6)$

These coordinates are the vertices of △*ABC*.

▶ A dilation of △*MNP* from the origin by a scale factor of $\frac{3}{4}$ would produce △*ABC*.

TRY

Describe how the smaller triangle, △*ABC*, could be dilated to form the larger triangle, △*MNP*.

Practice

Write *true* or *false* for each statement. If false, rewrite the statement to make it true.

1. The dilation of a line segment by a scale factor greater than 1 results in a shorter segment.

   _____

2. Similar figures have corresponding sides that are congruent.

   _____

3. All regular pentagons are similar to one another.

   _____

4. When a line contains the center of dilation, its image is parallel to the preimage.

   _____

5. A vertical stretch of a figure will preserve the measure of the angles in the figure but not the lengths of its sides.

   _____

   _____

Graph the image that results from the dilation indicated. State if the resulting image is identical to the preimage, parallel to the preimage, or neither.

6. $D_2(x, y) = (2 + 2(x - 2), 1 + 2(y - 1))$

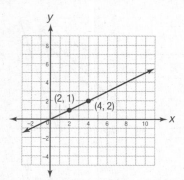

7. Scale factor: $\frac{1}{3}$

   Center of dilation: the origin

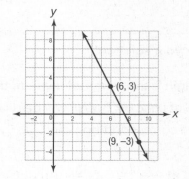

_____   _____

Dilate two points on the line.

For questions 8 and 9, determine if the two figures are similar. Explain how you know.

8. Trapezoids *ABCD* and *RSTV*

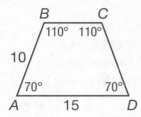 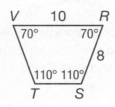

_____

_____

_____

9. Triangles *XYZ* and *MNO*.

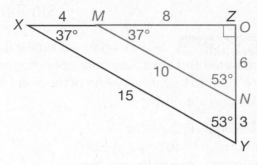

_____

_____

_____

10. **APPLY** Describe how △*ABC* was transformed to its image, △*A'B'C'*, both in words and in function notation.

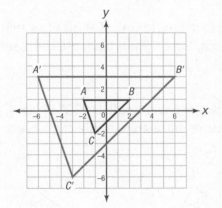

Words:_____

_____

Function Notation: _____

11. **IDENTIFY** Derek says that △*GHJ* could be transformed to △*G'H'J'* by dilating it from the origin by a scale factor of $\frac{2}{3}$. Is Derek correct? If not, identify the error Derek made and identify the correct dilation.

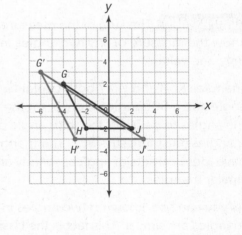

_____

_____

_____

_____

Similar Triangles

Similarity with Angles

UNDERSTAND Two triangles are similar if all of their corresponding angles have equal measures and all of their corresponding sides have proportional lengths. However, you do not need to know every one of those angle measures and side lengths to prove that two triangles are similar.

Each angle in △ABC is congruent to an angle in △EFG. However, none of the lengths of the sides of either triangle are known. If there is a dilation that carries △ABC on to △EFG, then the triangles must be similar. The dilated image △A′B′C′ exactly covers △EFG, so △ABC must be similar to △EFG.

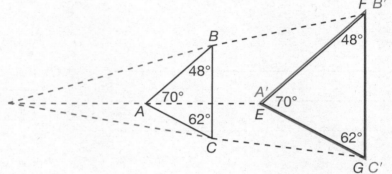

Dilating a figure produces a similar figure with congruent corresponding angles. The reverse is also true. If all corresponding angles in two triangles are congruent, dilating one triangle can produce the other triangle, so the triangles must be similar.

Notice that for figures with four or more sides, two figures can have identical angles but still not be similar. Consider a square and a rectangle. Even though the figures have the same set of angles, all right angles, they are not similar.

UNDERSTAND The sum of the measures of the interior angles of any triangle is 180°. If you know the measure of any two angles in a triangle, the measure of the third angle can have only one value.

Triangles KLM and WXY both contain a 78° angle and a 66° angle. In order for the sums of the angles to be 180°, the third angle of both triangles must measure 36°. The triangles have identical sets of angles, so they are similar triangles.

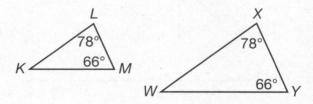

As you can see, knowing two angles in each triangle is enough information to determine if the triangles are similar. This fact is the basis for the postulate defined below.

Angle-Angle Similarity (AA~) Postulate: If two angles of one triangle are congruent to two angles of another triangle, then the triangles are similar.

88 Unit 2: Similarity, Proof, and Trigonometry

⌗ Connect

Prove that △ABC ∼ △DEF by the AA∼ Postulate.

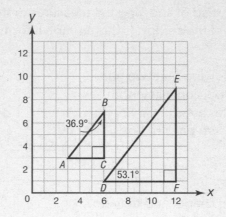

1

Identify corresponding angles.

If △ABC ∼ △DEF, the order of the letters in each triangle's name will identify corresponding angles. So, ∠A corresponds to ∠D, ∠B corresponds to ∠E, and ∠C corresponds to ∠F.

2

Show that one pair of corresponding angles are congruent.

∠C ≅ ∠F because both measure 90°.

3

Show that a second pair of corresponding angles are congruent.

To determine if ∠A ≅ ∠D, find m∠A.

m∠A + m∠B + m∠C = 180°

m∠A + 36.9° + 90° = 180°

m∠A = 180° − 36.9° − 90°

m∠A = 53.1°

This is equal to the measure of ∠D, so the triangles have two pairs of congruent corresponding angles.

▶ Since ∠A ≅ ∠D and ∠C ≅ ∠F, then △ABC ∼ △DEF by the AA∼ Postulate.

Check that the triangles are similar by finding a center of dilation and a scale factor that would transform △ABC into △DEF.

Similarity with Sides and Angles

UNDERSTAND Suppose that instead of knowing the measures of the angles in a pair of triangles, you know the length of their sides. Is this enough information to determine if the triangles are similar?

Unlike with angle measures, showing that two pairs of corresponding sides are proportional in length does not prove that two triangles are similar. For example, in △FGH and △ABC, two pairs of sides are in the same ratio.

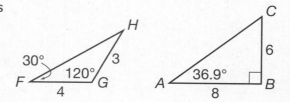

$$\frac{AB}{FG} = \frac{8}{4} = 2 \qquad \frac{BC}{GH} = \frac{6}{3} = 2$$

However, they are not the same shape, and they do not have corresponding angles that are congruent. They are not similar.

Now, consider △FGH and △JKL. In these triangles, all three pairs of sides are in the same ratio.

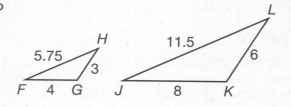

$$\frac{JK}{FG} = \frac{8}{4} = 2 \qquad \frac{KL}{GH} = \frac{6}{3} = 2 \qquad \frac{JL}{FH} = \frac{11.5}{5.75} = 2$$

Think of the three sides of △FGH as three line segments. Dilating $\overline{FG}$, which has a length of 4 units, by a scale factor of 2 will produce a line segment with a length of 8 units. Dilating $\overline{GH}$, with length 3, by the same scale factor will produce a line segment with a length of 6 units. Dilating $\overline{FH}$, with length 5.75, by this same scale factor will produce a line segment with a length of 11.5 units. If these dilated line segments are assembled to form a triangle, that triangle will be identical to △JKL.

As you can see, knowing the lengths of all of the sides of two triangles allows you to determine if they are similar. This is summarized in a mathematical theorem.

> **Side-Side-Side Similarity (SSS~) Theorem:** If the three sides of one triangle are proportional in length to the three sides of another triangle, then the triangles are similar.

UNDERSTAND As you saw above, showing that only two pairs of corresponding sides are proportional in length is not enough information to prove that two triangles are similar. However, if two pairs of sides are proportional in length and the angles between those sides have equal measures, then the two triangles must be similar.

> **Side-Angle-Side Similarity (SAS~) Theorem:** If two sides of one triangle have lengths that are proportional to two sides of another triangle and the included angles of those sides are congruent, then the triangles are similar.

On the next page, we will verify the SAS~ Theorem.

⊶Connect

Use what you know about dilations to show that △MNP ~ △QRP, according to the SAS~ Theorem.

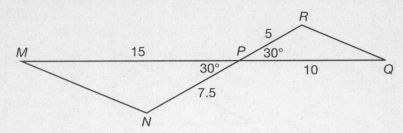

1

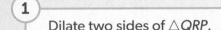

Dilate two sides of △QRP.

Treat the sides as separate line segments. Dilate $\overline{PR}$ by a scale factor of -1.5 from vertex *P*. For a negative scale factor, draw the image on the opposite side of the center of dilation. Notice that the dilated segment $\overline{P'R'}$ covers $\overline{PN}$.

$5 \cdot (-1.5) = -7.5$

Dilate $\overline{PQ}$ by a scale factor of -1.5 from point *P*. Notice that the dilated segment $\overline{P'Q'}$ covers $\overline{PM}$.

$10 \cdot (-1.5) = -15$

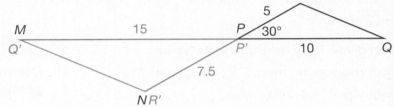

2

Complete the triangle.

Notice that, since they are dilations, $\overline{P'Q'}$ and $\overline{P'R'}$ form the same angle as $\overline{PQ}$ and $\overline{PR}$.

There is only one possible line segment that has endpoints *Q'* and *R'*. That segment, $\overline{Q'R'}$, covers $\overline{MN}$.

▶ $\overline{PR} \sim \overline{PN}$, $\overline{PQ} \sim \overline{PM}$, and ∠QPR ≅ ∠MPN, so △MNP ~ △QRP.

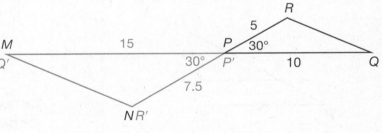

◁DISCUSS▷

If △QRP was dilated by positive 1.5, would the image be identical to △MNP?

EXAMPLE A Use △RST to show that a line parallel to one side of a triangle divides the other two sides proportionally.

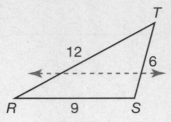

1

Dilate △RST from point T.

Begin by dilating $\overline{TR}$ by a factor of $\frac{2}{3}$. This produces segment $\overline{T'R'}$, which has length $\frac{2}{3} \cdot 12 = 8$ units.

Then dilate $\overline{TS}$ by the same scale factor. This produces segment $\overline{T'S'}$, which has length $\frac{2}{3} \cdot 6 = 4$ units.

Complete the image by drawing in segment $\overline{R'S'}$ to form dilated triangle R'S'T'.

When a polygon is dilated, corresponding sides are always parallel (or collinear). So, $\overline{R'S'}$ must be parallel to $\overline{RS}$.

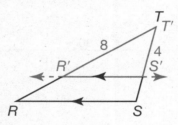

Notice that △RST ~ △R'S'T' according to the Side-Angle-Side Similarity Theorem.

2

Determine if the sides are divided proportionally.

Find the lengths of R'R and S'S.

TR' + R'R = TR	TS' + S'S = TS
8 + R'R = 12	4 + S'S = 6
R'R = 4	S'S = 2

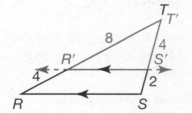

Compare line segments to see if the sides are partitioned in the same ratio.

$$\frac{TR'}{R'R} = \frac{8}{4} = 2 \qquad \frac{TS'}{S'S} = \frac{4}{2} = 2$$

▶ A line parallel to $\overline{RS}$ divides the other two sides proportionally.

DISCUSS

Suppose you had dilated △RST by a different scale factor. Would the sides intersected by the line parallel to $\overline{RS}$ still be divided proportionally?

EXAMPLE B Right triangle *DFG* is shown on the left. Altitude $\overline{FJ}$ divides it into two right triangles, as shown on the right. Use these figures to derive the Pythagorean Theorem.

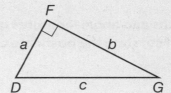
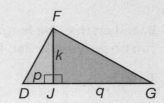

1

Compare △*DFG* and △*DJF*.

Triangle *DFG* contains ∠*D* and a right angle. Triangle *DJF* also contains ∠*D* and a right angle. So, △*DFG* ~ △*DJF* according to the Angle-Angle Similarity Postulate.

Copy △*DJF* and show the triangles with the same orientation to make comparing them easier.

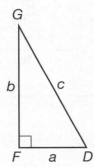

Corresponding sides of similar triangles are proportional, so ratios of corresponding sides can be set equal to each other. Substitute the variables for each side length.

$\dfrac{GD}{FD} = \dfrac{FD}{JD}$ Substitute *a*, *c*, and *p*.

$\dfrac{c}{a} = \dfrac{a}{p}$ Cross multiply.

$cp = a^2$

DISCUSS

Could you derive the Pythagorean Theorem if △*DFG* were not a right triangle?

2

Compare △*DFG* and △*FJG*.

Triangles *DFG* and *FJG* both contain ∠*G* and a right angle. So, △*DFG* ~ △*FJG* according to AA~.

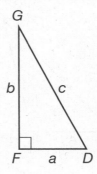
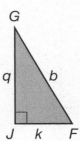

$\dfrac{GD}{GF} = \dfrac{GF}{GJ}$

$\dfrac{c}{b} = \dfrac{b}{q}$

$cq = b^2$

3

Derive the Pythagorean Theorem.

Examine $\overline{DG}$.

$DG = DJ + JG$

$\quad c = p + q$

$a^2 = cp$ and $b^2 = cq$, so:

$a^2 + b^2 = cp + cq$ Factor out *c*.

$a^2 + b^2 = c(p + q)$ Substitute *c* for *p* + *q*.

$a^2 + b^2 = c(c)$

▶ $a^2 + b^2 = c^2$

Practice

Based on the side lengths and angle measures given or indicated, determine if the triangles can be proven similar. If so, state the postulate or theorem that applies.

1.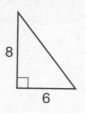

_____

2.

_____

HINT Identical angles marks indicate congruent angles.

3.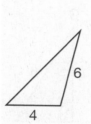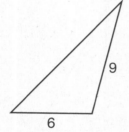

_____

4.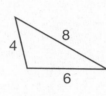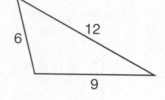

_____

Choose the best answer.

5. In $\triangle ABC$, $\overline{DE}$ is parallel to $\overline{AC}$. If $BA = 12$, what is the value of BD?

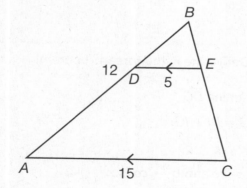

A. 2 units

B. 3 units

C. 4 units

D. 5 units

6. Using the information given in the figures below, which of the following allows you to prove that $\triangle FGH \sim \triangle JKL$?

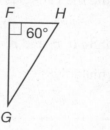 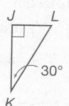

A. AA~ Postulate

B. SSS~ Theorem

C. SAS~ Theorem

D. Pythagorean Theorem

For questions 7 and 8, determine if each pair of triangles is similar or not. Explain which theorem you used and which sides or angles you compared to determine your answer.

7. △*RST* and △*RVU*

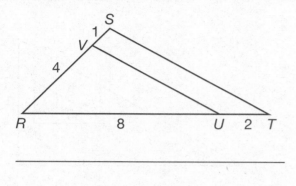

_____

_____

8. △*KLM* and △*NPQ*

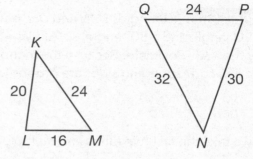

_____

_____

Solve.

9. [COMPARE] Ling went hiking one day. She measured the angle of the sun to be 55° from the horizon. At that time, her shadow was 3.5 feet long, and she is 5 feet tall. She measured the shadow of a tree to be 14.7 feet long. How tall is the tree?

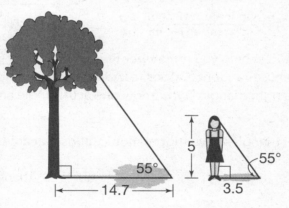

_____

_____

_____

LESSON 12 Trigonometric Ratios

UNDERSTAND Triangles *LMN* and *DEF* both have a 90° angle and a 30° angle, so $\triangle LMN \sim \triangle DEF$ by the AA~ Postulate. Because the triangles are similar, corresponding sides are proportional.

$$\frac{LM}{DE} = \frac{MN}{EF} = \frac{NL}{FD}$$

If we take the first two ratios and multiply by $\frac{EF}{LM}$, we get a new proportion: $\frac{EF}{DE} = \frac{MN}{LM}$. The ratio of the **leg** opposite the 30° angle divided by the **hypotenuse** is the same for both triangles. This ratio is called the **sine** ratio.

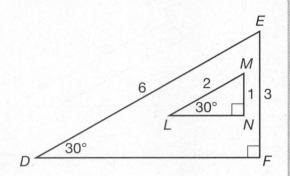

The ratios of the side lengths of a right triangle depend on the measures of its acute angles. These ratios are called **trigonometric ratios**.

Sine of $\angle A$ = sin A = $\dfrac{\text{Opposite leg length}}{\text{Hypotenuse}} = \dfrac{a}{c}$

Cosine of $\angle A$ = cos A = $\dfrac{\text{Adjacent leg length}}{\text{Hypotenuse}} = \dfrac{b}{c}$

Tangent of $\angle A$ = tan A = $\dfrac{\text{Opposite leg length}}{\text{Adjacent leg length}} = \dfrac{a}{b}$

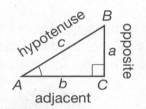

Thinking "SOH-CAH-TOA" can help you remember these ratios: Sine/Opposite/Hypotenuse-Cosine/Adjacent/Hypotenuse-Tangent/Opposite/Adjacent. Using these ratios, you can find the length of any side of a right triangle if you know one acute angle and any other side.

UNDERSTAND Some right triangles have trigonometric ratios that are easy to remember.

45°−45°−90° triangle:

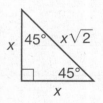

30°−60°−90° triangle:

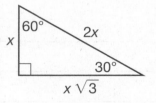

sin 45° = $\dfrac{1}{\sqrt{2}} = \dfrac{\sqrt{2}}{2}$

cos 45° = $\dfrac{1}{\sqrt{2}} = \dfrac{\sqrt{2}}{2}$

tan 45° = 1

sin 30° = $\dfrac{1}{2}$

cos 30° = $\dfrac{\sqrt{3}}{2}$

tan 30° = $\dfrac{1}{\sqrt{3}} = \dfrac{\sqrt{3}}{3}$

sin 60° = $\dfrac{\sqrt{3}}{2}$

cos 60° = $\dfrac{1}{2}$

tan 60° = $\sqrt{3}$

⊶ Connect

Consider right triangle *JKL*. What are the sine, cosine, and tangent ratios for ∠*K*?

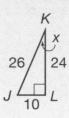

1

Identify the opposite and adjacent legs and the hypotenuse.

The leg opposite ∠*K* is $\overline{JL}$. Its length is 10 units.

The leg adjacent to ∠*K* is $\overline{KL}$. Its length is 24 units.

The hypotenuse is $\overline{JK}$. Its length is 26 units.

2

Find the trigonometric ratios.

The degree measure of ∠*K* is *x*, so use *x* in the equations.

$$\sin x = \frac{\text{opposite}}{\text{hypotenuse}} = \frac{10}{26} = \frac{5}{13}$$

$$\cos x = \frac{\text{adjacent}}{\text{hypotenuse}} = \frac{24}{26} = \frac{12}{13}$$

$$\tan x = \frac{\text{opposite}}{\text{adjacent}} = \frac{10}{24} = \frac{5}{12}$$

CHECK

The value of *x* in the triangle is approximately 22.6°. Use this angle measure and a calculator to check that the ratios found above are accurate. For example, press SIN, enter 22.6, and press ENTER. Then verify that the decimal found is about equal to $\frac{5}{13}$ by dividing 5 by 13. Use the COS and TAN keys to check the other ratios.

EXAMPLE A In isosceles right triangle PQR, an altitude has been drawn from angle Q. Use $\overline{QS}$ to find the area of $\triangle PQR$.

1

Find the length of $\overline{PR}$, the hypotenuse of $\triangle PQR$.

Triangle PQR is a $45°-45°-90°$ triangle with legs 4 centimeters long.

The hypotenuse of a $45°-45°-90°$ triangle is $\sqrt{2}$ times the length of a leg, so $PR = 4\sqrt{2}$ cm.

2

Find the length of $\overline{PS}$.

$\overline{QS}$ is an altitude, so $m\angle PSQ = 90°$.

Triangles PSQ and RSQ are both $45°-45°-90°$ triangles with a 4-cm hypotenuse, so they are congruent by ASA Theorem.

Because congruent parts of congruent triangles are congruent, $PS = RS$ and each segment is half of $\overline{PR}$.

$PS = \dfrac{4\sqrt{2}}{2} = 2\sqrt{2}$

3

Determine the length of $\overline{QS}$.

Because $\triangle PSQ$ is a $45°-45°-90°$ triangle, its legs have equal length.

$QS = PS = 2\sqrt{2}$

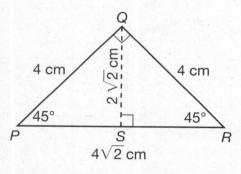

4

Calculate the area of $\triangle PQR$.

The area of a triangle is $\frac{1}{2}$ base times height.

$A = \dfrac{1}{2} \cdot PR \cdot QS$

$A = \dfrac{1}{2} \cdot 4\sqrt{2}$ cm $\cdot\ 2\sqrt{2}$ cm

$A = \dfrac{1}{2} \cdot 8(\sqrt{2})^2$

Recall that if $x^2 = 2$, then $x = \sqrt{2}$. So, substituting $\sqrt{2}$ for x, $(\sqrt{2})^2 = 2$.

$A = \dfrac{1}{2} \cdot 8(2)$

▶ $A = 8$ cm^2

CHECK

Find the area of $\triangle PQR$, using $\overline{PQ}$ and $\overline{QR}$. Compare the two results.

EXAMPLE B Use trigonometric ratios to find the missing lengths, *x* and *y*, in △*FGH*, to the nearest foot.

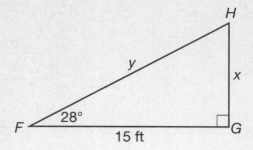

1

Calculate the value of *x*.

The given side, which has a length of 15 ft, is adjacent to the given angle, which has a measure of 28°.

The leg labeled *x* is opposite the 28° angle.

The tangent ratio compares the opposite and adjacent sides.

$$\tan 28° = \frac{x}{15}$$

$(15)(\tan 28°) = x$

On your calculator, enter 15 × TAN 28 and press ENTER.

▶ *x* ≈ 8 ft

2

Calculate the value of *y*.

The leg labeled *y* is the hypotenuse.

The cosine ratio compares the adjacent side and the hypotenuse.

$$\cos 28° = \frac{15}{y}$$

$(\cos 28°)(y) = 15$

$$y = \frac{15}{\cos 28°}$$

On your calculator, enter 15 ÷ COS 28 and press ENTER.

▶ *y* ≈ 17 ft

CHECK

Use the Pythagorean Theorem to verify that the side lengths you found for △*FGH* would form a right triangle.

Practice

Find the sine, cosine, and tangent ratios for ∠D in each triangle.

1.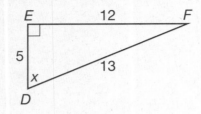

sin x = _____

cos x = _____

tan x = _____

2.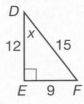

sin x = _____

cos x = _____

tan x = _____

> REMEMBER SOH-CAH-TOA

Find the indicated side length in each right triangle.

3.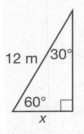

x = _____

4.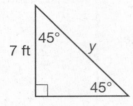

y = _____

5.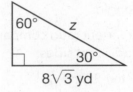

z = _____

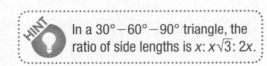

> **HINT** In a 30°−60°−90° triangle, the ratio of side lengths is $x : x\sqrt{3} : 2x$.

Fill in the blank with an appropriate word or number.

6. The _____ of an acute angle in a right triangle is the ratio of its adjacent side length to the hypotenuse.

7. If two right triangles are _____, then their corresponding acute angles have identical trigonometric ratios.

8. The hypotenuse of a 45°−45°−90° triangle is _____ times longer than each leg.

9. The hypotenuse of a 30°−60°−90° triangle is _____ times the length of its shorter leg.

Use trigonometric ratios to find the lengths *x* and *y* in each triangle to the nearest foot.

10.

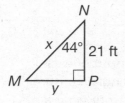

$x \approx$ _____

$y \approx$ _____

11.

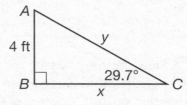

$x \approx$ _____

$y \approx$ _____

Triangle *JKL* was dilated by a scale factor of $\frac{2}{3}$ and translated to the right to form $\triangle J'K'L'$. Use this diagram for questions 12 and 13.

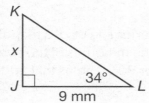

12. How does the tangent of $\angle L$ compare to the tangent of $\angle L'$? Explain.

_____

_____

_____

13. Find the value of *x* and the value of *y* to the nearest millimeter.

_____

_____

14. **COMPUTE** The diagonal $\overline{AC}$ in the square below is 10 inches long. Compute the exact area of square *ABCD*.

_____

15. **SHOW** Find the exact area of equilateral triangle *KLM*.

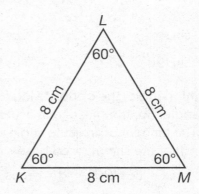

_____

LESSON 13

Relationships between Trigonometric Functions

UNDERSTAND Sine, cosine, and tangent are trigonometric **functions**. The **input** of each function is an angle measure. For each trigonometric function, every acute angle measure produces a different **output**, or value of the function. The values change in a predictable way over the domain $0° < x < 90°$.

Function	Relationship between Inputs and Outputs
$f(x) = \sin x$	As x increases, the value of the sine, $f(x)$, increases.
$f(x) = \cos x$	As x increases, the value of the cosine, $f(x)$, decreases.
$f(x) = \tan x$	As x increases, the value of the tangent, $f(x)$, increases.

UNDERSTAND The sum of the measures of the interior angles of a triangle is 180°. Every right triangle has one right angle, so the sum of the measures of the two acute angles in any right triangle must be equal to $(180 - 90)°$, or 90°. Angles that add up to 90° are **complementary angles**.

In $\triangle ABC$ below, the degree measure of $\angle A$ is x. Since $\angle B$ is the complement of $\angle A$, the degree measure of $\angle B$ is $90° - x$. Compare the trigonometric ratios for the two angles.

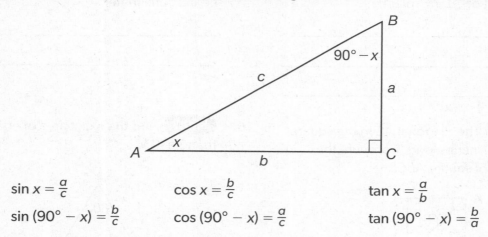

$$\sin x = \frac{a}{c} \qquad \cos x = \frac{b}{c} \qquad \tan x = \frac{a}{b}$$

$$\sin(90° - x) = \frac{b}{c} \qquad \cos(90° - x) = \frac{a}{c} \qquad \tan(90° - x) = \frac{b}{a}$$

In a right triangle, the opposite leg for one acute angle is the adjacent leg for the other acute angle. So, the sine of one acute angle is equal to the cosine of its complement, and vice versa. The tangent of an acute angle is the reciprocal of the tangent of its complement. These relationships are summarized below.

$$\sin x = \cos(90° - x) \qquad \cos x = \sin(90° - x) \qquad \tan x = \frac{1}{\tan(90° - x)}$$

⊸⊏ Connect

In △MNP, ∠N measures 74° and sine of ∠N is approximately 0.96. What is the measure of ∠M and the cosine of ∠M?

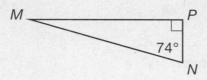

1

Find m∠M.

The acute angles of a right triangle are complementary.

m∠M + m∠N = 90°

m∠M = 90° − m∠N

m∠M = 90° − 74°

▶ m∠M = 16°

2

Find cos M.

The cosine of an angle is equal to the sine of its complement.

cos M = sin N

▶ cos M ≈ 0.96

TRY

The tangent of ∠N is approximately 3.5. What is the approximate value of the tangent of ∠M?

EXAMPLE A Make a chart showing the sine, cosine, and tangent values for angle measures in the domain {20, 40, 60, 80}. Analyze the values and describe how the outputs change as the inputs change.

1

Make a chart and use a calculator to approximate trigonometric ratios.

To estimate the sine of 20° by using your calculator, press SIN, enter 20, and press ENTER.

Use the COS key to estimate cosine and the TAN to estimate tangent.

Repeat this process for 40°, 60°, and 80°.

Measure of Angle	Sine of Angle	Cosine of Angle	Tangent of Angle
20°	0.34	0.94	0.36
40°	0.64	0.77	0.84
60°	0.87	0.5	1.73
80°	0.98	0.17	5.67

2

Analyze the chart.

As the angle measures increase, the sine values and tangent values also increase. However, as the angle measures increase, the cosine values decrease.

TRY

Use a calculator to determine the values of the sine, cosine, and tangent for the inputs 0° and 90°.

EXAMPLE B Use the triangle below to prove that $\tan x = \frac{\sin x}{\cos x}$.

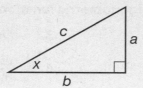

1

Write trigonometric ratios for x.

The side opposite the angle has length a. The side adjacent to the angle has length b.

The hypotenuse has length c.

$$\sin x = \frac{\text{opposite}}{\text{hypotenuse}} = \frac{a}{c}$$

$$\cos x = \frac{\text{adjacent}}{\text{hypotenuse}} = \frac{b}{c}$$

$$\tan x = \frac{\text{opposite}}{\text{adjacent}} = \frac{a}{b}$$

2

Divide the ratios for sine and cosine.

Remember that dividing by a fraction is the same as multiplying by its reciprocal.

$$\frac{\sin x}{\cos x} = \frac{\frac{a}{c}}{\frac{b}{c}}$$

$$\frac{\sin x}{\cos x} = \frac{a}{c} \cdot \frac{c}{b}$$

$$\frac{\sin x}{\cos x} = \frac{a}{b}$$

This is identical to the ratio for the tangent.

$$\frac{\sin x}{\cos x} = \tan x$$

DISCUSS

If $\sin y = \frac{4}{5}$ and $\cos y = \frac{3}{5}$, what is the value of $\tan y$? Is there only one way to determine this answer?

Practice

Let *x* be the degree measure of an acute angle in a right triangle. Fill in each blank with an equivalent expression containing a trigonometric function with *x* as the input.

1. $\cos(90° - x) = $ _____

3. $\tan(90° - x) = $ _____

2. $\sin(90° - x) = $ _____

4. $\dfrac{\cos(90° - x)}{\sin(90° - x)} = $ _____

> **REMEMBER** If *x* is the measure of one acute angle in a right triangle, the other angle measures $90° - x$.

Choose the best answer.

5. Which equation is true?

   A. $\cos 48° = \sin 42°$

   B. $\cos 48° = \sin 48°$

   C. $\cos 48° = \cos 42°$

   D. $\tan 48° = \tan 42°$

6. Which equation is true?

   A. $\tan 67° = \tan 23°$

   B. $\tan 67° = \dfrac{1}{\tan 23°}$

   C. $\tan 67° = \dfrac{\cos 67°}{\sin 67°}$

   D. $\tan 67° = \dfrac{\sin 23°}{\cos 23°}$

7. Which two angles are complementary angles?

   A. 95° and 85°

   B. 12° and 78°

   C. 36° and 36°

   D. 90° and 45°

8. If $\sin 14.25° \approx \dfrac{16}{65}$ and $\cos 14.25° \approx \dfrac{63}{65}$, what is the approximate value of $\tan 14.25°$?

   A. 65

   C. $\dfrac{16}{63}$

   B. $\dfrac{63}{16}$

   D. $\dfrac{16}{65}$

HINT Division is equivalent to multiplication by the reciprocal.

Use the given information to find the indicated measures.

9. $\sin 28° \approx 0.47$

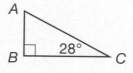

$m\angle A = $ _____ $\cos A = $ _____

10. $\cos 51.8° \approx 0.62$ $\sin 51.8° \approx 0.79$

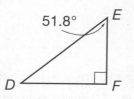

$m\angle D = $ _____ $\cos D = $ _____

Complete the chart and use it to answer questions 12 and 13.

11. Use a calculator to complete the chart below. Round to the nearest hundredth.

Measure of Angle	Sine of Angle	Cosine of Angle	Tangent of Angle
15°			
35°	0.57		
55°			1.43
75°		0.26	

12. Would you expect tan 70° to be less than or greater than 1.43? Explain.

_____

13. If cos $x \approx 0.89$, the value of x must lie between what two angle measures?

_____

_____

Solve without using a calculator.

14. **EXPLAIN** Given that sin 26.45° $\approx$ 0.45 and sin 63.55° $\approx$ 0.90, find the approximate value of tan 26.45°. Explain how you found your answer.

_____

_____

15. **PROVE** Follow the given steps and use the side lengths of the triangle below to prove the Pythagorean Identity: $\sin^2 x + \cos^2 x = 1$.

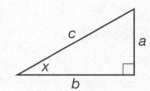

Use side lengths a, b, and c to write trigonometric ratios.	$\sin x = \frac{a}{c}$ $\cos x = -$
Write the formula for the Pythagorean Theorem.	$a^2 + b^2 = c^2$
Divide both sides of that equation by c^2.	$\frac{a^2}{c^2} + - = \frac{c^2}{c^2}$
Rewrite the expressions on the left side as ratios squared. Simplify the right side.	$\left(\frac{a}{c}\right)^2 + \left(-\right)^2 = $ _____
Substitute sin x and cos x for the ratios in the equation to show the Pythagorean Identity.	_____

14 Solving Problems with Right Triangles

Trigonometry can be applied to solve various geometric problems.

EXAMPLE A Find the area of a regular pentagon with sides 6 feet long and angles of 108°.

1

Draw the pentagon and divide it into five congruent triangles.

The result is five isosceles triangles, each with two base angles measuring 54°.

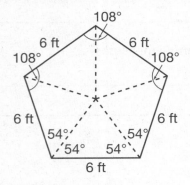

2

Draw an **apothem** of the pentagon.

The apothem connects the center to the midpoint of a side. It is also the altitude and median of one of the isosceles triangles. So, it bisects the base (the side of the pentagon) into two congruent 3-ft segments.

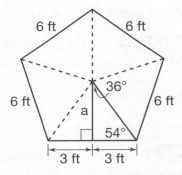

3

Find the length of the apothem.

$\tan 54° = \dfrac{a}{3}$

$3(\tan 54°) = a$

$4.13 \approx a$

DISCUSS

Leo says that if the pentagon had 8-foot sides, its area would be $A \approx 5 \cdot \dfrac{1}{2}(8)(4.13)$. What error did Leo make?

4

Find the area of the pentagon.

Find the area of the triangle.

$A_{triangle} = \dfrac{1}{2}ba \approx \dfrac{1}{2} \cdot 6 \cdot 4.13 = 12.39 \text{ ft}^2$

The pentagon is made up of five such triangles, so its area is $5A_{triangle}$

▶ $A_{pentagon} \approx 5(12.39 \text{ ft}^2) = 61.95 \text{ ft}^2$

EXAMPLE B Derive a formula for the area of △ABC using trigonometry.

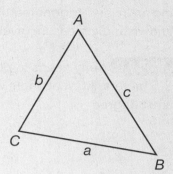

1

Draw an altitude from ∠A.

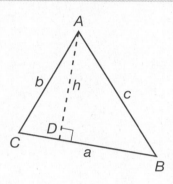

Let D be the point where the altitude meets side $\overline{BC}$, and let $AD = h$.

2

Find an expression for h.

Using right triangle ADC, find the sine ratio for angle C.

$\sin C = \dfrac{\text{opposite}}{\text{hypotenuse}}$

$\sin C = \dfrac{h}{b}$

Find the height, h, of the triangle by multiplying both sides of the trigonometric equation by b.

$\sin C = \dfrac{h}{b}$

$b \sin C = h$

3

Find the area of △ABC.

Substitute a for the base and h for the height.

$Area = \dfrac{1}{2} base \times height$

$Area = \dfrac{1}{2} ah$

Substitute $b \sin C$ for h.

▶ $Area = \dfrac{1}{2} ab \sin C$

TRY

Find the area of the triangle below.

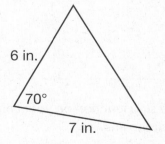

Using an inverse trigonometric function, such as $\sin^{-1}$, $\cos^{-1}$, or $\tan^{-1}$, allows you to determine an unknown angle measure given sides of a right triangle.

EXAMPLE C Amy needs to place a 6-meter ladder against a house so that it reaches a height of 5.5 meters. At what angle will she need to place the ladder? Find your answer to the nearest degree.

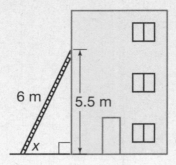

6 m
5.5 m
x

1

Write an equation using x.

The measure of the angle, x, is unknown.

The side opposite the unknown angle is 5.5 meters, and the hypotenuse is 6 meters. Since the opposite leg and hypotenuse are known, use the sine function.

$$\sin x = \frac{5.5}{6}$$

2

Use an inverse trigonometric function to solve for x.

The inverse of the sine function is the inverse sine function, $\sin^{-1}x$. Apply this function to both sides of the equation.

$$\sin^{-1}(\sin x) = \sin^{-1}\left(\frac{5.5}{6}\right)$$

$$x = \sin^{-1}\left(\frac{5.5}{6}\right)$$

The inverse function cancels out the sine function on the left side of the equation. To calculate the right side, press

[2nd] [SIN] on your calculator and enter

5.5 ÷ 6. Then press [ENTER]

$$x \approx 66.44$$

▶ Amy should place the ladder at about a 66° angle.

CHECK

Use the sine function on your calculator to check the answer.

An **angle of elevation** is the angle formed by a horizontal line and the line of sight to an object above that horizontal line. An **angle of depression** is the angle formed by a horizontal line and the line of sight to an object below that horizontal line.

EXAMPLE D An airplane is approaching a landing strip at a 3° angle of depression, starting from a height of 3,000 feet. To the nearest hundredth of a mile, what is d, the horizontal distance of the airplane from the airport?

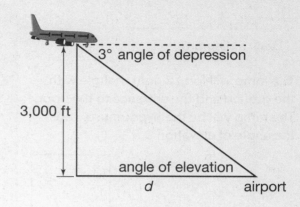

3° angle of depression

3,000 ft

angle of elevation
d airport

1

Write an equation using d

The dashed horizontal line, from which the angle of depression is measured, is parallel to the ground. This means that the angle of depression and the angle of elevation are alternate interior angles, so they are congruent. The angle of elevation is also 3°.

The altitude of the plane is the leg opposite the angle of elevation and the distance d is the adjacent leg. Use the tangent function.

$$\tan 3° = \frac{3,000}{d}$$

2

Solve for d.

$$\tan 3° = \frac{3,000}{d}$$

$$d(\tan 3°) = 3,000$$

$$d = \frac{3,000}{\tan 3°}$$

$$d \approx 57,243.41 \text{ ft}$$

3

Convert from feet to miles.

$$57,243.41 \text{ ft} \cdot \frac{1 \text{ mi}}{5,280 \text{ ft}} \approx 10.84 \text{ mi}$$

▶ The airplane is starting its descent when it is approximately 10.84 miles from the airport.

MODEL

If a plane began descending from an altitude of 10,000 feet at a vertical distance of 114,300 feet from the airport, what would be its angle of descent?

EXAMPLE E A wheelchair accessible ramp must have an angle of elevation of no more than 9.5°. Determine the length of ramp needed to reach a doorway that is 4.5 feet off the ground. How far from the door will the ramp start?

1

Draw a diagram.

The ramp will form a right triangle with the ground and the entrance to the door. The ramp will be the hypotenuse. Label the angle of elevation 9.5°.

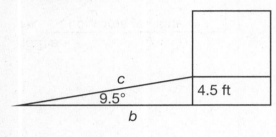

2

Find the length of the ramp.

The ramp forms the hypotenuse of a right triangle with one acute angle measuring 9.5° and the leg opposite it measuring 4.5 feet. Use the sine function to relate these known values to the length of the ramp.

$$\sin 9.5° = \frac{4.5}{c}$$

Solve for c.

$$c(\sin 9.5°) = 4.5$$

$$c = \frac{4.5}{\sin 9.5°}$$

$$c \approx 27.26$$

▶ The ramp must be at least 27.26 feet long.

3

Find the distance from the door to the start of the ramp.

The distance along the ground is the other leg of the right triangle. Note that this is the leg adjacent to the 9.5° angle.

$$\tan 9.5° = \frac{4.5}{b}$$

$$b = \frac{4.5}{\tan 9.5°}$$

$$b \approx 26.89$$

▶ The ramp must start at least 26.89 feet from the door.

CHECK

Use the Pythagorean Theorem to check these answers.

Problem Solving

READ

Juan is a firefighter. From the ground, he sees a cat in a tree. Juan is 90 feet from the tree, and his eye level is 5 feet above the ground. The angle of elevation from his eyes to the cat is 25°. What is the elevation of the cat above the ground to the nearest tenth of a foot?

PLAN

Draw a diagram to represent the problem. Account for the fact that the firefighter's eye level is 5 feet above the ground.

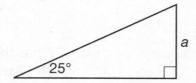

The 90-ft side is adjacent to the 25° angle. The side labeled a is _____ the 25° angle.

So, use the _____ function to find the value of a. Then you can add 5 feet to find the total elevation of the cat above the ground.

SOLVE

$$\tan 25° = \frac{a}{\boxed{}}$$

(_____)$\tan 25° = a$

_____ $\approx a$

Juan's eye level is _____ feet above the ground. So, add _____ feet to the value of a to find the cat's total elevation.

_____ + _____ = _____ feet

CHECK

Use the inverse of tangent, $\tan^{-1}$, to check your answer. Remember to use the value for a, not the elevation of the cat.

On your calculator, press 2nd TAN . Enter _____ ÷ 90 and press ENTER .

Is the result approximately equal to the original angle? _____

▶ The cat is about _____ feet above the ground.

Practice

Choose the best answer. You may use your calculator.

1. A jet is capable of a steady 15° climb. What is a, the approximate altitude of the jet, in meters, after it moves 800 meters through the air?

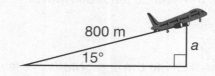

A. 207 m   **C.** 772 m

B. 309 m   **D.** 828 m

2. At a certain time of day, Sean, who is 6 feet tall, casts an 8-foot shadow. What is the approximate angle of elevation of the sun when this shadow is cast?

A. 37°   **C.** 53°

B. 49°   **D.** 68°

> **HINT** The figure and its shadow form a right triangle. The location of the sun determines the angle.

3. What is the area of $\triangle ABC$, to the nearest tenth of a square foot?

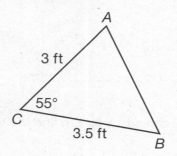

A. 3.9 ft^2 **C.** 4.6 ft^2

B. 4.3 ft^2 **D.** 4.9 ft^2

4. When the sun's angle of elevation is 56°, a tree casts a shadow that is 60 feet long. What is the height of the tree to the nearest foot?

A. 40 ft

B. 50 ft

C. 89 ft

D. 116 ft

Use the diagram of a 16-foot ladder leaning against a building for questions 5 and 6.

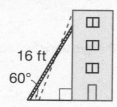

5. If the ladder makes an angle of 60° with the ground, how high does it reach? Give an exact answer and give an answer to the nearest inch.

_____

> **REMEMBER** The sides of a 30°-60°-90° triangle are in the ratio x; $x\sqrt{3}$; $2x$.

6. Suppose the ladder is adjusted to be at an angle of 70° with the ground. Approximately how many inches higher will it reach?

_____

Solve.

7. The bed of a mover's truck is 4 feet above the ground. The owner of the moving company needs to build a ramp with an angle of elevation of no more than 20°. How long should the ramp be?

   _____

8. A lighthouse keeper spots a boat out at sea. The angle of depression from the keeper to the boat is 4°. The keeper's viewing level from the top of the lighthouse is 102 feet above sea level. What is *d*, the distance from the boat to the lighthouse, to the nearest foot?

   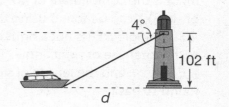

   _____

9. The Great Pyramid of Giza in Egypt is a right square pyramid with base lengths of approximately 230 meters. The faces of the pyramid are inclined at 52° angles. What is the approximate height of the Great Pyramid to the nearest tenth of a meter?

   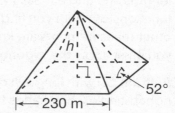

   _____

10. **APPLY** A tent for a party has a base shaped like a regular hexagon with each side measuring 4 yards and each angle measuring 120°. There should be 10 square feet of space for each guest at the party. How many people can fit in the tent? Explain.

   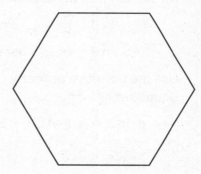

   _____

   _____

   _____

11. **MODEL** Forest rangers at two lookout towers each see the same forest fire. Tower *A* is 20 km west of Tower *B*. The fire is directly southeast of Tower *A* and directly southwest of Tower *B*. Approximately how far is the fire from each tower? Draw a model and use it to help explain your work.

   _____

Trigonometric Laws

LESSON 15

$$\boxed{\text{Law of Sines}}$$

UNDERSTAND Triangle *XYZ* is a right triangle, so m∠*X* is the compliment of 40° and the length of side $\overline{YX}$ can be found using the cosine ratio of 40°. Triangle *DEF* is not a right triangle, so it has no hypotenuse or right angle. The measures of ∠*E* and ∠*F* and the length of side $\overline{EF}$ cannot be found so easily.

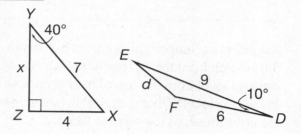

In earlier lessons, you learned how to use trigonometric functions to find missing side lengths and angle measures in right triangles. Now, you will see that trigonometric functions can help you find missing measurements in any triangle, as long as at least three other measurements are known. To find unknown angles and sides in nonright triangles, you must apply the trigonometric laws.

Altitude $\overline{CD}$ with length *h* divides △*ABC* on the right into two right triangles. Sine ratios for angles *A* and *B* can be written using these triangles. Solve both equations for *h*.

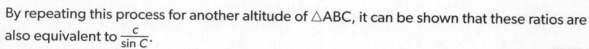

$$\sin B = \frac{h}{a} \qquad \sin A = \frac{h}{b}$$

$$a\sin B = h \qquad b\sin A = h$$

Use the transitive property of equality to combine the two equations into one.

$$a\sin B = b\sin A \qquad \text{Divide both sides by } (\sin A)(\sin B).$$

$$\frac{a}{\sin A} = \frac{b}{\sin B}$$

By repeating this process for another altitude of △ABC, it can be shown that these ratios are also equivalent to $\frac{c}{\sin C}$.

Law of Sines: $\frac{a}{\sin A} = \frac{b}{\sin B} = \frac{c}{\sin C}$, where *a*, *b*, and *c* are the lengths of the sides of a triangle and *A*, *B*, and *C* are their opposite angles.

The Law of Sines can be used when one angle in a triangle and the length of the side opposite that angle are known. As long as one other side length or angle measure is known, all other measurements can be found.

⊶€ Connect

Find *g* and *j*.

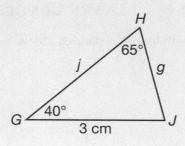

1

> Find the unknown angle measure.
>
> The angle measures of a triangle sum to 180°
>
> $\angle G + \angle H + \angle J = 180°$
>
> $40° + 65° + \angle J = 180°$
>
> $\angle J = 75°$

2

> Write a proportion using the Law of Sines.
>
> Write a general rule and then substitute in the known values.
>
> $$\frac{g}{\sin G} = \frac{h}{\sin H} = \frac{j}{\sin J}$$
>
> $$\frac{g}{\sin 40°} = \frac{3}{\sin 65°} = \frac{j}{\sin 75°}$$

3

> Solve for *g*.
>
> $$\frac{g}{\sin 40°} = \frac{3}{\sin 65°}$$
>
> $$g = \frac{3}{\sin 65°} \cdot \sin 40°$$
>
> ▶ $g \approx 2.13$ cm

4

> Solve for *j*
>
> $$\frac{j}{\sin 75°} = \frac{3}{\sin 65°}$$
>
> $$j = \frac{3}{\sin 65°} \cdot \sin 75°$$
>
> ▶ $j \approx 3.20$ cm

 TRY

Find m∠L, m∠M, and length of side *m*.

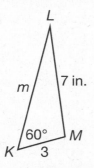

Law of Cosines

UNDERSTAND Altitude $\overline{BD}$ with length h divides $\triangle ABC$ below into two right triangles.

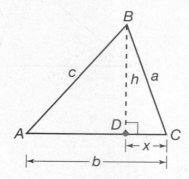

By using right triangle CBD, we can write the following trigonometric ratios:

$$\sin C = \frac{h}{a} \qquad \cos C = \frac{x}{a}$$

$$a\sin C = h \qquad a\cos C = x$$

Apply the Pythagorean Theorem to $\triangle ABD$, which has a hypotenuse of length c and legs of length h and $b - x$. Substitute expressions for h and x from the equations above.

$c^2 = h^2 + (b - x)^2$	Use the Pythagorean Theorem.
$c^2 = (a\sin C)^2 + (b - x)^2$	Substitute $a\sin C$ for h.
$c^2 = (a\sin C)^2 + (b - a\cos C)^2$	Substitute $a\cos C$ for x.
$c^2 = a^2\sin^2 C + b^2 - 2ab\cos C + a^2\cos^2 C$	Expand the binomial.
$c^2 = a^2(\sin^2 C + \cos^2 C) + b^2 - 2ab\cos C$	Factor out a^2.
$c^2 = a^2 + b^2 - 2ab\cos C$	Substitute 1 for $\sin^2 C + \cos^2 C$.

Law of Cosines: $c^2 = a^2 + b^2 - 2ab\cos C$, where C denotes the angle of a triangle contained between sides of lengths a and b and opposite the side of length c.

⟜Ξ Connect

Find the length of side n, m∠O, and m∠P in △NOP.

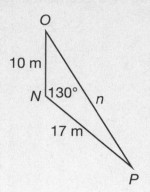

1

Use the Law of Cosines to find n.

Apply the Law of Cosines, letting $a = 10$, $b = 17$, $c = n$, and $C = 130°$.

$$c^2 = a^2 + b^2 - 2ab\cos C$$

$$n^2 = (10)^2 + (17)^2 - 2(10)(17)\cos(130°)$$

$$n^2 = 100 + 289 - 340\cos 130°$$

$$n^2 \approx 100 + 289 - 340(-0.6428)$$

$$n^2 \approx 100 + 289 + 218.5$$

$$n^2 \approx 607.5$$

$$n \approx 24.6$$

▶ The missing side length is approximately 24.6 meters.

2

Use the Law of Cosines to find the measure of one angle.

Let $a = 10$, $b = 24.6$, $c = 17$, and $C = m∠O$.

$$c^2 = a^2 + b^2 - 2ab\cos C$$

$$17^2 = (10)^2 + (24.6)^2 - 2(10)(24.6)\cos O$$

$$289 = 100 + 605.16 - 492\cos(O)$$

$$289 = 705.16 - 492\cos O$$

$$0 = 416.16 - 492\cos O$$

Isolate cos O and use the inverse cosine function to find m∠O.

$$492\cos O = 416.16$$

$$\cos O \approx 0.8459$$

$$\cos^{-1}(\cos O) \approx \cos^{-1}(0.8459)$$

▶ m∠$O \approx 32°$

3

Find the measure of the remaining angle.

The angle measures of a triangle sum to 180°.

$$m∠N + m∠O + m∠P = 180°$$

$$130° + 32° + m∠P \approx 180°$$

▶ m∠$P \approx 18°$

TRY

A triangle has side lengths 4, 8, and 10. Find the approximate angles of the triangle.

Practice

Use the Law of Sines to find the missing measurements. Round to the nearest tenth.

1.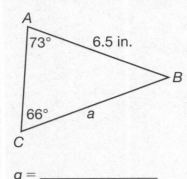

$a =$ _____

2.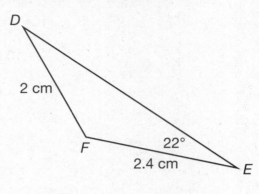

$m\angle D =$ _____

Use △GHJ below for questions 3 and 4. Choose the best answer.

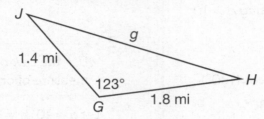

3. What is the length of *g*?

   A. 1.2 mi   **C.** 5.1 mi

   B. 2.8 mi   **D.** 7.9 mi

 HINT In the Law of Cosines, *C* is the angle between sides *a* and *b*.

4. What is m∠*H*?

   A. 8.5°

   B. 12.2°

   C. 24.8°

   D. 32.6°

Solve.

5. Brenda and Tim are on a scavenger hunt. They are 55 feet apart when they both spot the last item on their list, a blue teddy bear. The diagram to the right shows their positions.

Who is closer to the teddy bear? By approximately how much?

_____

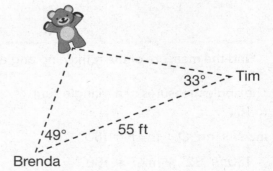

Solve.

6. A plane is flying from Topeka to St. Louis. In order to avoid a tornado, the pilot diverts the plane 31° from the original flight path. After flying 232 miles, the plane turns at an angle of 95° back toward St Louis.

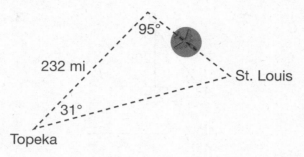

What is the total length of the modified flight path, to the nearest mile? _____

About how much farther did the plane travel than it would have if it had flown a direct route?

_____

7. **APPLY** A surveyor took some measurements of a triangular plot of land that is for sale. He made the following sketch of his measurements.

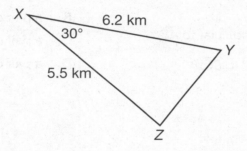

What is the approximate perimeter of the land? _____

What is the approximate area of the land? _____

If the plot of land is sold for $29,000, what is the approximate price per square kilometer?

_____

8. **GENERALIZE** When does it make sense to use the Law of Sines? When does it make sense to use the Law of Cosines?

_____

_____

_____

_____

Write the sine, cosine, and tangent ratios for ∠A in each triangle.

1.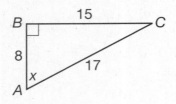

sin x = _____

cos x = _____

tan x = _____

2.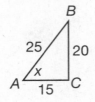

sin x = _____

cos x = _____

tan x = _____

3.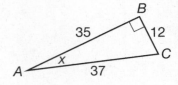

sin x = _____

cos x = _____

tan x = _____

Choose the best answer.

4. In △ABC, D is the midpoint of $\overline{AB}$ and E is the midpoint of $\overline{AC}$. What must be true of this figure?

   A. Segment DE is perpendicular to $\overline{AB}$.

   B. Segment DE is parallel to $\overline{BC}$.

   C. $\frac{DE}{BC} = \frac{AD}{AC}$

   D. DE = AB

5. Which pair of figures must be similar?

   A. a pair of equilateral triangles

   B. a pair of isosceles triangles

   C. a pair of obtuse triangles

   D. a pair of right triangles

6. $\overline{MQ}$ and $\overline{NR}$ intersect at point P. Can it be shown that △MNP ~ △QRP?

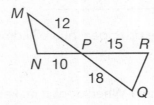

   A. Yes, by the AA ~ Postulate.

   B. Yes, by the SAS ~ Theorem.

   C. Yes, by the SSS ~ Theorem.

   D. No, the information given is not sufficient.

7. Using only the information given, can it be shown that △CDE ~ △FGE?

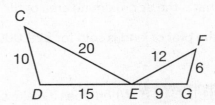

   A. Yes, by the AA ~ Postulate.

   B. Yes, by the SAS ~ Theorem.

   C. Yes, by the SSS ~ Theorem.

   D. No, the information given is not sufficient.

Dilate each line or segment as indicated. State whether the resulting image is *parallel to the preimage*, *collinear with the preimage*, or *neither parallel nor collinear with the preimage*.

8. $D_{\frac{2}{3}}(x, y) = \left(\frac{2}{3}x, \frac{2}{3}y\right)$

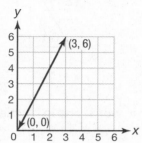

9. Scale factor: 2
    Center of dilation: (4, 3)

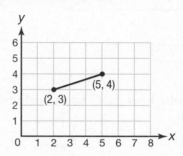

_____

_____

Determine if the figures are similar. If they are similar, describe a dilation (including the scale factor) that would transform one figure into the other. If not, explain how you know.

10.

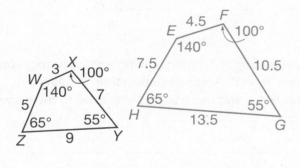

11.

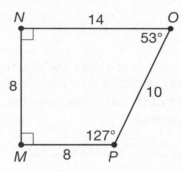

_____

_____

_____

_____

Solve.

12. At a certain time of day, a 24-foot flagpole casts a shadow that is 18 feet long. What is the angle of elevation of the sun at that time, to the nearest tenth of a degree? _____

Find the indicated side length in each right triangle. Give an exact value.

13.

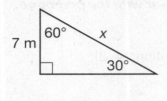

$x =$ _____

14.

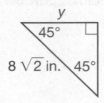

$y =$ _____

15.

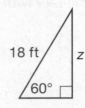

$z =$ _____

16. Describe how △*DEF* was transformed to its image, △*D'E'F'*, both in words and in function notation.

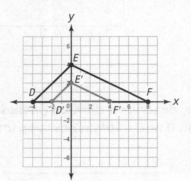

Words: _____

_____

Function Notation:

_____

17. A blimp hovers near a baseball stadium at an altitude of 250 meters, taking aerial photographs. The camera operator sights the baseball diamond at an 8° angle of depression. What is the line-of-sight distance, *d*, between the camera operator and the baseball diamond to the nearest hundred meters?

_____

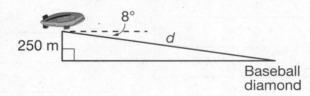

Complete the chart and use it to answer questions 19–21.

18. Use a calculator to complete the chart below. Fill in sine and cosine values to the nearest thousandth.

Measure of Angle	Sine of Angle	Cosine of Angle
5°		
25°		
65°		0.423
85°	0.996	

19. Based on the chart, how do the cosine values change as the input values increase?

_____

20. Would you expect sin 70° to be less than or greater than 0.9? Explain.

_____

21. What do you notice about sin 5° and cos 85°? How do you account for this? Do any other values in the chart demonstrate this relationship between sine and cosine values?

_____

_____

_____

Use the Law of Sines to find the missing measurements. Round to the nearest tenth.

22.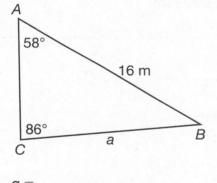

$a =$ _____

23.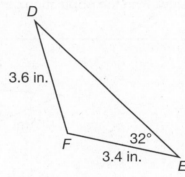

$m\angle D =$ _____

Use △PQR for questions 24 and 25.

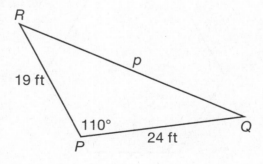

24. What is p to the nearest tenth? _____

25. What is the area of △PQR to the nearest tenth? _____

Solve.

26. What postulate or theorem can be used to show that
    △ABC ~ △AB′C′? Cite the relevant angles and/or sides.
    Then describe a dilation that would transform △ABC ~ △AB′C′.

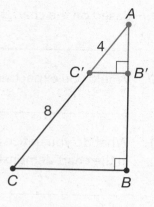

_____

_____

_____

27. Smith County, which is shaped like a triangle, has 12,615 residents. A diagram of the county is shown below. Find the population density in people per square mile.

_____

Smith County

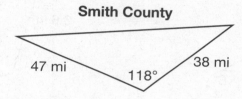

28. A honeycomb is made up of cells shaped like regular hexagons. The length of one side of each hexagon is 4 millimeters, and the angles in a hexagon sum to 720°. Find the area of one cell by using the model below. Describe the process you use.

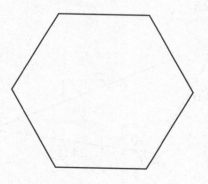

_____

_____

_____

29. **PROVE** Lucia drew △GHJ. Then she drew $\overleftrightarrow{KL}$ parallel to $\overleftrightarrow{HJ}$ as shown below. She wants to prove that $\overleftrightarrow{KL}$ divides sides $\overline{GH}$ and $\overline{GJ}$ proportionally. How could she do this?

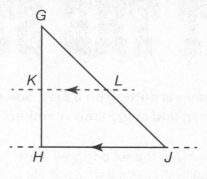

_____

_____

_____

_____

30. **DESIGN** A set designer is working on a set for an opera. Part of the set must include a ramp from the floor to a platform that is 6 feet tall. The angle of elevation can be no greater than 15° to be comfortable for the performers. What is the shortest ramp that can be designed? If the ramp is 3 feet wide, how many square feet of area on the stage floor will it cover? Draw a sketch.

_____

_____

_____

SET THE STAGE

The local community theater is putting on a play. Solve the problems to help the set designer, lighting designer, and stage crew members get the stage set for the play.

The play takes place on a farm, so the set designer must create a wooden facade that looks like a barn door. He wants the door to have a rectangle with an X inside it as shown. The stage crew saws two boards, each 9 feet long, to form the top and bottom of the rectangle. They paint the boards white.

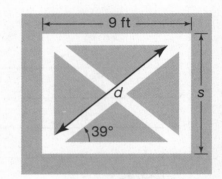

1. What is *s*, the length of the boards that must be cut to form the left and right sides?

   Give your answer to the nearest tenth of a foot. Show or explain your work.

   _____

   _____

2. What is *d*, the length of the boards that must be cut to form the diagonals?

   Give your answer to the nearest tenth of a foot. Show or explain your work.

   _____

   _____

The crew places a 14-foot ladder against one wall of the set to paint a tractor on the wall. The ladder must reach 13.5 feet up from the floor.

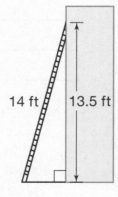

3. In order to be safely climbed, a ladder should be placed at an angle of about 75° with the floor. Will the ladder be safe to climb as shown?

   _____

4. How far from the base of the wall should the painter place the bottom of the ladder in order to ensure that the ladder reaches high enough? Give your answer to the nearest tenth of a foot.

   _____

Finally, the crew hangs a pair of lights 30 feet above the stage. For one monologue, both lights must be on one actor.

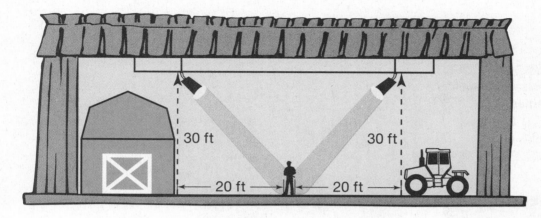

5. If the actor stands in the center of the stage, as shown, at what angle from horizontal should the lights be set, to the nearest degree? Show or explain your work.

_____

_____

_____

_____

_____

6. The director decides to change the scene so the actor is now standing 5 feet closer to the barn than he was previously. How will the lighting designer need to change the angles at which the lights are set? Show or explain your work.

_____

_____

_____

_____

_____

_____

Grades 6–8 & Algebra I

Geometry

Algebra II

Number and Quantity
Quantities
Reason quantitatively and use units to solve problems.

Algebra
Creating Equations
Create equations that describe numbers or relationships.

Grade 8 Geometry
Solve real-world and mathematical problems involving volume of cylinders, cones, and spheres.

Grade 7 Geometry
Draw, construct, and describe geometrical figures and describe the relationships between them.

Solve real-life and mathematical problems involving angle measure, area, surface area, and volume.

Geometry
Geometric Measurement and Dimension
Explain volume formulas and use them to solve problems.

Visualize relationships between two-dimensional and three-dimensional objects.

Modeling with Geometry
Apply geometric concepts in modeling situations.

Functions
Trigonometric Functions
Extend the domain of trigonometric functions using the unit circle.

Unit 3
Extending to Three Dimensions

Circumference and Area of Circles

UNDERSTAND Compare a **circle** to a square or other regular polygon. The shapes have corresponding characteristics and parts. For example, a diagonal of a square extends across the figure and through its center, much like a **diameter** of a circle. An **apothem** connects the center of a regular polygon to its side, and a **radius** connects the center of a circle to a point on the circle. Perimeter is the distance around a polygon, and **circumference** is the distance around a circle.

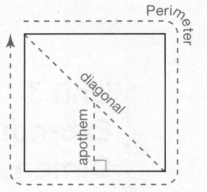

UNDERSTAND Line segments and perimeters are measured in linear units, such as meters (m) or feet (ft). So, when a circle is dilated by a factor of 2, its diameter, its radius, and its circumference all double, or increase by a factor of 2. Because these measurements change by the same factor, they are proportional to one another. For example, the circumference is directly proportional to the diameter, and the constant of proportionality is π.

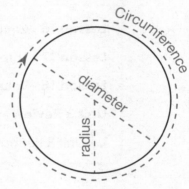

$$\frac{C_1}{d_1} = \frac{C_2}{d_2} \qquad \frac{C}{d} = \pi$$

This relationships leads to the formula for circumference, $C = \pi d$.

UNDERSTAND Look at the figures below. Notice how the sides of the polygons become closer to the curve of the circle as the number of sides increases. The perimeters of the polygons become better and better approximations of the circumference of the circle.

$C \approx 6.28$ cm $\qquad A \approx 3.14$ cm^2

2 cm

| $P \approx 5.66$ cm | $P \approx 5.88$ cm | $P = 6$ cm | $P \approx 6.07$ cm | $P \approx 6.12$ cm |
| $A = 2$ cm^2 | $A \approx 2.38$ cm^2 | $A \approx 2.60$ cm^2 | $A \approx 2.74$ cm^2 | $A \approx 2.83$ cm^2 |

Notice also how, as the number of sides increases, the polygons cover more and more of the circle's area. The areas of the polygons become better and better approximations of the area of the circle.

—€ Connect

Derive the formula for the area of a circle by dissecting a circle and rearranging its slices.

1 Dissect a circle.

Diameters can be used to cut a circle into identical slices. Notice that as more diameters are added to the circle, the slices become smaller.

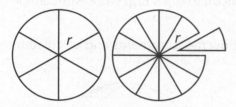

2 Find the length of the curved side of each slice.

Each curved side is a part of circle. If all of the curved sides were added together, the total would equal the circumference of the circle.

If every slice is identical, each curved side will be the same length. Call this length *s*. This length can be found by dividing the circle's circumference by the number of slices.

$$s = \frac{C}{n} = \frac{2\pi r}{n}$$

3 Rearrange the slices into a parallelogram-like shape.

Reassembling the slices into a shape like a parallelogram allows you to use the formula $A = bh$ to approximate their total area.

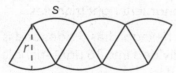

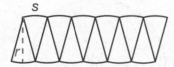

Assembling smaller sectors makes the shape look more like a parallelogram.

DISCUSS

If the circle were cut into 100 slices, would the assembled figure look more like a parallelogram or less?

4 Derive the formula for the area of a circle.

The length along the top of the 12-slice figure consists of half of the slices' arcs.

So, if the circle is divided into *n* slices, $\frac{n}{2}$ curves make up the base of the figure.

$$\text{base} \approx \frac{n}{2} \cdot s = \frac{n}{2} \cdot \frac{2\pi r}{n} = \pi r$$

The height from the top of the figure to the bottom is equal to the radius of the circle.

$$\text{height} = r$$

Multiply these two expressions to derive a formula for the area of the figure.

$$\text{Area} = \text{base} \cdot \text{height} \approx \pi r \cdot r = \pi r^2$$

This is the formula for the area of a circle.

EXAMPLE A Use regular polygons drawn in a circle to derive the formula for the area of a circle in terms of the radius, *r*.

1

Draw polygons into congruent circles.

A polygon with many sides is a better approximation of a circle than a polygon with fewer sides. So, you might want to use a polygon with a large number of sides to find the formula.

But a polygon with 1,000 sides, for example, would be difficult to draw and work with, and it still would not produce the exact formula for a circle.

Instead, draw several figures in congruent circles and see how measurements and calculations change as the number of sides increases.

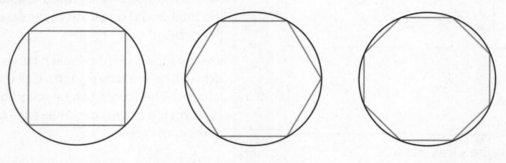

2

Divide the polygons into congruent triangles.

Drawing radii to the vertices of each polygon divides the figure into congruent isosceles triangles. Drawing in the apothems divides them further into congruent right triangles.

The square has 4 sides and is divided into 8 right triangles. The hexagon has 6 sides and is divided into 12 right triangles. The octagon has 8 sides and is divided into 16 right triangles. So, a polygon with *n* sides would be divided into 2*n* right triangles.

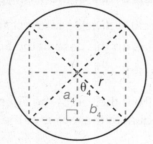 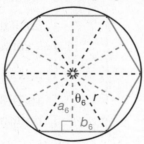 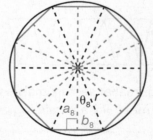

Label the radii, *r*, and apothems, *a*, in each figure.

In each figure, the triangles are congruent, so the angles formed by each apothem and radius are congruent. Let θ represent the measure of these angles in each figure.

In each triangle, the leg opposite θ is half of the length of the side of the polygon. Label this length *b* in each figure.

3

Find an expression for the perimeter of the polygon.

Each side of the polygon has a length of $2b$.

The perimeter of the square is $4 \cdot 2b_4$.

The perimeter of the hexagon is $6 \cdot 2b_6$.

The perimeter of the octagon is $8 \cdot 2b_8$.

In general, the perimeter of a polygon with n sides is $n \cdot 2b$, or $P = 2nb$.

4

Find an expression for a.

Consider one of the right triangles. The hypotenuse is the length of the radius, r.

The side adjacent to θ has a length of a. Relate them with the cosine function.

$$\cos \theta = \frac{a}{r}$$

$$a = r \cos \theta$$

5

Find the polygon's area.

The area of one of the right triangles is

$$A_{tri} = \frac{1}{2}ab = \frac{1}{2}(r \cos \theta)b$$

A regular polygon with n sides contains $2n$ triangles, so its area is:

$$A_{poly} = 2n \cdot A_{tri}$$
$$A_{poly} = 2n \cdot \frac{1}{2}br \cos \theta$$
$$A_{poly} = \frac{1}{2}(2nb)r \cos \theta$$

Notice that $2nb$ is the expression for the perimeter of the polygon.

6

Consider what happens as n increases.

As n increases, the polygon looks more and more like a circle. When n is very large, the perimeter of the polygon will be approximately equal to the circumference of the circle. So, replace $2nb$ in the equation with $2\pi r$.

Notice that as the number of sides, n, increases, angle θ becomes smaller. When n is very large, θ will be approximately 0°. So, replace θ with 0°.

$$A = \frac{1}{2}(2\pi r)r \cos (0°) = \pi r \cdot r(1)$$
$$A = \pi r^2$$

This formula gives the area of the circle.

 CHECK

There are 360° in a circle, so $\theta = \frac{360°}{2n}$.

Use your calculator to check that $\frac{360°}{2n}$ gets closer to 0° as n increases.

EXAMPLE B Suppose that a polygon is drawn within a circle having a radius of 1 meter. Find the difference between the circumference of the circle and the perimeter of the polygon if the polygon has 10 sides, 100 sides, or 1,000 sides.

1

Find the circumference of the circle

Remember that the diameter is twice the length of the radius, $d = 2r$.

$C = \pi d$

$C = \pi(2r)$

$C \approx 3.14159 \cdot 2 \cdot (1 \text{ m})$

$C \approx 6.28318 \text{ m}$

2

Find an expression for the perimeter of the polygon.

The same technique of dividing the polygon into right triangles can be used in this problem.

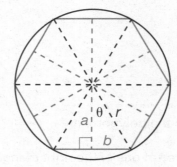

Each side of the polygon is equal to $2b$. Recall that the length $b = r \sin \theta$. There are a total of 360° in a circle, and the circle is divided into $2n$ right triangles, where n is the number of sides, so $\theta = \frac{360°}{2n}$.

So, the length, l, of a side of the polygon is given by:

$l = 2b = 2r \sin \theta = 2r \sin \frac{360°}{2n}$

The perimeter of the polygon is equal to the number of sides times the length of a side.

$P = nl = 2nr \sin \frac{360°}{2n}$

3

Find the perimeter of each polygon and the difference between its perimeter and the circle's circumference.

Remember that $r = 1$ meter. Use the formula for perimeter and let n equal 10, 100, and 1,000. Then subtract the perimeter values from the approximate circumference of the circle.

n	P	C – P
10	6.18034 m	0.10284 m
100	6.28215 m	0.00103 m
1,000	6.28317 m	0.00001 m

Repeat these calculations for a circle with a diameter of 1 meter.

Problem Solving

READ

Ariana has a weekend job driving the children's train ride at the amusement park. The two rails of the track form circles with the same center. The radius of the inner circle is 24 feet. The width of the track is 3 feet. In one lap, approximately how much farther does a wheel on the outer track travel than a wheel on the inner track?

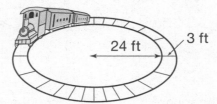

PLAN

The distance that each wheel travels is equal to the length around its circular track.

To find how much farther a wheel on the outer track travels than a wheel on the inner track,

find the _____ of each circle and subtract.

SOLVE

Find the exact circumferences in terms of π.

The radius of the inner circle is 24 ft.

C of inner circle $= 2\pi r = 2\pi(_____) = _____$

The radius of the outer circle is: _____ $+ 3 =$ _____ ft.

C of outer circle $= 2\pi r = 2\pi(_____) = _____$

The difference is: _____ $-$ _____ $=$ _____

Substitute 3.14 for π and approximate the difference: _____ $\cdot$ 3.14 $\approx$ _____

CHECK

All circles are similar, so the ratio of the radius of the inner track to the radius of the

outer track should equal the ratio of the _____ of the inner track to the

_____ of the outer track.

$\frac{24}{27} = $ _____

Is this proportion a true number sentence? _____

▶ A wheel on the outer track travels approximately _____ more feet than a wheel on the inner track.

Practice

The circles below have radii of 3 units. A square is drawn within the first circle. An octagon is drawn within the second circle. Use these figures for questions 1–5.

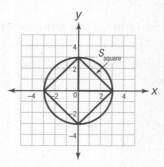
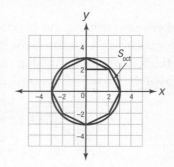

1. Find the exact side length of the square. Estimate its perimeter to the nearest hundredth.

   $s_{square} =$ _____

   $P_{square} = 4 \cdot s_{square} \approx$ _____

   HINT Use the Pythagorean Theorem or a trigonometric ratio to find s_{square}.

2. Find the exact side length of the octagon. Estimate its perimeter to the nearest hundredth.

   $s_{oct} =$ _____

   $P_{oct} = 8 \cdot s_{oct} \approx$ _____

   HINT The hypotenuse of the small right triangle is equal to s_{oct}.

3. The circle's circumference is greater than the square's perimeter. Complete the inequality.

   $2\pi r > P_{square}$

   $2\pi ($_____$) >$ _____

   $\pi >$ _____

4. The circle's circumference is greater than the octagon's perimeter. Complete the inequality.

   $2\pi r > P_{oct}$

   $2\pi ($___$) >$ _____

   $\pi >$ _____

5. Suppose you keep increasing the number of sides of the inscribed polygon. What will happen to your approximation of π?

   _____

Find the circumference and area of circles with the given dimensions.

6. a radius of 4 inches

   Circumference: _____

   Area: _____

7. a diameter of 10 centimeters

   Circumference: _____

   Area: _____

Polygon *HJKLMN* is drawn around circle *O*. Use this figure for questions 8–11.

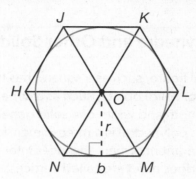

8. What is the perimeter P of a polygon with *n* sides if each side has a length of *b* units?

   P = _____

9. Write an expression for the area of △*MNO* in terms of *b* and *r*.

   _____

10. A polygon with *n* sides could be broken into *n* such triangles. What would be the total area of that polygon, in terms of *n*, *b*, and *r*?

    _____

    What is the polygon's area in terms of its perimeter P and *r*?

    _____

11. For very large values of *n*, the perimeter of the polygon would be about equal to the circumference of the circle. Substitute $2\pi r$ for the P in your equation for the polygon's area and simplify.

    _____

    _____

Solve.

12. **ILLUSTRATE** Julissa's bedroom floor is 12 feet by 12 feet. She places a circular rug on her floor so that it touches each side of the room. Approximately how many square feet of her bedroom floor will **not** be covered by the rug? Give an exact answer and an approximate answer to the nearest square foot.

    _____

    _____

13. **ANALYZE** A circle has a circumference of 5π meters. What is its area? _____

LESSON 17 — Three-Dimensional Figures

Polyhedra and Other Solids

UNDERSTAND A two-dimensional figure, such as a square, has two dimensions: length and width. A three-dimensional (or solid) object, such as a cube, has three dimensions: length, width, and height. The length and width of a solid generally refer to the dimensions of its base. A **polyhedron** (plural: polyhedra) is a three-dimensional figure bounded by polygons, called faces. The line segments where the faces intersect are called edges, and the points where three or more edges meet are called vertices.

A **prism** is a polyhedron having two congruent, parallel bases and parallelograms for all other faces. The faces that are not bases, the parallelograms, are called lateral faces. If one base of a prism lies directly above the other base, then the lateral faces are rectangles and the figure is a right prism. If not, the figure is an oblique prism. A prism is categorized by the shape of its bases. For example, a prism with triangles for bases is a triangular prism.

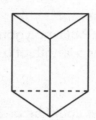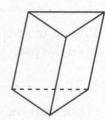

A **pyramid** is a polyhedron with one base, which can be any polygon. Like prisms, pyramids are also categorized by their bases. For example, a pyramid with a square base is a square pyramid. The lateral faces are triangles that meet at a common vertex, called the apex. If the apex of a pyramid is directly above the center of its base, then it is a right pyramid. Otherwise, it is an oblique pyramid. The slant height of a pyramid is the distance from the base to the apex along the center of a lateral face. In other words, it is the altitude of a triangular face.

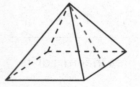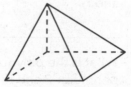

If a solid figure has any curved edge or face, it is not a polyhedron. A **cylinder** has two congruent bases, like a prism, but the bases are circles. A **cone** is similar to a pyramid in that it has a single base and an apex, but its base is a circle and its lateral surface is curved. Cones, like pyramids, have slant height. Like prisms and pyramids, cylinders and cones can be right or oblique.

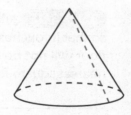

Recall that a circle is the set of all points in a plane that are a given distance from the center. A **sphere** is the set of all points in three-dimensional space that are a given distance from a point, also called the center. Like a circle, a sphere has radii, chords, and diameters. A sphere is a continuous curved surface, so it has no faces, edges, or vertices.

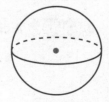

⊣€ Connect

The monument shown below is made up of several different solid figures. Identify each of them.

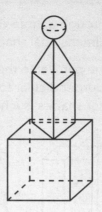

1 Identify the base.

The base is a rectangular prism in which each face is a square. This figure is called a cube.

2 Identify the solid resting on the base.

The solid resting on the base has two congruent triangular bases and lateral faces that are rectangles. This solid is a triangular prism.

3 Identify the next solid up.

The next solid also has a triangular base, but it has only one. Its lateral faces are triangles that meet at a single point. This solid is a triangular pyramid.

4 Identify the solid on top.

The solid on top has no faces, edges, or vertices. It is made up of a continuous, curved surface. The solid on top is a sphere.

DISCUSS

Which of the solids in the monument are right? oblique?

Cross Sections and Rotations

UNDERSTAND Imagine slicing a plane through a three-dimensional solid. The portion of solid inside that plane would be a two-dimensional shape called a **cross section**.

Consider the square prism below. A plane parallel to the bases produces a square cross section, identical to the bases. A plane perpendicular to the bases produces a rectangular cross section. Other planes produce other shapes, such as the hexagon shown.

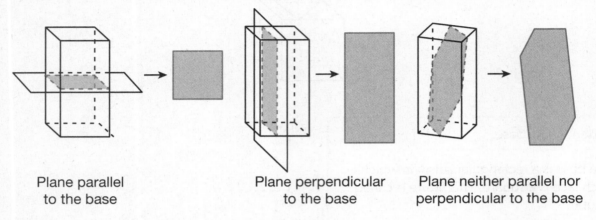

Plane parallel to the base   Plane perpendicular to the base   Plane neither parallel nor perpendicular to the base

Every cross section of a polyhedron is a polygon. Figures that are not polygons, such as cylinders and cones, have some cross sections that are circles or ellipses. For prisms and cylinders, all cross sections made parallel to the bases are congruent to the bases. For pyramids and cones, all cross sections made parallel to the base are similar to the base but different in size.

UNDERSTAND You can produce a three-dimensional solid by rotating a two-dimensional figure around a line called an axis. This is not the same as the rotational transformations that were done on the plane. During those transformations, the points of the figure moved in the plane. During this type of rotation, each point is spread over an area of space.

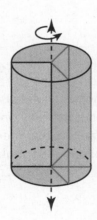

The rectangle on the right is rotated 360° around one of its sides. The result is a cylinder. Notice how the left vertices become the circular edges of the bases.

UNDERSTAND You can think of a solid as a stack of cross sections. For example, in a cylinder, all cross sections made parallel to the bases will be congruent circles. You can imagine "building" a cylinder by stacking these flat circles, like a roll of very thin coins. For a prism or cone, the stacked shapes would be similar, but not congruent. The closer a cross section is to the apex, the smaller it would be.

⊏ Connect

Take several cross sections of a right cone. Identify the shape of each cross section and compare it to the base of the cone.

1

Take a cross section parallel to the base.

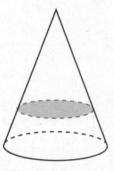

Any cross section parallel to the base of a cone is a circle. Since the base is a larger circle, the cross section is similar to the base.

2

Take another cross section parallel to the base, but at a different height.

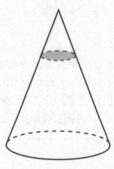

This cross section is also a circle, but because it was taken closer to the apex, it is smaller than the previous cross section. All circles are similar, so the cross section is similar to the base as well as the previous cross section.

3

Take a cross section at an angle to the base.

The cross section taken at this angle produces an ellipse. It is not similar to the base.

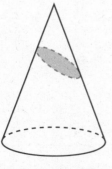

TRY

Take a cross section perpendicular to the base and through the apex. Describe the shape of the cross section.

EXAMPLE A Use △ABC to create solid figures in the following ways. Identify the solids created.

- Stack congruent triangles on top of each other.
- Stack increasingly smaller similar triangles on top of each other.
- Rotate the triangle 360° around $\overline{AB}$.

1 Stack congruent triangles to create a solid.

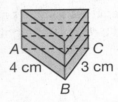

All triangles in the stack are congruent, so every horizontal cross section will be congruent to △ABC. This solid is a triangular prism whose base is △ABC.

2 Stack similar triangles to create a solid.

Each similar triangle becomes smaller as we go up from the base. Eventually, it will become so small that it will be a single point.

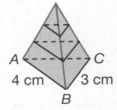

A solid with a triangular base and flat sides that meet at a point is a triangular pyramid. The base of the pyramid is △ABC.

3 Rotate the triangle to create a solid.

Rotate 360° around $\overline{AB}$.

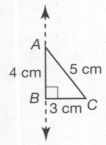 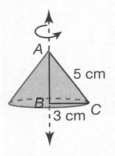

The solid has a circular base and a curved lateral face that tapers to a point, so it is a cone. The base has a radius equal to the length of $\overline{BC}$. The height is equal to the length of $\overline{AB}$. The slant height is equal to the hypotenuse, 5 cm.

DISCUSS

Could you create an oblique prism or pyramid by stacking triangles? Could you create an oblique cone by rotating a triangle around one of its sides?

EXAMPLE B Rotate a circle 360° about its diameter and identify the solid created. Then, take cross sections of the solid and identify their shapes.

1

Sketch a circle and extend one of its diameters.

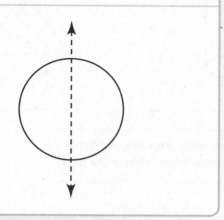

2

Rotate the circle about the diameter.

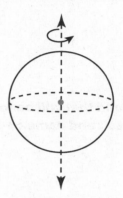

▶ The resulting solid is a sphere with the same diameter and radius as the circle.

3

Take several cross sections.

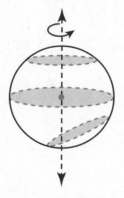

Every cross section is a circle, though not all are the same size. The largest possible circular cross sections, which contain the center, are congruent to the original circle that was rotated to create the sphere.

▶ All of the cross sections of a sphere are circles.

DISCUSS

Imagine rotating a circle around a line through only one of its points. What shape results from this rotation?

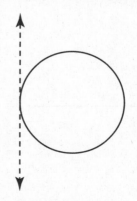

Practice

Identify the cross section that results from slicing through each solid as indicated.

1. Plane parallel to the base

_____

2. Plane perpendicular to the base

3. Plane perpendicular to the base through the apex

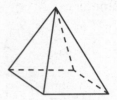

_____

 HINT A cross section made perpendicular to the base will resemble a front view of the solid.

Identify the solid that will be formed by rotating the figure 360° around the dashed line. Sketch the result and name or describe the solid.

4.

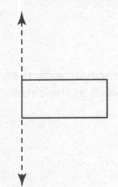

_____

5.

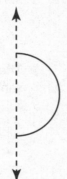

_____

6.

 HINT A rotated figure may be a combination of two or more solids that you studied.

7. What solid would be created by stacking many congruent hexagons, one on top of another?

_____

8. A café owner slices limes to put in water and iced tea. She slices some lengthwise and others widthwise. Sketch two types of slices that could result.

9. **DESCRIBE** What solid will result from rotating the triangle below 360° around the dashed line?

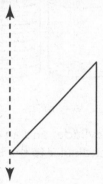

Describe the solid. _____

_____

Describe a cross section taken parallel to the base of the solid. _____

_____

Sketch an example of this cross section.

10. **THINK CRITICALLY** Is it possible to produce a polyhedron by rotating a figure around a line? Why or why not?

_____

_____

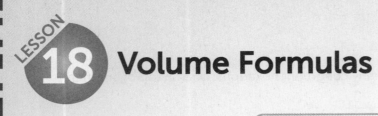

Volume Formulas

$\boxed{\text{Volume and Cylinders}}$

UNDERSTAND The **volume** of a solid object is the amount of space that it occupies. It is measured in cubic units.

Recall that every cross section of a cylinder is a circle congruent to the bases, and that you can think of a cylinder as a stack of circles. If the height of the cylinder is h units, you would stack the circles h units high. So, to find the volume of a cylinder, multiply the area of the circular base by the height.

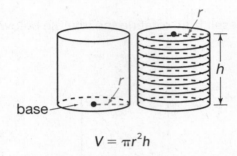

$$V = \pi r^2 h$$

This formula is the same for both a right cylinder and an oblique cylinder. However, remember that the height must be measured perpendicular to the bases.

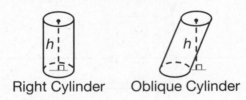

Right Cylinder   Oblique Cylinder

To understand why the formula is the same for both cylinders, think of a stack of coins. Each coin has a certain volume, and the volume of the stack is the sum of the volumes of the coins. Whether the coins are stacked straight up or displaced to form an oblique cylinder, the volume of each coin stays the same, so the volume of the stack remains the same.

Imagine cutting a cross section from each cylinder at the same height and parallel to the bases. If the cross sections have the same area and the cylinders have the same height, the cylinders must have the same volume.

The volume of a cylinder equals the area of the base multiplied by its height, $V = Bh$. This formula can also be used to find the volume of any prism.

←€ Connect

Dayshawn will buy either the two small cans of tomato soup shown or the one family-size can. Which would provide more soup? Approximately how much more?

1

Find the total volume of the two small cans.

The diameter of each small can is 6 cm. The radius is half the length of the diameter, so $r = 3$ cm. The cans have a height, h, of 10 cm.

$V = Bh = \pi r^2 h$

$V = \pi(3)^2(10)$

$V = 90\pi$

$V \approx 282.60 \text{ cm}^3$

The volume of two cans would be about $2 \cdot 282.60$, or 565.20 cm^3.

2

Find the volume of the family-size can.

The diameter of the family-size can is 8 cm, so $r = 4$ cm. Its height, h, is 11 cm.

$V = \pi r^2 h$

$V = \pi(4)^2(11)$

$V = 176\pi$

$V \approx 552.64 \text{ cm}^3$

3

Compare the volumes.

$565.20 > 552.64$

$565.20 - 552.64 = 12.56$

▶ Buying two small cans would provide approximately 12.56 cubic centimeters more soup.

TRY

The volume of a large cylindrical can of vegetable broth is 200 cm^3. If the radius of the can is tripled, how much broth could the new can hold?

Dimensions and Formulas

UNDERSTAND The area of a two-dimensional figure is proportional to its two dimensions: length and width. For example, the area of a rectangle is equal to the product of its length and its width. If its length or width is doubled, its area will also be doubled. So, the area is proportional to both the length and width. This means that there is a constant of proportionality, k_{rect}, such that $A_{rect} = k_{rect} \cdot l \cdot w$. In this case, $k_{rect} = 1$.

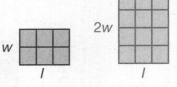

Draw a diagonal within one of the rectangles. This divides the rectangle into two congruent triangles. Since the area of the rectangle is divided between the two triangles, the area of each triangle must be equal to half of the area of the rectangle. If either the base length or height of a triangle is doubled, the area will also be doubled, just as it is with a rectangle. So, as with a rectangle, the area of a triangle is proportional to both its base length and its height: $A_{tri} = k_{tri} \cdot b \cdot h$. This area is half that of the rectangle, so $k_{tri} = \frac{1}{2}$, and $A_{tri} = \frac{1}{2} \cdot b \cdot h$.

Since all sides of a square are congruent, the same length is used to measure both dimensions. So, $A_{squ} = k_{squ} \cdot s \cdot s = k_{squ} \cdot s^2$. The constant of proportionality, k_{squ}, is 1, just as for the rectangle. According to this formula, $A_{squ} = s^2$, if the side length is doubled (or increased by a factor of 2), the area will increase by a factor of 2^2, or 4.

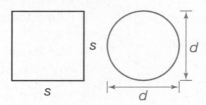

In a circle, the diameter is the same across the figure's width and its length. As with the side of a square, if the diameter is doubled, the area will be quadrupled. A circle is more commonly defined by its radius than its diameter, though. Doubling the radius of a circle will also quadruple its area, just as with the diameter. Therefore, the circle must have an area formula similar to that of the square: $A_{circ} = k_{circ} \cdot r^2$. In a previous lesson, you derived the formula for area of a circle: $A_{circ} = \pi r^2$. Thus, the constant of proportionality, k_{circ}, relating the area of a circle to its radius squared is π.

The formula for the volume of a sphere is $V = \frac{4}{3}\pi r^3$. Notice that the radius is raised to the second power in the circle's area formula and to the third power in the sphere's volume formula.

As you saw above, the area of a plane figure is proportional to its two dimensions. The volume of a three-dimensional figure is proportional to its three dimensions: length, width, and height. For a rectangular prism or a cube, the constant of proportionality is $k = 1$, just as it is for rectangles and squares, so $V = lwh$. Is the constant of proportionality for a pyramid $\frac{1}{2}$, as it is for triangles, or is it a different value? We will find out on the next page.

⊏ Connect

Use a cube to derive the formula for the volume of a pyramid.

1 Find the volume formula of a cube.

A cube is a type of square prism. The volume of any prism is given by:

$$V_{cube} = Bh$$

The base is a square, so its area is the square of its side length, s. The height of a cube is this same distance, s.

$$V_{cube} = (s^2)(s) = s^3$$

2 Divide a cube into 6 square pyramids.

Draw in the diagonals of the cube. Notice how the triangles formed by the diagonals and edges of the cube form 6 congruent pyramids. Each face of the cube is the base of a pyramid.

The volume of the cube is equal to the sum of the volumes of these 6 pyramids.

$$V_{cube} = 6 \cdot V_{pyr}$$

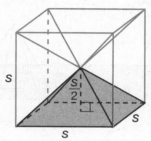

3 Consider one of these pyramids.

The volume of each pyramid must be proportional to its three dimensions.

$$V_{pyr} = k_{pyr} \cdot l \cdot w \cdot h$$

The length and width of each pyramid's base are equal to the side length of the cube, s. One pyramid stacked on top of another is equal to the height of the cube, so the height of each pyramid is half the height of the cube.

$$V_{pyr} = k_{pyr} \cdot s \cdot s \cdot \frac{s}{2} = k_{pyr} \cdot \frac{s^3}{2}$$

4 Find the general formula for the volume of a pyramid.

Find the constant of proportionality by substituting into the equation below.

$$V_{cube} = 6 \cdot V_{pyr}$$

$$(s^3) = 6 \cdot \left(k_{pyr} \cdot \frac{s^3}{2} \right)$$

$$s^3 = 3 \cdot k_{pyr} \cdot s^3$$

$$1 = 3 \cdot k_{pyr}$$

$$\frac{1}{3} = k_{pyr}$$

The volume of a square pyramid is given by:

$$V_{sqpyr} = \frac{1}{3}lwh$$

More generally, the volume of a pyramid is proportional to the area of its base times its height.

▶ $$V_{pyr} = \frac{1}{3}Bh$$

Could you use the formula $V = \frac{1}{3}Bh$ to find the volume of this pyramid? Could you use $V = \frac{1}{3}lwh$? Explain.

EXAMPLE A square pyramid and a cone have the same height, H. The base of the cone is a circle with radius R. This circle could be inscribed in the base of the pyramid, so the square base of the pyramid has an apothem of length R. Use these solids to derive the formula for the volume of a cone.

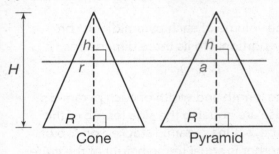

1

Take a cross section of each figure.

Slice a plane through the cone and the pyramid parallel to each base and at the same height.

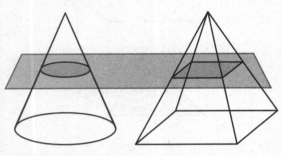

2

Examine the figures from the front.

The cross section of the cone is a circle. Let its radius be r. The cross section of the pyramid is a square. Let its apothem be a.

Cone   Pyramid

3

Compare radius r to apothem a.

Since the plane is parallel to the base, the small triangles above the plane line are similar to the large triangles. Corresponding sides are proportional.

$$\frac{r}{R} = \frac{h}{H} \qquad \frac{a}{R} = \frac{h}{H}$$

Because R, H, and h are the same for each figure, $r = a$, meaning the radius of the circular cross section is equal to the apothem of the square cross section.

4

Approximate the figures with cylinders and prisms.

Imagine taking several cross sections of the figures and then using those cross sections as the bases of short cylinders and prisms. These cylinders and prisms could be stacked to form figures like the cone and the pyramid.

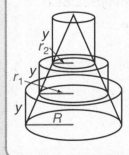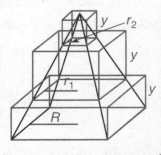

5

Find the volumes of the stacked cylinders and prisms.

The volume of one cylinder in the stacked figure is given by $V_{cyl} = \pi r^2 y$.

The volume of the corresponding prism is given by $V_{pri} = (2r)^2 y = 4r^2 y$.

Relate these two volumes by finding their ratio.

$$\frac{V_{cyl}}{V_{pri}} = \frac{\pi r^2 y}{4r^2 y}$$

$$\frac{V_{cyl}}{V_{pri}} = \frac{\pi}{4}$$

$$V_{cyl} = \frac{\pi}{4} \cdot V_{pri}$$

6

Determine a formula for the volume of the cone.

If the height, y, of the cylinders and prisms is decreased, more are needed to build the figures. As the cylinders become thinner, the approximations come closer to the real volume of the figures. This process becomes like stacking circles and squares to build the figures.

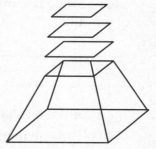

$$V_{cone} = V_{cyl1} + V_{cyl2} + V_{cyl3} + V_{cyl4} + \ldots$$
$$V_{pyr} = V_{pri1} + V_{pri2} + V_{pri3} + V_{pri4} + \ldots$$

Recall that for any corresponding cylinder and prism in the "stacks," $V_{cyl} = \frac{\pi}{4} V_{pri}$.

$$V_{cone} = V_{cyl1} + V_{cyl2} + V_{cyl3} + V_{cyl4} + \ldots$$
$$V_{cone} = \frac{\pi}{4} V_{pri1} + \frac{\pi}{4} V_{pri2} + \frac{\pi}{4} V_{pri3} + \frac{\pi}{4} V_{pri4} + \ldots$$
$$V_{cone} = \frac{\pi}{4}(V_{pri1} + V_{pri2} + V_{pri3} + V_{pri4} + \ldots)$$
$$V_{cone} = \frac{\pi}{4}(V_{pri})$$

Insert the formula for the volume of a prism.

$$V_{cone} = \frac{\pi}{4}\left(\frac{1}{3}BH\right)$$
$$V_{cone} = \frac{\pi}{4}\left(\frac{1}{3}(2R)^2 H\right) = \frac{\pi}{4}\left(\frac{1}{3}(4R^2)H\right)$$
▶ $$V_{cone} = \frac{1}{3}\pi R^2 H$$

TRY

Ling is selling snow cones at a carnival. She uses cone-shaped paper cups that are 4 inches deep and 3 inches wide. She molds the top of each snow cone into a half-sphere. What is the volume of each snow cone?

Practice

Identify the value of k, the constant of proportionality.

1. The rectangle is divided into two congruent triangles.

$$A_{rect} = l \cdot w$$

$$A_{tri} = k_{tri} \cdot l \cdot w$$

$$k_{tri} = \underline{\hspace{1.5cm}}$$

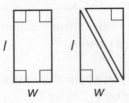

The images below show a cube and the cube cut into three congruent pyramids. Use these diagrams for questions 2–4.

2. Compare the base area and height of each oblique pyramid to the dimensions of the cube.

_____

_____

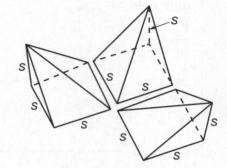

3. The cube has a volume of $V = s \cdot s \cdot s$. Each oblique pyramid has a volume of $V = k_{pyr} \cdot s \cdot s \cdot s$. What is the value of k_{pyr}? Explain how you know.

_____

_____

_____

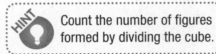

HINT Count the number of figures formed by dividing the cube.

4. A right pyramid is one in which the apex is directly above the center of the base. The pyramids shown are oblique pyramids, because their apexes are not above the center of the base. Is the formula for finding the volume of an oblique pyramid the same as the formula for finding a right pyramid? Explain why this is or is not the case.

_____

_____

Find the volume of each solid figure shown. Give an exact answer.

5.

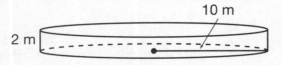

2 m   10 m

_____

6.

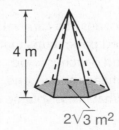

4 m

$2\sqrt{3}\ m^2$

_____

Use the cones below for questions 7 and 8.

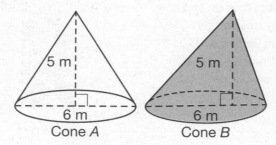

Cone A Cone B

7. Find the volume of each cone above. Give exact answers.

$V_A =$ _____

$V_B =$ _____

8. If the cones are cut by a horizontal plane parallel to their bases, will the areas of their cross sections be the same or different? Why? If different, which will have the greater area?

_____

Solve. Give answers to the nearest tenth.

9. The entrance to the Louvre Museum in Paris, France, is a pyramid with a height of 20.6 meters and a square base with sides measuring 35 meters. What is the volume of the pyramid?

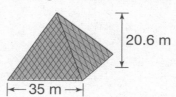

20.6 m

35 m

_____

10. Leah bought a plastic ball for her hamster. The ball has a diameter of 7 inches. What is the volume of the ball?

_____

7 in.

Use the diagrams to the right for questions 11 and 12.

11. Arnaldo stacked 18 quarters one on top of another. Approximately how many cubic centimeters of metal were used to make all the quarters in Arnaldo's stack? Give your answer to the nearest tenth of a cubic centimeter.

Arnaldo's Stack   Norma's Stack

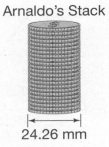 

31.5 mm

24.26 mm

_____

12. Norma made a stack of quarters, nickels, and pennies. She says the volume of her stack must be the same as the volume of Arnaldo's stack because the total height of her stack is the same as his. Is she correct? Explain your reasoning.

_____

_____

Find the volume of the figures below in terms of π.

13. The figure below was rotated 360° around the dashed line to form a solid.

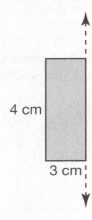

4 cm

3 cm

Find the volume of the solid formed. _____

14. The figure on the right is made of congruent isosceles triangles. It was rotated 360° around the dashed line to form a solid.

Find the volume of the solid formed. _____

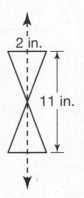

2 in.

11 in.

Choose the best answer.

15. A cylindrical fish tank has a base radius of 7 inches. The volume of the tank is approximately 3,080 cubic inches. What is the approximate height of the fish tank?

    A. 62 in.   **C.** 11 in.

    B. 20 in.   **D.** 10 in.

16. The volume of a small ice cream cone made by a company is 16π cubic centimeters. If the company doubles the base radius of the ice cream cone, what will be the volume of the new cone?

    A. $10.\overline{6}\pi$ cm^3 **C.** 64π cm^3

    B. 32π cm^3 **D.** 128π cm^3

Solve.

17. **APPLY** Three tennis balls, each with diameter 6.8 centimeters, fit in their container so that the top tennis ball touches the lid of the container and each tennis ball touches the sides of the container. The part of the container not taken up by the tennis balls contains air. How many cubic centimeters of this air are in the container? (Give your answer in terms of π.)

6.8 cm

---

18. **ANALYZE** A furniture company sells sculptures in the shape of an oblique cone. Each sculpture has a base diameter of 6 inches and a height of 20 inches. The sculpture's apex lies directly above one of the points on the circular boundary of the base.

The company packs the sculptures in cylindrical containers with diameter and height equal to that of the sculpture. Two sculptures fit in each container. Do the sculptures completely fill the container? If not, what volume of air is in the packed container?

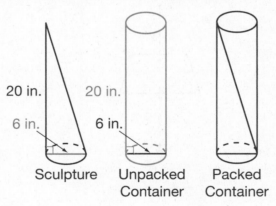

20 in.   20 in.

6 in.   6 in.

Sculpture   Unpacked   Packed
          Container   Container

Identify the cross section that results from slicing through each solid as indicated.

1. Plane parallel to the base

_____

2. Plane through the apex and the base

_____

3. Plane neither parallel nor perpendicular to the base

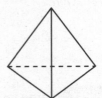

_____

Identify the solid that will be formed by rotating the figure 360° around the dashed line. Sketch the result and name or describe the solid.

4.

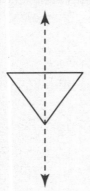

_____

5.

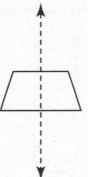

_____

6.

_____

Choose the best answer.

7. A cylindrical swimming pool has a volume of 25 cubic meters. The company that makes the pools wants to make an even larger pool by doubling the radius of their current model. How many cubic meters of water would the new pool hold?

    A. 12.5 m³

    B. 50 m³

    C. 100 m³

    D. 200 m³

8. A souvenir pyramid has a square base measuring 10 cm by 7 cm and a height of 12 cm. It comes in the smallest possible box. What is the volume of air in the souvenir box when the pyramid is packed inside?

    A. 280 cm²

    B. 420 cm³

    C. 560 cm²

    D. 840 cm³

9. The rectangle below will be rotated 360° around the dashed line to create a solid. Which is closest to the volume of that solid?

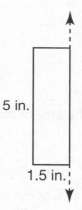

5 in.

1.5 in.

    A. 7.5 in.³   **C.** 11.3 in.³

    B. 8.8 in.²   **D.** 35.3 in.²

10. The following cross sections were taken from a solid.

Plane perpendicular to the base

Plane parallel to the base

Which of the following could be the solid?

    A. cone   **C.** sphere

    B. cylinder   **D.** cube

Solve.

11. Rosie is building a sand pyramid at the beach. She wants the pyramid to have a square base with a side length of 24 inches, and she wants the height of the pyramid to be 11 inches. How many cubic inches of sand will Rosie need to build the pyramid?

_____

Regular polygon *ABCDEFGH* is drawn within Circle *O*. Use this figure for questions 12–15.

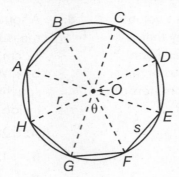

12. Use the triangle area formula $A = \frac{1}{2}ab\sin C$ to write an expression for the area of $\triangle FOG$.

    $A_{tri} =$ _____

    A circle contains 360°. A regular polygon with *n* sides can be broken into *n* congruent triangles, each with vertex angle θ. Write an expression for the measure of θ in terms of *n*.

    $\theta =$ _____

    Substitute this value for θ into your area formula.

    $A_{tri} = \frac{1}{2}$ _____ sin _____

13. Use your formula for the area of one triangle to find a formula for the area of the entire regular polygon (with *n* sides) in terms of *r* and *n*.

    $A_{poly} =$ _____ $\cdot A_{tri} =$ _____

14. When the polygon has very many sides (when *n* is very large), the area of the polygon will be approximately equal to the area of the circle. Set the area of the circle equal to your formula for the area of the polygon. Solve for π

    $\pi r^2 =$ _____

    $\pi =$ _____

15. Substitute 10, 100, and 1,000 for *n* in your expression for π and evaluate the expression. Are these values good approximations for π?

    _____

N	π = _____
10	
100	
1,000	

Solve.

16. **SEPARATE** Isaiah melted wax and used it to make the candle shown on the right. In terms of π, how many cubic centimeters of wax did he use to make the candle?

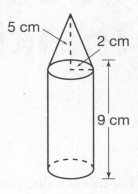

5 cm
2 cm
9 cm

_____

17. **ANALYZE** The cone and square pyramid on the left below have a height of 12 units. The cone has a base radius of 4 units, and the square pyramid has a base side length of $4\sqrt{\pi}$ units. The figures were cut by a horizontal plane that is parallel to their bases, forming the cross sections shown in the center below. A side view of both figures is shown on the right below.

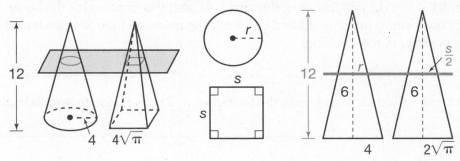

Find the area of each base.

Area of cone base = _____   Area of pyramid base = _____

Use the side-view diagram and your knowledge of similar triangles to find the values of r and s.

r = _____ s = _____

Find the area of each cross section.

Area of circle = _____   Area of square = _____

How does the volume of the cone compare to the volume of the pyramid? Explain how you know.

_____

_____

_____

Circular Thinking

MATERIALS

- Math Tools: Circular Thinking (pp. 339, 341)
- tape
- piece of string at least 80 inches long
- scissors

For this activity, you will work with a partner or in groups to explore measurements of circles.

1 Tear out the Math Tools: Circular Thinking pages. Notice that one circle has radius 2 inches and one has radius 3 inches. Cut the two circles out of the paper.

2 Wrap a piece of string completely around the outside of the smaller circle. Cut the string so that it is equal to the circumference of the circle. Repeat this process for the larger circle as well. Lay the pieces of string out straight and use a ruler to measure their lengths (which are equal to the circumferences of the circles).

$C_{2 \text{ in.}} \approx$ _____ $C_{3 \text{ in.}} \approx$ _____

Substitute these values for C and r into the formula $C = 2\pi r$ to calculate approximate values for π.

_____

3 Are the circles on the Math Tools sheet similar figures? Explain how you know.

_____

4 Cut the larger circle along the dashed lines, dividing it into 16 slices. Use 8 slices to form a semicircle. Use the string and ruler to find the length of the semicircular arc.

_____

_____

5 Assemble the slices so they resemble a parallelogram, as shown. Tape them together.

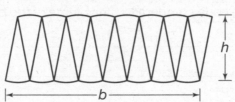

6 The formula for the area of a parallelogram is $A = bh$. Because the parallelogram consists of all 16 slices, its area must be equal to the area of the circle.

Measure the base length and height of the figure using your ruler. Find its area.

$b =$ _____ $h =$ _____

$A = b \cdot h =$ _____ $\cdot$ _____ $=$ _____

7 How does the height of the figure compare to the radius of the large circle? How does the base length of the figure compare to the arc length of the semicircle?

_____

_____

8 Based on your comparisons and the equation for circumference, $C = 2\pi r$, write expressions for b and h in terms of the radius of the original circle, r.

$b =$ _____ $h =$ _____

Substitute these expressions into the formula for area.

$A = b \cdot h =$ _____ $\cdot$ _____ $=$ _____

9 Rearrange the slices to form the taller "parallelogram" shown.

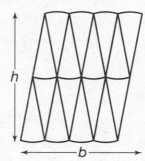

Use both formulas to find the area of this figure. How do they compare?

_____

10 Suppose the large circle were the base of a cone with a volume of 27π cubic inches. A certain cross section of the cone would be congruent to the smaller circle that you cut out. At what height above the base would this cross section be found?

_____

Grades 6–8 & Algebra I

Geometry

Algebra II

Algebra

Creating Equations

Create equations that describe numbers or relationships.

Statistics and Probability

Interpreting Categorical and Quantitative Data

Summarize, represent, and interpret data on a single count or measurement variable.

Functions

Interpreting Functions

Interpret functions that arise in applications in terms of the context.

Analyze functions using different representations.

Building Functions

Build a function that models a relationship between two quantities.

Linear, Quadratic, and Exponential Models

Construct and compare linear, quadratic, and exponential models and solve problems.

Interpret expressions for functions in terms of the situation they model.

Grade 8 Geometry

Understand and apply the Pythagorean Theorem.

Geometry

Expressing Geometric Properties with Equations

Translate between the geometric description and the equation for a conic section.

Use coordinates to prove simple geometric theorems algebraically.

Number and Quantity

The Complex Number System

Perform arithmetic operations with complex numbers.

Use complex numbers in polynomial identities and equations.

Algebra

Arithmetic with Polynomials and Rational Expressions

Understand the relationship between zeros and factors of polynomials.

Creating Equations

Create equations that describe numbers or relationships.

Functions

Interpreting Functions

Interpret functions that arise in applications in terms of the context.

Analyze functions using different representations.

Building Functions

Build a function that models a relationship between two quantities.

Build new functions from existing functions.

Linear, Quadratic, and Exponential Models

Construct and compare linear, quadratic, and exponential models and solve problems.

Unit 4
Connecting Algebra and Geometry through Coordinates

LESSON 19 · Parallel and Perpendicular Lines

UNDERSTAND **Parallel lines** lie in the same plane but never intersect. On a coordinate plane, lines that are parallel to each other have the same slope but different *y*-intercepts.

Consider two cars traveling in the same direction at the same constant speed. Both cars are traveling at a rate of 50 miles per hour, but Car A is 100 miles ahead of Car B. The following functions describe the distance of each car from Car B's starting point, in miles, after *t* hours.

Car A: $d_A(t) = 50t + 100$

Car B: $d_B(t) = 50t$

The graphs of these equations are shown on the right.

The equations have the same slope, 50, but different *y*-intercepts. The function for Car A has a *y*-intercept of 100, and the function for Car B has a *y*-intercept of 0. In real terms, at the time when Car B leaves, Car A is 100 miles away. Since the cars travel at the same rate, they will always be 100 miles apart and will never meet, just as the parallel lines in the graph will never intersect.

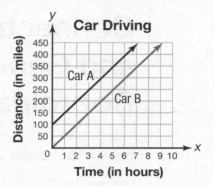

UNDERSTAND **Perpendicular lines** intersect to form right angles. On a coordinate plane, lines that are perpendicular have slopes that are opposite reciprocals of each other. This means that if one line has a slope of *m*, then a line perpendicular to it will have a slope of $-\frac{1}{m}$. The product of a number and its opposite reciprocal is always -1.

$$m \cdot -\frac{1}{m} = -1$$

The two lines shown on the right are perpendicular. Use the slope formula, $m = \frac{y_2 - y_1}{x_2 - x_1}$ to find the slope of each line.

One line passes through the points (2, 3) and (4, 2).

$$m = \frac{2 - 3}{4 - 2} = \frac{-1}{2} = -\frac{1}{2}$$

The other line passes through the points (1, 1) and (2, 3).

$$m = \frac{3 - 1}{2 - 1} = \frac{2}{1} = 2$$

The negative reciprocal of $-\frac{1}{2}$ is $\frac{2}{1}$, or 2, so the lines are perpendicular.

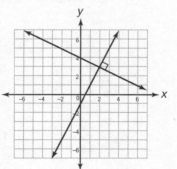

⊏ Connect

Are lines *a* and *b* parallel?

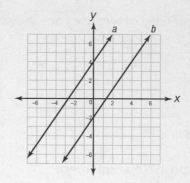

1

Observe the lines.

The lines do not intersect at any visible point, so they appear to be parallel. However, the lines may intersect at some point not on the grid, so observation alone is not enough to prove that they are parallel.

2

Find the slope of line *a*.

Find two points on the line, and use the slope formula to calculate its slope.

Line *a* passes through the points $(0, 4)$ and $(-2, 1)$.

$$m_a = \frac{1-4}{-2-0} = \frac{-3}{-2} = \frac{3}{2}$$

3

Find the slope of line *b*.

Line *b* passes through the points $(0, -2)$ and $(2, 1)$.

$$m_b = \frac{1-(-2)}{2-0} = \frac{3}{2}$$

4

Compare the slopes of lines *a* and *b*.

Both lines have a slope of $\frac{3}{2}$. The *y*-intercept of line *a* is 4, and the *y*-intercept of line *b* is -2. The slopes are the same, and the *y*-intercepts are different.

▶ Lines *a* and *b* are parallel.

TRY

Find the equation of another line that is parallel to lines *a* and *b*. Then graph that line on the same coordinate plane.

EXAMPLE A The equations of two lines are shown below. Are lines r and s perpendicular?

Line r: $4y + 12 = x$

Line s: $8y + 2x = 16$

1

Find the slope of line r.

Rewrite the equation in slope-intercept form. The coefficient of x will be the slope.

Solve for y.

$4y + 12 = x$

$4y = x - 12$

$y = \frac{1}{4}x - 3$

The slope is $\frac{1}{4}$.

2

Find the slope of line s.

Rewrite the equation in slope-intercept form. The coefficient of x will be the slope.

Solve for y.

$8y + 2x = 16$

$8y = -2x + 16$

$y = -\frac{1}{4}x + 2$

The slope is $-\frac{1}{4}$.

3

Compare the slopes of lines r and s.

$\frac{1}{4} \cdot \left(-\frac{1}{4}\right) = -\frac{1}{16}$

The product of the slopes is not -1, so the slopes are not opposite reciprocals.

▶ Lines r and s are not perpendicular.

TRY

Determine whether the following lines are perpendicular.

$3y - 2x = 6$

$3x = 14 - 2y$

EXAMPLE B Line p is represented by the equation $2y + 2 = 6x$. Find the following:

- line n, a line that is parallel to line p and that passes through the point $(6, 2)$
- line q, a line that is perpendicular to line p and that passes through the point $(6, 2)$.

1

Rewrite the equation for line p in slope-intercept form. Find the slope.

Solve for y.

$2y + 2 = 6x$

$2y = 6x - 2$

$y = 3x - 1$

The slope of line p is 3.

2

Find the equation of line n.

A line parallel to line p has the same slope, 3. Use point-slope form to write the equation of a line with a slope of 3 that passes through $(6, 2)$. Then, convert the equation to slope-intercept form.

$y - y_1 = m(x - x_1)$

$y - 2 = 3(x - 6)$

$y - 2 = 3x - 18$

▶ $y = 3x - 16$

3

Find the equation of line q.

A line perpendicular to line p has a slope that is the opposite reciprocal of 3. The opposite reciprocal of 3 is $-\frac{1}{3}$ because $3 \cdot \left(-\frac{1}{3}\right) = -1$.

Use point-slope form to write the equation of a line with a slope of $-\frac{1}{3}$ that passes through $(6, 2)$. Then convert the equation to slope-intercept form.

$y - y_1 = m(x - x_1)$

$y - 2 = -\frac{1}{3}(x - 6)$

$y - 2 = -\frac{1}{3}x + 2$

▶ $y = -\frac{1}{3}x + 4$

CHECK

Graph lines p, n, and q on the same coordinate plane. Confirm that line p is parallel to line n and is perpendicular to line q.

Practice

Fill in the blank or write the answer to the question.

1. A line that is parallel to $y = \frac{3}{4}x - 9$ has slope $m = $ _____.

REMEMBER The slopes of perpendicular lines are opposite reciprocals.

2. A line that is perpendicular to $3y = 11 - 8x$ has slope $m = $ _____.

3. A line that is parallel to $y = 12$ has slope $m = $ _____.

4. Are the lines $2y - x = 6$ and $6x - 3y - 33 = 0$ parallel, perpendicular, or neither?

HINT Write the equation of a line in slope-intercept form to find its slope.

Choose the best answer.

5. Which equation represents a line that is perpendicular to the line shown below?

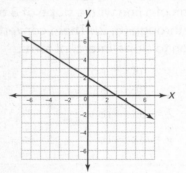

   A. $y = \frac{2}{3}x + 5$

   B. $y = \frac{3}{2}x - 4$

   C. $y = -\frac{2}{3}x - 6$

   D. $y = -\frac{3}{2}x + 1$

6. Which equation represents a line that is parallel to the line shown below?

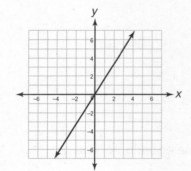

   A. $y = \frac{3}{5}x + 1$

   B. $y = -\frac{3}{5}x + 1$

   C. $y = \frac{5}{3}x - 1$

   D. $y = -\frac{5}{3}x - 1$

7. Which describes the lines $y = \frac{7}{8}x + 12$ and $y = -\frac{8}{7}x + 7$?

   A. parallel

   B. perpendicular

   C. neither parallel nor perpendicular

8. Which describes the lines $x - 2y = -6$ and $4y + 4 = 2x$?

   A. parallel

   B. perpendicular

   C. neither parallel nor perpendicular

Choose the best answer.

9. Which describes the lines shown below?

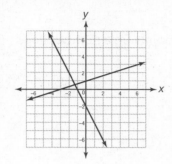

A. parallel

B. perpendicular

C. neither parallel nor perpendicular

10. Which describes the lines shown below?

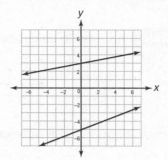

A. parallel

B. perpendicular

C. neither parallel nor perpendicular

Write the equation of the line that is described. Give your answer in slope-intercept form.

11.

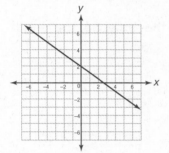

A line that is parallel to the one shown above and that passes through the point $(8, -7)$.

_____

13. A line that is parallel to $3y = x + 12$ and that passes through the point $(6, -8)$.

_____

12.

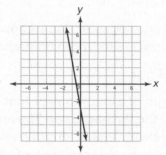

A line that is perpendicular to the one shown above and that passes through the point $(12, 3)$.

_____

14. A line that is perpendicular to $y - x = 7$ and that passes through the point $(-2, -2)$.

_____

Solve.

15. **EXPLAIN** Lines s, t, and u all lie on the same plane. Line s is parallel to line t. Line t is perpendicular to line u. What is the relationship between lines s and u? How do you know?

_____

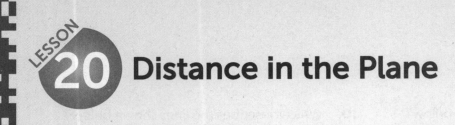

Distance in the Plane

LESSON 20

UNDERSTAND It's easy to calculate the distance between two points on a number line.

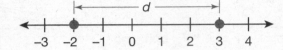

The distance is equal to the difference of the two numbers.

$$d = 3 - (-2) = 5$$

It's just as easy to calculate the length of a vertical or horizontal line segment on the coordinate plane.

For a vertical line segment, the x-coordinates of the endpoints are the same. So, the length of the line segment is simply the difference of the y-coordinates.

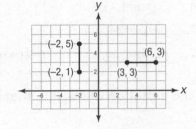

$$d = 5 - 1 = 4$$

For a horizontal line segment, the y-coordinates of the endpoints are the same. So, the length of the line segment is simply the difference of the x-coordinates.

$$d = 6 - 3 = 3$$

Finding the length of a line segment that is not horizontal or vertical is trickier. Recall the **Pythagorean Theorem**, which states that, for any right triangle with legs of length a and b and hypotenuse of length c, $a^2 + b^2 = c^2$. You can think of a diagonal line on the coordinate plane as the hypotenuse of a triangle with one vertical leg and one horizontal leg.

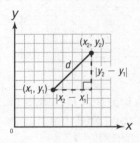

The horizontal leg has a length of $|x_2 - x_1|$. The vertical leg has a length of $|y_2 - y_1|$. You can substitute these expressions into the Pythagorean Theorem and solve for d, the length of the diagonal line.

$$a^2 + b^2 = c^2$$
$$(x_2 - x_1)^2 + (y_2 - y_1)^2 = d^2$$
$$\sqrt{(x_2 - x_1)^2 + (y_2 - y_1)^2} = d$$
$$d = \sqrt{(x_2 - x_1)^2 + (y_2 - y_1)^2}$$

This formula is called the distance formula. It can be used to find the length of any line segment on the coordinate plane, as long as its endpoints are known.

⊷Connect

The coordinate plane shows point *A*, point *B*, and the line segment connecting them.

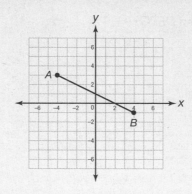

Use the distance formula to find *AB*, the length of the line segment.

1

Find the coordinates of the endpoints.

Point *A* is located at $(-4, 3)$.

Point *B* is located at $(4, -1)$.

Let $A(-4, 3) = (x_1, y_1)$ and
let $B(4, -1) = (x_2, y_2)$.

2

Apply the distance formula.

Substitute the coordinates into the formula
and evaluate the radicand.

$$d = \sqrt{(x_2 - x_1)^2 + (y_2 - y_1)^2}$$
$$= \sqrt{(4 - (-4))^2 + (-1 - 3)^2}$$
$$= \sqrt{(8)^2 + (-4)^2}$$
$$= \sqrt{64 + 16}$$
$$= \sqrt{80}$$

3

Determine if the result can be
simplified further.

The radicand, 80, is not a perfect square.
However, it has factors that are perfect
squares. Simplify by factoring out any
perfect square factors.

$$d = \sqrt{80}$$
$$d = \sqrt{16 \cdot 5}$$
$$d = \sqrt{16} \cdot \sqrt{5}$$
▶ $d = 4\sqrt{5}$

TRY

Substitute the points in the reverse
order: Let $B(4, -1) = (x_1, y_1)$ and let
$A(-4, 3) = (x_2, y_2)$. Do you get the
same result? Why do you think this is?

EXAMPLE A Parallelogram *DEFG* is shown on the coordinate plane.

What is the perimeter of parallelogram *DEFG*?

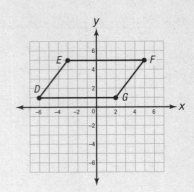

1

Determine what lengths to find.

Recall that opposite sides of a parallelogram are congruent. So, you only need to find the lengths of two adjacent sides. Find the lengths of $\overline{DE}$ and $\overline{EF}$.

2

Find the length of $\overline{EF}$.

The coordinates of the endpoints of $\overline{EF}$ are $E(-3, 5)$ and $F(5, 5)$. Since $\overline{EF}$ is horizontal, you do not need to use the distance formula. The *y*-coordinates are the same. To find the length, find the absolute value of the difference of the *x*-coordinates.

$$EF = |-3 - 5| = |-8| = 8$$

Opposite sides of a parallelogram are congruent, so $GD = EF$.

$$GD = EF = 8$$

3

Find the length of $\overline{DE}$.

The coordinates of the endpoints of $\overline{DE}$ are $D(-6, 1)$ and $E(-3, 5)$. Since $\overline{DE}$ is diagonal, use the distance formula. Let $D(-6, 1) = (x_1, y_1)$ and $E(-3, 5) = (x_2, y_2)$.

$$DE = \sqrt{(-3 - (-6))^2 + (5 - 1)^2}$$

$$DE = \sqrt{(3)^2 + (4)^2}$$

$$DE = \sqrt{9 + 16}$$

$$DE = \sqrt{25}$$

$$DE = 5$$

Opposite sides of a parallelogram are congruent, so $FG = DE$.

$$FG = DE = 5$$

4

Find the perimeter.

$$P = DE + EF + FG + GD$$

$$P = 5 + 8 + 5 + 8$$

$$P = 26$$

▶ The perimeter of parallelogram *DEFG* is 26 units.

DISCUSS

Imagine a regular octagon in a coordinate plane. How many side lengths would you need to find in order to calculate its perimeter?

EXAMPLE B Right triangle *QRS* is shown on the coordinate plane.

Find the area of △*QRS*.

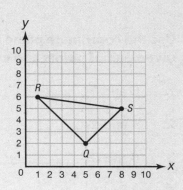

1

Determine what lengths to find.

△*QRS* is a right triangle with the right angle at ∠*Q*. In a right triangle, the legs form the base and the height. So, find *QR* and *QS*.

2

Find the length of $\overline{QR}$.

Let $Q(5, 2) = (x_1, y_1)$ and $R(1, 6) = (x_2, y_2)$.

$QR = \sqrt{(1 - 5)^2 + (6 - 2)^2}$

$QR = \sqrt{(-4)^2 + (4)^2}$

$QR = \sqrt{32}$

$QR = 4\sqrt{2}$

3

Find the length of $\overline{QS}$.

Let $Q(5, 2) = (x_1, y_1)$ and $S(8, 5) = (x_2, y_2)$.

$QS = \sqrt{(8 - 5)^2 + (5 - 2)^2}$

$QS = \sqrt{(3)^2 + (3)^2}$

$QS = \sqrt{18}$

$QS = 3\sqrt{2}$

4

Find the area of △*QRS*.

The area of a triangle is half of the base times the height. Let $\overline{QR}$ be the base and let $\overline{QS}$ be the height.

$A = \frac{1}{2}bh$

$A = \frac{1}{2}QR \cdot QS$

$A = \frac{1}{2}(4\sqrt{2})(3\sqrt{2})$

$A = 12$

▶ The area of △*QRS* is 12 square units.

TRY

Find the area of △*XYZ* with vertices $X(-4, 2)$, $Y(2, 2)$ and $Z(-1, 5)$.

Practice

Use the coordinate plane below for questions 1–4. Find the distance in units between each given pair of points and write it in simplest form.

1. *D* and *E* _____

2. *A* and *C* _____

3. *B* and *D* _____

4. *A* and *E* _____

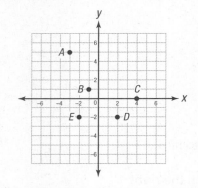

Use the information below for questions 5 and 6. Choose the best answer.

Figure *WXYZ* on the coordinate plane below is a square.

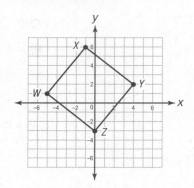

5. What is the perimeter of *WXYZ*?
    - **A.** $2\sqrt{41}$ units
    - **B.** 20 units
    - **C.** $4\sqrt{39}$ units
    - **D.** $4\sqrt{41}$ units

6. What is the area of *WXYZ*?
    - **A.** 25 units^2
    - **B.** 39 units^2
    - **C.** 41 units^2
    - **D.** 82 units^2

Solve.

7. The distance between points *A* and *B* is $\sqrt{113}$. Point *A* is located at $(-3, 6)$, and point *B* is located at $(4, y)$. What is a possible value of *y*? _____

8. The distance between points *C* and *D* is $6\sqrt{2}$. Point *C* is located at the origin. Point *D* is located at the point (a, a). What is a possible value of *a*? _____

9. Triangle *FGH* is isosceles with base $\overline{GH}$. Point *M* is the midpoint of $\overline{GH}$.

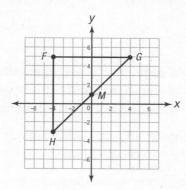

Find the length of altitude $\overline{FM}$, the perimeter of △*FGH*, and the area of △*FGH*.

Altitude: _____

Perimeter: _____

Area: _____

Use the information below to answer questions 10 and 11.

Rectangle *PQRS* is shown on the coordinate plane below.

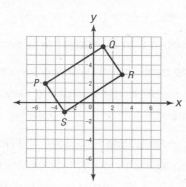

10. PLAN How can you find the area of rectangle *PQRS*?

_____

_____

11. APPLY Find the area of rectangle *PQRS*.

Area: _____

Dividing Line Segments

LESSON 21

UNDERSTAND The **midpoint** of a line segment divides, or **partitions**, the segment in half, producing two line segments of equal length, so the lengths have a ratio of 1:1. It is possible to find the point that divides a given line segment into two segments of any given ratio.

For a vertical or horizontal line segment, finding such a point is a straightforward process. Look at the coordinate plane.

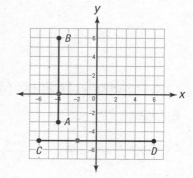

Notice that all points on $\overline{AB}$ have the same x-coordinate, -4. So, the point $\frac{1}{3}$ of the way from A to B "rises" only $\frac{1}{3}$ of the way along the line. To find this point, add $\frac{1}{3}$ of the length of $\overline{AB}$ to the y-coordinate of A.

$$(-4, -3 + \tfrac{1}{3}AB) = (-4, -3 + \tfrac{1}{3} \cdot 9)$$
$$= (-4, -3 + 3) = (-4, 0)$$

The point $(-4, 0)$ is $\frac{1}{3}$ of the way from A to B, and it partitions $\overline{AB}$ in a ratio 1:2.

A similar process can be used to find the point $\frac{1}{3}$ of the way from C to D. This point "runs" only $\frac{1}{3}$ of the length along the line from C to D.

$$(-6 + \tfrac{1}{3}CD, -5) = (-6 + \tfrac{1}{3} \cdot 12, -5) = (-6 + 4, -5) = (-2, -5)$$

The point $(-2, -5)$ is $\frac{1}{3}$ of the way from C to D, and it partitions $\overline{CD}$ in a ratio 1:2.

A diagonal line segment can also be partitioned by using a point. A point that is, for example, $\frac{1}{3}$ of the way from one endpoint to another "rises" $\frac{1}{3}$ of the way along the segment and also "runs" $\frac{1}{3}$ of the way along the segment.

Look at line segment $\overline{MN}$ on the coordinate plane below. To find the point P that is $\frac{1}{3}$ of the way from M to N, add $\frac{1}{3}$ of the "rise" to the y-coordinate of M and add $\frac{1}{3}$ of the "run" to its x-coordinate. Point M is located at $(-6, -5)$, and N is located at $(6, 4)$.

$$rise = 4 - (-5) = 9$$
$$run = 6 - (-6) = 12$$
$$P = (-6 + \tfrac{1}{3} \cdot 12, -5 + \tfrac{1}{3} \cdot 9) = (-6 + 4, -5 + 3)$$
$$= (-2, -2)$$

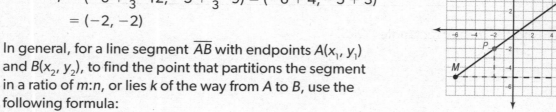

In general, for a line segment $\overline{AB}$ with endpoints $A(x_1, y_1)$ and $B(x_2, y_2)$, to find the point that partitions the segment in a ratio of $m:n$, or lies k of the way from A to B, use the following formula:

$$(x_1 + k(x_2 - x_1), y_1 + k(y_2 - y_1)) \quad \text{where } k = \frac{m}{m+n}$$

⸰Connect

The line segment $\overline{AB}$ is shown on the coordinate plane on the right.

Find the point Q that is $\frac{3}{4}$ the distance from A to B.
Then, plot and label Q on the coordinate plane.

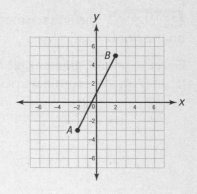

1

Identify the endpoints of $\overline{AB}$.

The coordinates of the endpoints are $A(-2, -3)$ and $B(2, 5)$.

Since the problem states that Q is $\frac{3}{4}$ the distance from A to B, let $A = (x_1, y_1)$ and let $B = (x_2, y_2)$.

2

Use the formula to find point Q.

Let $k = \frac{3}{4}$, $(x_1, y_1) = (-2, -3)$, and $(x_2, y_2) = (2, 5)$.

$Q = (x_1 + k(x_2 - x_1), y_1 + k(y_2 - y_1))$

$Q = (-2 + \frac{3}{4}[2 - (-2)], -3 + \frac{3}{4}[5 - (-3)])$

$Q = (-2 + \frac{3}{4}(4), -3 + \frac{3}{4}(8))$

$Q = (-2 + 3, -3 + 6)$

$Q = (1, 3)$

▶ Point $Q(1, 3)$ is $\frac{3}{4}$ the distance from A to B.

3

Plot Q on the coordinate plane.

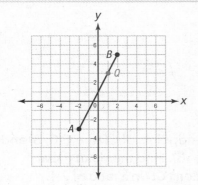

CHECK

Use the distance formula to find the lengths of $\overline{AQ}$ and $\overline{AB}$. Does $AQ = \left(\frac{3}{4}\right)AB$?

EXAMPLE A The line segment $\overline{BA}$ is shown on the coordinate plane on the right.

Find the point Q that partitions $\overline{BA}$ in a ratio of 1:3. Then, plot and label Q on the coordinate plane.

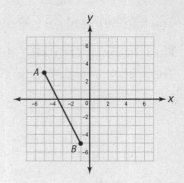

1

Identify the endpoints of $\overline{BA}$.

The coordinates of the endpoints are $A(-5, 3)$ and $B(-1, -5)$.

To partition $\overline{BA}$ in a ratio of 1:3, find the point that is $\frac{1}{1+3}$, or $\frac{1}{4}$, of the distance from B to A. Let $B = (x_1, y_1)$ and let $A = (x_2, y_2)$.

2

Use the formula to find point Q.

Let $k = \frac{1}{4}$, $(x_1, y_1) = (-1, -5)$, and $(x_2, y_2) = (-5, 3)$.

$Q = (x_1 + k(x_2 - x_1), y_1 + k(y_2 - y_1))$

$Q = (-1 + \frac{1}{4}[-5 - (-1)], -5 + \frac{1}{4}[3 - (-5)])$

$Q = (-1 + \frac{1}{4}(-4), -5 + \frac{1}{4}(8))$

$Q = (-1 + (-1), -5 + 2)$

$Q = (-2, -3)$

▶ Point $Q(-2, -3)$ partitions $\overline{BA}$ in a ratio of 1:3.

3

Plot Q on the coordinate plane.

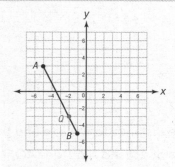

TRY

The endpoints of $\overline{CD}$ are $C(0, 3)$ and $D(12, 18)$. Find the point P that partitions $\overline{CD}$ in a ratio of 2:1.

EXAMPLE B The line segment $\overline{AB}$ is shown on the coordinate plane on the right.

Find the midpoint of $\overline{AB}$.

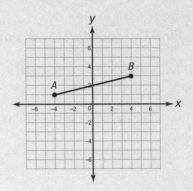

1

Identify the endpoints of $\overline{AB}$.

The coordinates of the endpoints are $A(-4, 1)$ and $B(4, 3)$.

The midpoint of $\overline{AB}$ is the point that is $\frac{1}{2}$ of the distance from A to B.

Let $A = (x_1, y_1)$ and $B = (x_2, y_2)$.

2

Use the formula to find the midpoint.

Let Q be the midpoint of $\overline{AB}$.

Let $k = \frac{1}{2}$, $(x_1, y_1) = (-4, 1)$, and $(x_2, y_2) = (4, 3)$.

$Q = (x_1 + k(x_2 - x_1), y_1 + k(y_2 - y_1))$

$Q = (-4 + \frac{1}{2}[4 - (-4)], 1 + \frac{1}{2}(3 - 1))$

$Q = (-4 + \frac{1}{2}(8), 1 + \frac{1}{2}(2))$

$Q = (-4 + 4, 1 + 1)$

$Q = (0, 2)$

▶ Point $(0, 2)$ is the midpoint of $\overline{AB}$.

DISCUSS

The formula for finding the midpoint of a segment with endpoints (x_1, y_1) and (x_2, y_2) is

$$\left(\frac{x_1 + x_2}{2}, \frac{y_1 + y_2}{2} \right)$$

How does this formula relate to the formula that you have been using?

Practice

Find the coordinates of point Q.

1. The line segment $\overline{AB}$ is shown on the coordinate plane on the right.

    Find the point Q that is $\frac{1}{5}$ the distance from A to B.

    _____

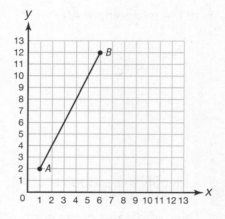

2. The line segment $\overline{CD}$ is shown on the coordinate plane on the right.

    Find the point Q that is $\frac{2}{3}$ the distance from C to D.

    _____

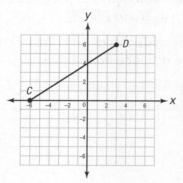

3. The line segment $\overline{GF}$ is shown on the coordinate plane on the right.

    Find the point Q that partitions $\overline{GF}$ in a ratio of 1:3.

    _____

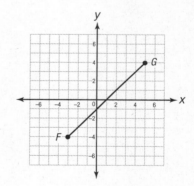

4. The line segment $\overline{JK}$ is shown on the coordinate plane on the right.

    Find the point Q that partitions $\overline{JK}$ in a ratio of 3:2.

    _____

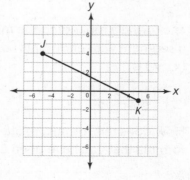

Use the information below for questions 5 and 6. Find the point described.

The endpoints of line segment $\overline{XY}$ are $X(-6, 2)$ and $Y(6, -10)$.

5. Find the point P that is $\frac{1}{3}$ the distance from X to Y. _____

6. Find the point Q that partitions $\overline{YX}$ in a ratio of 3:1. _____

Solve.

7. Point A is located at $(1, 4)$. Point P at $(3, 5)$ is $\frac{1}{3}$ the distance from A to point B.

   What are the coordinates of point B? _____

8. Point C is located at the origin. Point Q at $(-1, -2)$ partitions $\overline{CD}$ in a ratio of 1:6.

   What are the coordinates of point D? _____

9. The line segment $\overline{HJ}$ is shown on the coordinate plane to the right.

   Find the point Q that is $\frac{4}{5}$ the distance from J to H. _____

   Plot point Q on $\overline{HJ}$.

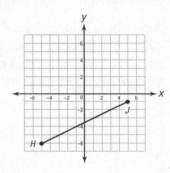

Fill in the blank.

10. **REASON** If point P is $\frac{3}{7}$ the distance from A to B, then it is _____ the distance from B to A.

Plot points L and P as described.

11. **SHOW** Point K is shown on the coordinate plane on the right.

    Plot a point L so that it is 15 units from point K and so that $\overline{KL}$ is not vertical or horizontal. (Hint: Find a Pythagorean triple where the largest number is 15.) Then, add point P that is $\frac{1}{3}$ the distance from K to L.

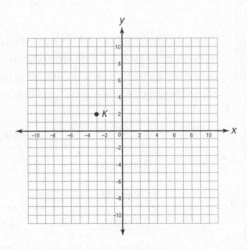

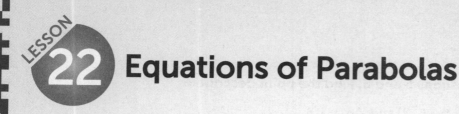

UNDERSTAND A conic section is a two-dimensional cross section formed by the intersection of a plane and a double cone. When the plane intersects at an angle and passes through one of the bases, the cross section is a U-shaped curve called a **parabola**.

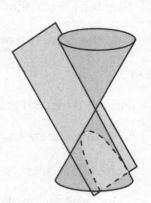

A conic section can also be defined as a curve having an equation of degree 2—a quadratic equation. The general form for the equation of any conic section is $Ax^2 + By^2 + Cx + Dy + E = 0$, in which A and B cannot both equal zero. If $B = 0$, the equation can be written in the form $y = ax^2 + bx + c$. This describes a parabola that opens up or down. If $A = 0$, the equation can be written in the form $x = ay^2 + by + c$. This describes a parabola that opens right or left.

A parabola is formally defined as the set of all points that are equidistant from a fixed line, called the **directrix**, and from a fixed point not on the line, called the **focus**. The parabola has an axis of symmetry that passes through the focus and is perpendicular to the directrix. The **vertex** lies on this line halfway between the focus and the directrix.

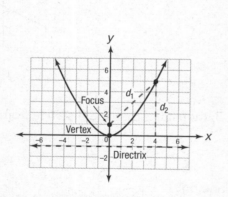

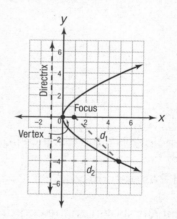

$d_1 = d_2$

The standard forms of an equation for a parabolic conic section with vertex (h, k) are given in the table below. The coordinates (h, k) give the vertex of the parabola. The variable p represents the shortest distance from the vertex to the focus and to the directrix. So, the coordinates of the focus and the equation of the directrix can be found from these equations.

	Vertical Parabola	Horizontal Parabola
Equation	$y - k = \frac{1}{4p}(x - h)^2$	$x - h = \frac{1}{4p}(y - k)^2$
Vertex	(h, k)	(h, k)
Focus	$(h, k + p)$	$(h + p, k)$
Directrix	$y = k - p$ (horizontal directrix)	$x = h - p$ (vertical directrix)

⊢€ Connect

Find the vertex, focus, and directrix of the parabola represented by $x^2 + 2x - 16y + 33 = 0$

1

Put the equation in standard form.

The equation contains an x^2 term. So, begin by grouping only terms containing x on one side of the equation. Then apply the method of completing the square: compare the expression to $ax^2 + bx + c$ and add $\left(\frac{b}{2a}\right)^2$ to both sides of the equation. Then factor.

$$x^2 + 2x - 16y + 33 = 0$$
$$x^2 + 2x = 16y - 33$$
$$x^2 + 2x + \left(\frac{2}{2(1)}\right)^2 = 16y - 33 + \left(\frac{2}{2(1)}\right)^2$$
$$x^2 + 2x + 1 = 16y - 33 + 1$$
$$(x + 1)^2 = 16y - 32$$
$$\frac{1}{16}(x + 1)^2 = y - 2$$

2

Identify the vertex.

Compare the given equation to the standard form of a vertical parabola, $y - k = \frac{1}{4p}(x - h)^2$.

$$y - 2 = \frac{1}{16}(x + 1)^2$$
$$y - 2 = \frac{1}{16}(x - (-1))^2$$

We can see that $k = 2$ and $h = -1$.

▶ The vertex of the parabola, (h, k), is $(-1, 2)$.

3

Find the value of p.

To find the value of p, set $\frac{1}{4p}$ equal to the number in front of the squared binomial, $(x + 1)^2$.

$$\frac{1}{4p} = \frac{1}{16}$$
$$4p = 16$$
$$p = 4$$

4

Identify the focus and directrix.

This equation represents a vertical parabola. Its focus is given by $(h, k + p)$.

$$(-1, 2 + 4) = (-1, 6)$$

Its directrix is given by $y = k - p$.

$$y = 2 - 4 = -2$$

▶ The focus of the parabola is $(-1, 6)$ and the directrix is $y = -2$.

 TRY

Find the vertex, focus, and directrix of $y^2 + x - 8y + 18 = 0$.

EXAMPLE A The focus of a parabola is (3.75, 5), and its directrix is $x = 4.25$. Write the equation of the parabola. Describe its appearance.

1

Determine the orientation of the parabola.

The directrix is a vertical line. So, the parabola is horizontal. Its equation has the form $x - h = \frac{1}{4p}(y - k)^2$.

2

Find the coordinates of the vertex.

Because the parabola is horizontal, the vertex is the midpoint between the focus (3.75, 5) and the point on the directrix with the same y-coordinate, (4.25, 5).

$$\left(\frac{3.75 + 4.25}{2}, \frac{5 + 5}{2}\right) = (4, 5)$$

The vertex is located at (4, 5).

3

Find the value of p.

The vertex (h, k) is (4, 5), so $h = 4$ and $k = 5$.

Because the parabola is horizontal, the formula for the focus is $(h + p, k)$. The focus of this parabola is (3.75, 5).

$$h + p = 3.75$$
$$4 + p = 3.75$$
$$p = -0.25 \text{ or } -\frac{1}{4}$$

This means the focus is $\frac{1}{4}$ unit to the left of the vertex.

4

Substitute the values of h, k, and p into the general form of the equation.

$h = 4$, $k = 5$, and $p = -0.25$

$$x - h = \frac{1}{4p}(y - k)^2$$
$$x - 4 = \frac{1}{4(-0.25)}(y - 5)^2$$
$$x - 4 = \frac{1}{-1}(y - 5)^2$$

▶ The equation of the parabola is $x - 4 = -(y - 5)^2$. Because the parabola is horizontal and $p < 0$, the parabola opens left.

MODEL

Graph the parabola. The point (0, 7) is on the parabola. What is the distance between this point and the focus, (3.75, 5)? What is the shortest distance between this point and the directrix, $x = 4.25$?

EXAMPLE B Identify the focus and the directrix for the parabola graphed below.

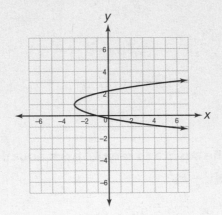

1

Identify the vertex and one other point.

The graph is a horizontal parabola that opens right. The vertex, or turning point, is the point with the lowest x-coordinate. The leftmost point appears to be $(-3, 1)$.

The point $(-1, 0)$ also appears to be on the graph.

2

Find the value of p.

The standard form equation of a horizontal parabola is $x - h = \frac{1}{4p}(y - k)^2$. Substitute the values from the vertex, $(-3, 1)$.

$$x - h = \frac{1}{4p}(y - k)^2$$

$$x + 3 = \frac{1}{4p}(y - 1)^2$$

Substitute $(-1, 0)$ into the equation and solve for p.

$$-1 + 3 = \frac{1}{4p}(0 - 1)^2$$

$$2 = \frac{1}{4p}(-1)^2$$

$$2 = \frac{1}{4p}(1)$$

$$8p = 1$$

$$p = \frac{1}{8}$$

3

Identify the focus and the directrix.

Because the parabola opens right, the focus is to the right of the vertex.

The formula for the focus is $(h + p, k)$.

$$(-3 + \tfrac{1}{8}, 1) = (-\tfrac{23}{8}, 1)$$

The directrix will be vertical and lie to the left of the parabola.

The formula for the directrix is $x = h - p$.

$$x = -3 - \frac{1}{8} = -\frac{23}{8}$$

▶ The focus is $(-\frac{25}{8}, 1)$, and the directrix is $x = -\frac{25}{8}$.

TRY

Write the equation of the parabola in the form $x = ay^2 + by + c$.

Practice

For each equation of a parabola, identify the vertex and the distance between the vertex and the focus, _p_.

1. $y + 10 = 2(x - 5)^2$

vertex: (_____, _____)

$p =$ _____

2. $x = -3(y - 1)^2 + 4$

vertex: (_____, _____)

$p =$ _____

3. $x - 2 = \frac{1}{4}(y + 8)^2$

vertex: (_____, _____)

$p =$ _____

Use the method of completing the square to rewrite each equation in standard form $y - k = \frac{1}{4}p(x - h)^2$ or $x - h = \frac{1}{4}p(y - k)^2$.

4. $x = y^2 + 6y + 10$

_____

5. $x = 2y^2 + 4y - 3$

_____

6. $\frac{1}{2}x^2 - y - 6x + 20 = 0$

_____

 HINT Factor out the coefficient 2 before completing the square.

Identify the focus and directrix for the parabola represented by each equation.

7. $y + 3 = -\frac{1}{12}x^2$

focus: (_____, _____)

directrix: _____

8. $x - 1 = \frac{1}{8}(y - 2)^2$

focus: (_____, _____)

directrix: _____

9. $y = x^2 - 10x + 27$

focus: (_____, _____)

directrix: _____

> **REMEMBER** For a horizontal parabola, the focus is $(h + p, k)$ and the directrix is $x = h - p$.

Write the equation for the parabola with the given focus and directrix. Also identify the vertex and the direction (_up_, _down_, _left_, or _right_) in which the parabola opens.

10. focus: $(0, -2)$

directrix: $y = 2$

vertex: (_____, _____)

equation: _____

opens _____

11. focus: $(4, -4)$

directrix: $x = -2$

vertex: (_____, _____)

equation: _____

opens _____

12. focus: $\left(\frac{3}{2}, 3\right)$

directrix: $x = 5$

vertex: (_____, _____)

equation: _____

opens _____

Write an equation in standard form to represent each parabola. Identify the focus and directrix.

13.

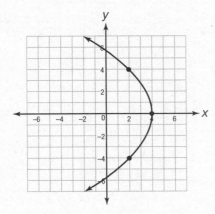

equation: _____

focus: (_____, _____)

directrix: _____

14.

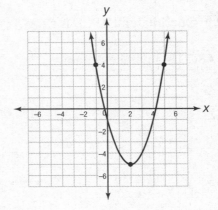

equation: _____

focus: (_____, _____)

directrix: _____

Solve.

15. [MODEL] The mirrored reflector in a flashlight is shaped like a parabola. The reflector is 4 inches across and 2 inches deep. The lightbulb of the flashlight is located at the focus of the parabola. Label the location of the lightbulb on the diagram. How far from the vertex is the lightbulb positioned?

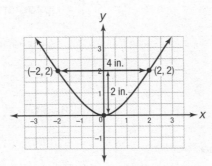

_____

LESSON 23
Using Coordinate Geometry to Prove Theorems

EXAMPLE A Quadrilateral *ABCD* is shown on the coordinate plane.

Prove that *ABCD* is a parallelogram.

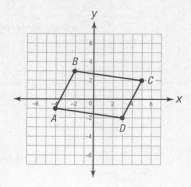

1

Make a plan.

A parallelogram is a quadrilateral in which opposite sides are parallel. To prove that *ABCD* is a parallelogram, find the slope of each side and show that the slopes of opposite sides are the same.

2

Find the slope of each side of the quadrilateral.

Use the slope formula $m = \frac{y_2 - y_1}{x_2 - x_1}$.

$\overline{AB}$: $m = \frac{3 - (-1)}{-2 - (-4)} = \frac{4}{2} = 2$

$\overline{BC}$: $m = \frac{2 - 3}{5 - (-2)} = \frac{-1}{7} = -\frac{1}{7}$

$\overline{CD}$: $m = \frac{-2 - 2}{3 - 5} = \frac{-4}{-2} = 2$

$\overline{DA}$: $m = \frac{-1 - (-2)}{-4 - 3} = \frac{1}{-7} = -\frac{1}{7}$

3

Analyze the results.

$\overline{AB}$ and $\overline{CD}$ are opposite sides, and they have the same slope, 2.

$\overline{BC}$ and $\overline{DA}$ are opposite sides, and they have the same slope, $-\frac{1}{7}$.

▶ Since both pairs of opposite sides are parallel, *ABCD* is a parallelogram.

DISCUSS

The definition of a rectangle is a parallelogram with four right angles. Is *ABCD* a rectangle? How do you know?

EXAMPLE B Circle *O* in the graph below has center *O*(1, 1). The point (−4, 1) lies on the circle. Prove that the point (4, 5) also lies on circle *O*.

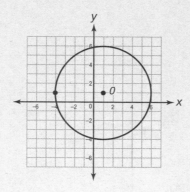

1

Make a plan.

The definition of a circle is all points that are equidistant from a given point, called the center. That distance is the radius. So, find the length of the radius, and then find the distance between (4, 5) and the center. If those distances are equal, the point lies on the circle.

2

Find the length of the radius.

The point (−4, 1) lies on the circle, so the radius is equal to the distance between (−4, 1) and the center, (1, 1). Since this segment is horizontal, find the difference of their *x*-coordinates to find the length.

$r = |1 - (-4)| = 5$

The radius of circle *O* is 5 units.

3

Find the distance between point *O* and (4, 5). Compare it to the radius.

Find the distance between (1, 1) and (4, 5). Use the distance formula.

$d = \sqrt{(x_2 - x_1)^2 + (y_2 - y_1)^2}$

$d = \sqrt{(5 - 1)^2 + (4 - 1)^2}$

$d = \sqrt{4^2 + 3^2}$

$d = \sqrt{25}$

$d = 5$

▶ This is equal to the radius, so the point (4, 5) does lie on circle *O*.

TRY

Circle *C* has center (−5, −6) and radius $2\sqrt{3}$. Is the point (−8, −4) on the circle?

EXAMPLE C Triangle *JKL* is shown on the coordinate plane on the right. Is △*JKL* a right triangle? Is it an isosceles triangle?.

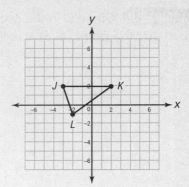

1

Make a plan.

A right triangle contains one right angle. This means that two of the sides of the triangle will be perpendicular, so they will have slopes that are opposite reciprocals. Find the slopes of all sides of △*JKL*.

An isosceles triangle has two congruent sides. Find the side lengths of △*JKL*.

2

Find the slopes of all sides and compare them.

Use the slope formula $m = \frac{y_2 - y_1}{x_2 - x_1}$.

$\overline{JK}$: $m = \frac{2 - 2}{2 - (-3)} = \frac{0}{5} = 0$

$\overline{KL}$: $m = \frac{2 - (-1)}{2 - (-2)} = \frac{3}{4}$

$\overline{JL}$: $m = \frac{2 - (-1)}{-3 - (-2)} = \frac{3}{-1} = -3$

▶ No two slopes are opposite reciprocals of each other, so △*JKL* is not a right triangle.

3

Find the lengths of the sides and compare them.

$\overline{JK}$ is horizontal, so find the difference of the *x*-coordinates to find its length.

$JK = |2 - (-3)| = 5$

For the remaining sides, use the distance formula: $d = \sqrt{(x_2 - x_1)^2 + (y_2 - y_1)^2}$.

$KL = \sqrt{(-2 - 2)^2 + (-1 - 2)^2}$

$KL = \sqrt{25}$

$KL = 5$

$JL = \sqrt{(-2 - (-3))^2 + (-1 - 2)^2}$

$JL = \sqrt{10}$

▶ $JK = KL = 5$, so △*JKL* is isosceles.

TRY

To what point could you move *L* to make *JKL* an isosceles right triangle?

EXAMPLE D Triangle *NOP* is shown on the coordinate plane on the right.

Prove that the centroid of △*NOP* divides each of the triangle's medians in a ratio of 2:1.

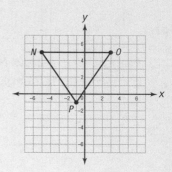

1

Find the endpoints of the medians of △*NOP*.

A median connects a vertex of a triangle to the midpoint of the opposite side. Find the midpoint of each side of the triangle. Use the formula $(x_1 + k(x_2 - x_1), y_1 + k(y_2 - y_1))$ with $k = \frac{1}{2}$.

$\overline{NO}$: $\left(-5 + \frac{1}{2}[3 - (-5)], 5 + \frac{1}{2}(5 - 5)\right) = (-1, 5)$

$\overline{OP}$: $\left(3 + \frac{1}{2}(-1 - 3), 5 + \frac{1}{2}(-1 - 5)\right) = (1, 2)$

$\overline{NP}$: $\left((-5 + \frac{1}{2}[-1 - (-5)], 5 + \frac{1}{2}(-1 - 5)\right) = (-3, 2)$

2

Graph the medians and find the centroid.

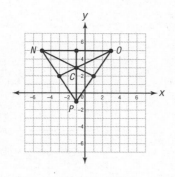

The centroid appears to be at $(-1, 3)$.

3

Find the points that partition each median in a ratio of 2:1.

A ratio of 2:1 indicates the point $\frac{2}{3}$ of the way from the vertex to the opposite side. Use the partition formula and let $k = \frac{2}{3}$.

Median from *N*:

$\left(-5 + \frac{2}{3}[1 - (-5)], 5 + \frac{2}{3}(2 - 5)\right) =$
$(-5 + 4, 5 + (-2)) = (-1, 3)$

Median from *O*:

$\left(3 + \frac{2}{3}(-3 - 3), 5 + \frac{2}{3}(2 - 5)\right) =$
$(3 + (-4), 5 + (-2)) = (-1, 3)$

Median from *P*:

$\left(-1 + \frac{2}{3}[-1 - (-1)], -1 + \frac{2}{3}[5 - (-1)]\right) =$
$(-1 + 0, -1 + 4) = (-1, 3)$

The point $(-1, 3)$ lies on all three lines, so it must be the centroid.

▶ The centroid, $(-1, 3)$, partitions each median in a ratio of 2:1.

CHECK

Pick a median and find its length. Then, find the distance from the vertex of that median to $C(-1, 3)$. Is that distance $\frac{2}{3}$ the length of the median?

Practice

Solve.

1. Triangle *GHJ* is shown on the coordinate plane on the right. Is △*GHJ* a right triangle? Explain your answer.

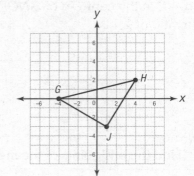

_____

_____

_____

> **REMEMBER** Lines that form a right angle are perpendicular to each other.

2. The point (−4, 6) lies on the parabola graphed to the right. Prove that this point is equidistant from the focus, (2, −2), and the directrix, $y = -4$.

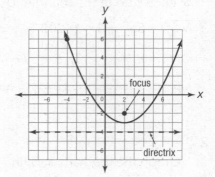

_____

_____

_____

_____

_____

3. Triangle *ABC* is shown on the coordinate plane on the right.

   Draw the line segment connecting the midpoint of $\overline{AB}$ to the midpoint of $\overline{BC}$ on the coordinate plane. Then prove that this line segment is parallel to $\overline{AC}$ and half its length.

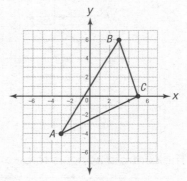

_____

_____

_____

_____

_____

_____

4. The diagram on the right represents a park with a plane imposed on it. Each unit length on the plane represents 1 foot. The point *S* represents the planned placement for a sprinkler head that sprays water in a circle. The point *F* represents a flowerbed.

If the sprinkler has a radius of 6 feet, will the water from the sprinkler reach the flowerbed? Explain your answer.

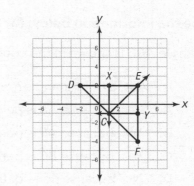

_____

_____

5. Right triangle *DEF* is shown on the coordinate plane on the right.

Find the intersection of the perpendicular bisectors of the triangle.

Prove that this point is the midpoint of $\overline{DF}$.

_____

_____

_____

_____

_____

_____

6. **CONSTRUCT** Draw a rhombus on the coordinate plane on the right so that no side of the rhombus is vertical or horizontal.

Prove that your figure is a rhombus. Then prove that your figure is also a parallelogram.

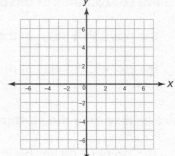

_____

_____

_____

_____

_____

_____

UNIT 4 Review

Find the equation of the line that fits each description.

1. the line parallel to $y = \frac{1}{4}x + 3$ that passes through the point $(-8, -7)$ _____

2. the line parallel to $2x + 3y = 24$ that passes through the point $(12, -4)$ _____

3. the line perpendicular to $4y + x + 40 = 0$ that passes through the point $\left(\frac{1}{2}, 0\right)$ _____

Use the information below for questions 4 and 5. Choose the best answer.

Triangle *ABC* is shown in the coordinate plane on the right.

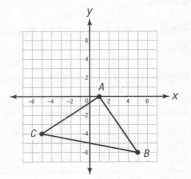

4. Is $\triangle ABC$ a right triangle?
   A. Yes, because $\overline{AB}$ is perpendicular to $\overline{BC}$.
   B. Yes, because $\overline{AB}$ is perpendicular to $\overline{AC}$.
   C. Yes, because $\overline{BC}$ is perpendicular to $\overline{AC}$.
   D. No, because none of the sides are perpendicular to one another.

5. What is the area of $\triangle ABC$ in square units?
   A. 13   C. 26
   B. 21   D. 52

Find the coordinates of the point that fits each description.

6. the point that lies $\frac{1}{3}$ of the distance from $(-10, 4)$ to $(14, -11)$ _____

7. the point that lies $\frac{5}{6}$ of the distance from $(3, 5)$ to $(15, 23)$ _____

Prove or disprove the statement below by finding an equation describing the parabola.

8. The point $(4, 4)$ lies on the parabola with vertex at the origin and with focus $(0, 2)$.

_____

_____

_____

_____

Use the information below for questions 9 and 10. Choose the best answer.

Quadrilateral *DFGH* is shown in the coordinate plane below.

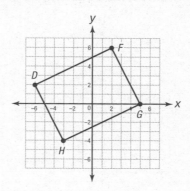

9.   Is *DFGH* a square?

   A.   Yes, because all of the angles are right angles and all of the sides are congruent.

   B.   No, because not all of the angles are right angles.

   C.   No, because opposite sides are not parallel.

   D.   No, because not all of the sides are congruent.

10.   What is the perimeter of *DFGH* in units?

   A. $12\sqrt{5}$ **C.** $16\sqrt{5}$

   B. $14\sqrt{5}$ **D.** $18\sqrt{5}$

Prove or disprove the statement below.

11.   The point (13, 16) lies on circle *O* with center (7, 8) and radius 10.

   _____

   _____

   _____

Write the equation for the parabola with the given focus and vertex. Also identify the vertex and the direction (*up*, *down*, *left*, or *right*) that the parabola opens.

12.   focus: (2, 0)

   directrix: $x = -6$

   vertex: (_____, _____)

   equation: _____

   opens _____

13.   focus: $\left(-1, \dfrac{7}{8}\right)$

   directrix: $y = \dfrac{9}{8}$

   vertex: (_____, _____)

   equation: _____

   opens _____

14.   focus: (1, 4)

   directrix: $x = 5$

   vertex: (_____, _____)

   equation: _____

   opens _____

Solve.

15. Square *PQRS* is shown on the coordinate plane below.

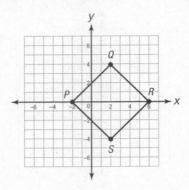

What is the area of *PQRS*? _____

16. $\overline{BA}$ is shown on the coordinate plane below.

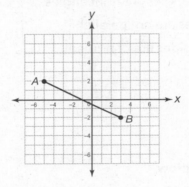

What point partitions $\overline{BA}$ in a ratio of 3:1? _____

17. Triangle *NOP* is shown on the coordinate grid below.

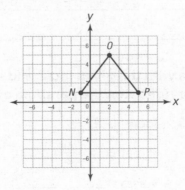

Find the perimeter of △*NOP*. _____

Solve.

18. **VERIFY** $\overline{CD}$ is shown on the coordinate plane below.

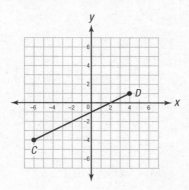

Find the point P that is $\frac{1}{5}$ the distance from C to D and plot it on the plane. Then find the lengths of $\overline{CD}$ and $\overline{CP}$. Verify that $CP = \frac{1}{5}CD$.

_____

_____

_____

19. **PROVE** Quadrilateral $JKLM$ is shown on the coordinate plane below.

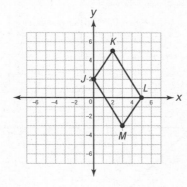

Prove that $JKLM$ is a parallelogram but not a rectangle. Give your proof in the form of a paragraph.

_____

_____

_____

_____

_____

_____

LANDSCAPE DESIGN

A landscape designer is making a plan for a client's backyard. He has made a scale drawing of the yard, shown below. Each unit on the grid represents one foot.

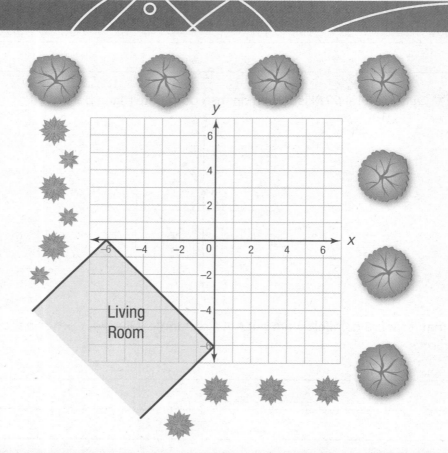

1. The yard will have several features, including a rectangular wooden deck. The corners of the deck will be $(-5, 0)$, $(-3, 2)$, $(1, -2)$, and $(-1, -4)$. Draw the deck on the scale drawing.

2. The deck will be made out of cedar or pine. Cedar costs $33 per square foot, and pine costs $28 per square foot. What would the cost be for each type of wood?

   _____

   _____

3. There will also be a circular pool with its center at $(3, 3)$ and a radius of 2 feet. There is currently a tree at $(4, 1)$. Will it need to be removed to put in the pool? Explain how you know.

   _____

   _____

4. Draw the pool on the scale drawing.

5. There is a plan for a string of lights to hang between two poles at $(-4, 5)$ and $(2, -4)$. Additional support poles will stand at $\frac{1}{3}$ the distance from each end of the lights. Where will these support poles be located?

   _____

   _____

6. On the scale drawing, draw the line segment representing the string of lights and plot the point where each support pole will stand.

7. Will the string of lights be parallel to the wall between the living room and the yard? Explain how you know.

   _____

   _____

Grades 6–8 & Algebra I

Geometry

Algebra II

Algebra

Creating Equations
Create equations that describe numbers or relationships.

Reasoning with Equations and Inequalities
Solve systems of equations.

Functions

Interpreting Functions
Interpret functions that arise in applications in terms of the context.

Analyze functions using different representations.

Grade 8 Geometry
Understand congruence and similarity using physical models, transparencies, or geometry software.

Understand and apply the Pythagorean Theorem.

Grade 7 Geometry
Draw, construct, and describe geometrical figures and describe the relationships between them.

Solve real-life and mathematical problems involving angle measure, area, surface area, and volume.

Geometry

Circles
Understand and apply theorems about circles.

Find arc lengths and areas of sectors of circles.

Expressing Geometric Properties with Equations
Translate between the geometric description and the equation for a conic section.

Use coordinates to prove simple geometric theorems algebraically.

Modeling with Geometry
Apply geometric concepts in modeling situations.

Functions

Trigonometric Functions
Extend the domain of trigonometric functions using the unit circle.

Unit 5
Circles With and Without Coordinates

Circles and Line Segments

Chords, Radii, and Diameters

UNDERSTAND A **circle** is the collection of points that are equidistant from a given point, which is called the center. The distance from the center to a point on the circle is the length of a **radius** of the circle. So, every radius that can be drawn in the circle has the same length. A circle is usually named by its center, so a circle whose center is point Q is named circle Q, or $\bigcirc Q$.

A **chord** is a line segment that has both endpoints on a circle. Two chords within the same circle can have different lengths. A **diameter** is a chord that passes through the center of a circle. Diameters are the longest possible chords in a circle, so all of a circle's diameters are the same length. The length of the diameter of a circle is twice the length of its radius.

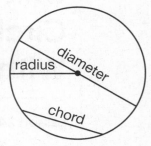

UNDERSTAND Relationships among these line segments can help you determine their lengths.

If two chords intersect and divide each other into segments, the product of the segments of one chord equals the product of the segments of the other chord.

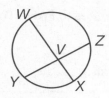

$$WV \cdot VX = YV \cdot VZ$$

If a radius or a diameter intersects a chord and is perpendicular to the chord, it bisects the chord.

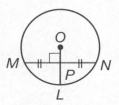

In circle O, $\overline{OL} \perp \overline{MN}$ and $MP = PN$.

The converse is also true. If a radius or diameter bisects a chord, then it is perpendicular to the chord.

◀€ Connect

Chords $\overline{FG}$ and $\overline{HJ}$ intersect at point Z. $HZ = 6$, $FZ = 3$, and $ZG = 8$.
Find the length of $\overline{ZJ}$.

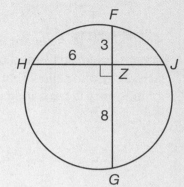

Set up an equation and solve for ZJ.

$HZ \cdot ZJ = FZ \cdot ZG$

$\quad 6 \cdot ZJ = 3 \cdot 8$

$\quad\quad 6ZJ = 24$

▶ $\quad\quad ZJ = 4$

Diameter $\overline{PQ}$ intersects chord $\overline{RS}$ at point T. The segments
are perpendicular to each other. $PT = 9$ and $TQ = 4$. Find the
length of $\overline{RT}$.

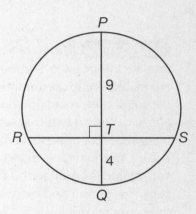

1

Compare $\overline{RT}$ and $\overline{TS}$.

Since $\overline{PQ}$ is a diameter perpendicular to $\overline{RS}$,
it must bisect $\overline{RS}$. Therefore, $RT = TS$.

2

Set up an equation and solve for RT.

A diameter is a special type of chord, so
use the equation for parts of a chord.

$\quad RT \cdot TS = PT \cdot TQ$

$\quad RT \cdot TS = 9 \cdot 4$

Because $RT = TS$, substitute RT for TS.

$\quad RT \cdot RT = 9 \cdot 4$

$\quad\quad RT^2 = 36$

▶ $RT = 6$

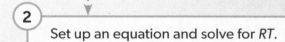

If two chords intersect such that each
chord is the perpendicular bisector of
the other chord, what is true about the
chords? Where do they intersect?

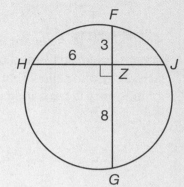

Secant Lines and Tangent Lines

UNDERSTAND A **secant line** is a line in the plane that intersects a circle at two points. A secant could be formed by extending the ends of a chord. A **tangent line** intersects a circle at exactly one point. That point is called the point of tangency. The radius drawn to a point of tangency is perpendicular to the tangent line through that point.

point of tangency

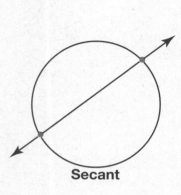

Secant

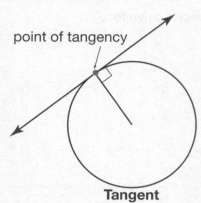

Tangent

UNDERSTAND $\overleftrightarrow{KL}$ and $\overleftrightarrow{MN}$ are secant lines that intersect at point P. Segments such as KP and MP are called secant segments. The portion of a secant segment outside the circle, such as $\overline{LP}$ or $\overline{NP}$, is called an external segment. If two secant lines intersect outside a circle, the product of the secant segment and external segment of one secant line is equal to the product of the secant segment and external segment of the other secant line.

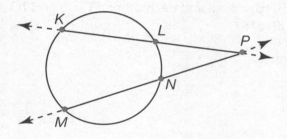

$$KP \cdot LP = MP \cdot NP$$

Imagine pulling secant $\overleftrightarrow{MN}$ down. Points M and N, which are located where the line intersects the circle, would move down the circle and come closer together. If you pulled the line down far enough, M and N would become the same point. The line would now be tangent to the circle.

If we call this single point of tangency S, the diagram is now changed so that secant $\overleftrightarrow{MN}$ is replaced by tangent $\overleftrightarrow{SP}$. Segment MP is replaced by segment SP, and segment NP is also replaced by segment SP. So, the product of KP and LP is equal to SP squared.

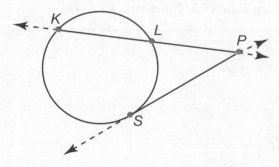

$$KP \cdot LP = SP \cdot SP$$
$$KP \cdot LP = SP^2$$

← Connect

In the diagram, $AB = 2$, $BC = 15$, and $AD = 3$. What is the length of chord DE?

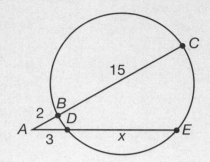

1

Identify the types of lines and line segments.

$\overleftrightarrow{AC}$ intersects the circle at two points, B and C. So, it is a secant. $\overline{AC}$ is its secant segment, and $\overline{AB}$ is its external segment.

$\overleftrightarrow{AE}$ also intersects the circle at two points, D and E. It is also a secant. $\overline{AE}$ is its secant segment, and $\overline{AD}$ is its external segment.

2

Find the lengths of the secant segments.

The length of secant segment $\overline{AC}$ is the sum of the length of external segment $\overline{AB}$ and internal segment $\overline{BC}$.

$AC = AB + BC = 2 + 15 = 17$

The length of secant segment $\overline{AE}$ is the sum of the length of external segment $\overline{AD}$ and internal segment $\overline{DE}$.

$AE = AD + DE = 3 + x$

3

Find the length of the internal segment.

The product of the secant segment and external segment must be the same for each secant line.

$AC \cdot AB = AE \cdot AD$

$17 \cdot 2 = (3 + x) \cdot 3$

$34 = 9 + 3x$

$25 = 3x$

$8\frac{1}{3} = x$

▶ Chord DE is $8\frac{1}{3}$ units long.

 TRY

If tangent line $\overleftrightarrow{AF}$ were drawn so that point F were on the circle above, what would be the length of $\overline{AF}$?

EXAMPLE A Circles *A* and *B* have different radii, as shown. Show that these two circles are similar figures.

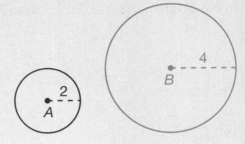

1

Select a transformation that will show similarity.

Dilations produce similar images.

So, if circle *A* can be dilated to form circle *B*, the two figures are similar.

The radius of circle *B* is 4, which is 2 times the radius of circle *A*. So, the dilation should have a scale factor of 2.

2

Transform circle *A*.

Translate circle *A* to the right so that it has the same center as circle *B*.

Then dilate circle *A* by a factor of 2 from its center.

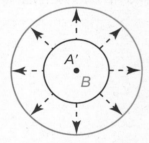

3

Compare the circles.

Circle *B* has a radius of 4 units.

Circle *A* has a radius of 2 units. Circle *A′*, its image after a translation and a dilation by a factor of 2, has distances twice that of circle *A*. So, circle *A′* has a radius of 4.

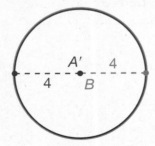

All points on circles *A′* and *B* are 4 units from the center, so the circles are congruent.

▶ Since a dilation of circle *A* produced an image congruent to circle *B*, circles *A* and *B* are similar.

DISCUSS

Are all circles similar to one another? Why or why not?

EXAMPLE B Sachit wants to buy an above-ground swimming pool with a diameter of 20 feet or more. He has found one pool that he likes, but he cannot find a salesperson to tell him its size or help him measure it. He stands in front of the pool and lays his tape measure along the floor. He measures 4 feet to the nearest point on the circular wall of the pool and 10 feet to the outermost edge that he can see. Might Sachit be interested in buying this pool?

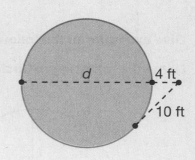

1 Identify the types of segments.

The line extending from where Sachit is standing to the farthest edge of the pool is a secant segment. Its length is the sum of his distance from the pool, 4 ft, and the diameter of the pool. His distance from the pool is the external segment of that secant line.

The outermost edge of the pool that Sachit can see is a point of tangency. So, the distance from where he is standing to that point is a tangent segment.

2 Identify a relationship that can be used to solve for d, the diameter of the pool.

The lengths of a tangent segment and the external segment of a secant are known. The unknown quantity, the diameter, is the internal segment of the secant.

These quantities are related because the product of one secant segment and its external segment equals the square of the tangent segment.

$(d + 4)(4) = (10)^2$

3 Solve for the diameter.

$(d + 4)(4) = (10)^2$

$4d + 16 = 100$

$4d = 84$

$d = 21$

▶ The pool has a diameter of 21 feet, so this is a pool that Sachit might consider buying.

CHECK

Extend a radius from the center of the pool to the point of tangency to form a right triangle. Use the Pythagorean Theorem to check that the answer is correct.

Practice

Give examples of the following in the given circles.

Name the following in Circle O:

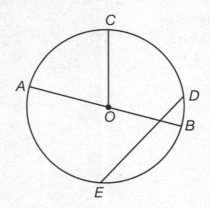

Name the following in Circle Z:

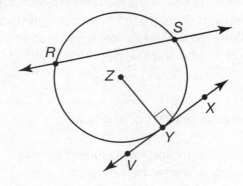

1. The center: _____

2. A diameter: _____

3. Three radii: _____

4. Two chords: _____

5. A radius: _____

6. A chord: _____

7. A secant line: _____

8. A tangent line: _____

> REMEMBER A secant line contains a chord.

Write *true* or *false* for each statement. If the statement is false, rewrite it so that it is true.

9. Every chord of a circle is also a diameter of the circle.

    _____

10. When two chords intersect inside a circle, the product of the divided segments of one chord equals the product of the divided segments of the other chord.

    _____

    _____

11. A diameter that intersects a chord bisects the chord.

    _____

12. A radius drawn to a point of tangency is perpendicular to the tangent line through that point.

    _____

13. A secant line intersects a circle in exactly one point.

    _____

Each circle shows intersecting chords. Find the length represented by *x* in each circle.

14.

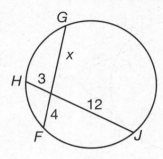

x = _____

15.

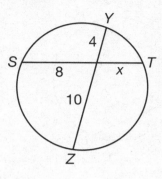

x = _____

16.

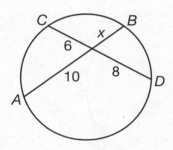

x = _____

17.

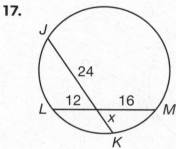

x = _____

18. Point *O* is the center of this circle.

QR = 10

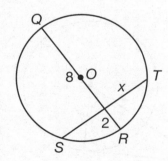

x = _____

19. Point *O* is the center of this circle.

AB = 5*x*

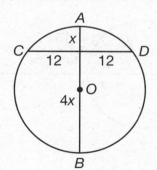

x = _____

Find the length represented by *x* in each diagram.

20.

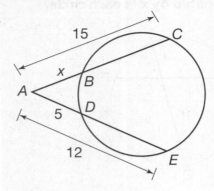

x = _____

21.

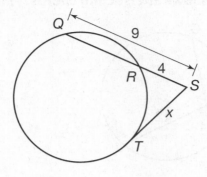

x = _____

22.

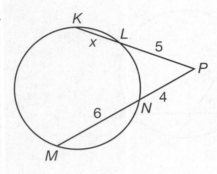

x = _____

23.

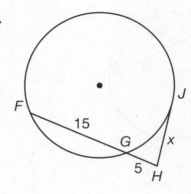

x = _____

Find the length of the radius, *r*, for each circle.

24.

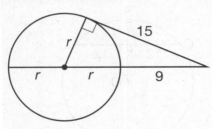

r = _____

25.

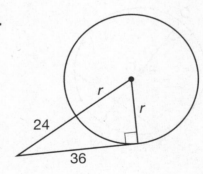

r = _____

Choose the best answer.

26. A diameter of a circle is perpendicular to a chord whose length is 14 centimeters. If the length of the shorter segment of the diameter is 5 centimeters, what is the length of its longer segment?

    A. 2.8 cm   **C.** 9.8 cm

    B. 9 cm   **D.** 19 cm

27. The diameter of a circle is 7 meters. If the diameter is extended 2 meters beyond the circle to point P, how long is a tangent segment from point P to the circle? Give your answer to the nearest tenth of a meter.

    A. 3.7 m   **C.** 9.0 m

    B. 4.2 m   **D.** 18.0 m

Solve.

28. A scientist uses a satellite in orbit to estimate the diameter of Earth. When the satellite is directly overhead, she sends a signal to the satellite in order to measure its altitude. She records a distance above her of 1,000 miles. As the Earth turns, the satellite eventually moves to the horizon. At this time, the scientist sends another signal and calculates that the satellite is 3,000 miles from her. What is the approximate diameter of the Earth, based on these measures?

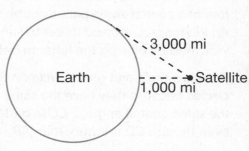

_____

29. **EXPLAIN** Dilate the circle below twice. One dilation should produce an enlargement. The other should produce a reduction. Identify the scale factor you used for each. Are all three circles similar to one another? Explain why this is so.

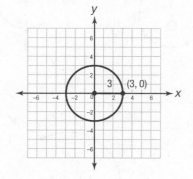

_____

_____

_____

30. **PROVE** Marcus made this statement: "Two tangent segments drawn from the same point P outside of a circle must be congruent." Is he correct? Use Circle O, tangent segments PM and PN, and secant segment PK to justify your answer.

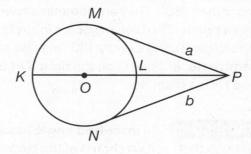

_____

_____

_____

Circles, Angles, and Arcs

LESSON 25

Measuring Arcs and Angles

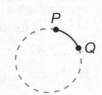

UNDERSTAND An **arc** is an unbroken part of a circle. An arc contains two endpoints and all the points on a circular curve between those points. The name of an arc contains its endpoints covered by an arc-like symbol, such as $\overset{\frown}{PQ}$. Sometimes, another point on the arc is included in the name.

An arc can be measured in two ways: by the length along its curve and by the measure of its **central angle**. A central angle is an angle whose vertex is the center of a circle. The rays of a central angle pass through the circle and cut off an arc called the **intercepted arc**. An intercepted arc and its central angle have the same measure. The measure of an arc is indicated by placing the letter m before the arc name, such as $m\overset{\frown}{PQ}$.

The blue circle and green circle on the right are **concentric circles** because they have the same center. $\overset{\frown}{AB}$ and $\overset{\frown}{CD}$ have the same central angle, $\angle COD$, and thus same measure, even though $\overset{\frown}{CD}$ is longer than $\overset{\frown}{AB}$.

$$m\overset{\frown}{AB} = m\overset{\frown}{CD} = m\angle COD$$

If the central angle increases, the measure of both arcs will likewise increase. If $\overrightarrow{OD}$ is rotated clockwise to lie on top of $\overrightarrow{OC}$, the angle will measure 360°, so one full circle measures 360°.

Circular arcs are classified according to their measure. **Minor arcs** measure less than 180°. They are typically named using only two points. The green minor arc in circle Q on the right is called $\overset{\frown}{KM}$. **Major arcs** measure more than 180°. They are sometimes named using three points. The blue major arc in circle Q is named $\overset{\frown}{KLM}$. An arc measuring exactly 180° may be called a **semicircle**. In circle G on the right, $\overset{\frown}{FJH}$ is a semicircle and $\overline{FH}$ is a diameter.

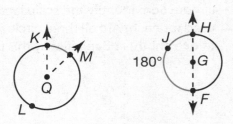

UNDERSTAND An **inscribed angle** has a vertex on the circle and has rays that contain chords of the circle. An inscribed angle will intercept an arc, just as a central angle does. In the circle on the right, inscribed angle RPS intercepts $\overset{\frown}{RS}$. The measure of an inscribed angle is equal to half the measure of its intercepted arc.

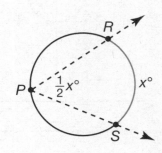

⟜ Connect

In Circle *E*, m∠*ABD* = 49°. Find the measures of $\overset{\frown}{AD}$, ∠*AED*, and ∠*ACD*.

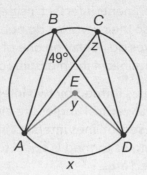

1

Determine the measure of $\overset{\frown}{AD}$.

Let *x* be the measure of $\overset{\frown}{AD}$.

$x = m\overset{\frown}{AD}$

Angle *ABD* is an inscribed angle that intercepts $\overset{\frown}{AD}$. So:

$m\angle ABD = \frac{1}{2} \cdot m\overset{\frown}{AD}$

$49° = \frac{1}{2} \cdot x$

$98° = x$

▶ $m\overset{\frown}{AD} = 98°$

2

Find the measure of ∠*AED*.

Let *y* be the measure of ∠*AED*.

$y = m\angle AED$

Angle *AED* is a central angle that intercepts $\overset{\frown}{AD}$. So:

$m\angle AED = m\overset{\frown}{AC}$

$y = 98°$

▶ $m\angle AED = 98°$

3

Find the measure of ∠*ACD*.

Let *z* be the measure of ∠*ACD*.

$z = m\angle ACD$

Angle *ACD* is an inscribed angle that intercepts $\overset{\frown}{AD}$. So:

$m\angle ACD = \frac{1}{2} \cdot m\overset{\frown}{AD}$

$z = \frac{1}{2} \cdot 98°$

$z = 49°$

▶ $m\angle ACD = 49°$

DISCUSS

Based on this example, what can you conclude about two inscribed angles that intercept the same arc? What can you conclude about an inscribed angle and a central angle that intercept the same arc?

Angles Formed by Intersecting Lines

UNDERSTAND When lines and line segments intersect inside a circle, they can form angles that are neither central angles (because their vertexes do not fall on the circle's center) nor inscribed angles (because their vertexes do not fall on one of the circle's points). However, the measures of these angles can be determined if the measures of the arcs they cut off are known.

Recall that a pair of non-adjacent angles formed by two intersecting lines are called vertical angles and that vertical angles are always congruent. When two chords or two secant lines intersect inside a circle, the measure of both vertical angles formed is equal to half the sum of the measures of the intercepted arcs.

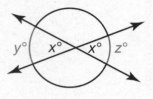

$$x° = \frac{1}{2}(y° + z°)$$

UNDERSTAND Secant lines and tangent lines can intersect outside a given circle. When two such lines intersect outside a circle, the measure of the angle at which they intersect is equal to half the difference of the measures of the intercepted arcs.

Two Secant Lines

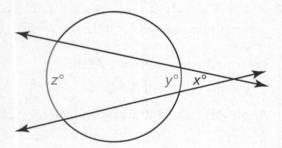

Two Tangent Lines

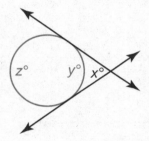

In each of these three diagrams
$x° = \frac{1}{2}(z° - y°)$.

A Secant Line and a Tangent Line

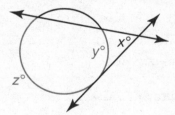

In the case where a tangent line and a secant line intersect, imagine shrinking the smaller arc until $y = 0$. This would produce a special case in which the secant line intersects the tangent line at the point of tangency. Substituting 0 for y in the formula above tells us that the measure of the angle formed is equal to half the measure of its intercepted arc.

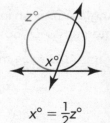

$$x° = \frac{1}{2}z°$$

◀€Connect

In the circle, chord $\overline{FG}$ intersects chord $\overline{HJ}$ at point K. What are the measures of the four angles formed by the intersection of the chords?

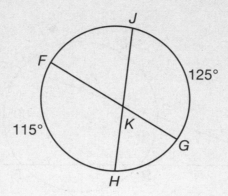

1

Relate the angles to one another.

Angles *FKH* and *JKG* are vertical angles, so they are congruent.

Angles *FKJ* and *HKG* are also vertical angles, so they are congruent.

Every pair of adjacent angles, such as ∠*FKH* and ∠*HKG*, form a linear pair, so adjacent angles are supplementary.

2

Find the measure of ∠*FKH* and ∠*JKG*.

Arc *FH* and arc *GJ* are intercepted by vertical angles *FKH* and *JKG*.

$m\angle FKH = \frac{1}{2}(m\widehat{FH} + m\widehat{GJ})$

$m\angle FKH = \frac{1}{2}(115 + 125)$

$m\angle FKH = \frac{1}{2}(240)$

$m\angle FKH = 120°$

Because angles *FKH* and *JKG* are congruent, they have the same measure.

▶ The measures of ∠*FKH* and ∠*JKG* are 120°.

3

Find the measure of ∠*FKJ* and ∠*HKG*.

Because angles *FKH* and *HKG* are supplementary, they sum to 180°.

$m\angle FKH + m\angle HKG = 180°$

$120° + m\angle HKG = 180°$

$m\angle HKG = 60°$

Because angles *FKJ* and *HKG* are congruent, they have the same measure.

▶ The measures of ∠*FKJ* and ∠*HKG* are 60°.

TRY

What is the measure of $\widehat{PR}$?

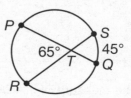

EXAMPLE A Secants $\overleftrightarrow{BC}$ and $\overleftrightarrow{DE}$ intersect at point A. $\overleftrightarrow{CF}$ is tangent to the circle at point C and intersects $\overleftrightarrow{DE}$ at point F. What are the measures of $\angle BAD$ and $\angle CFE$?

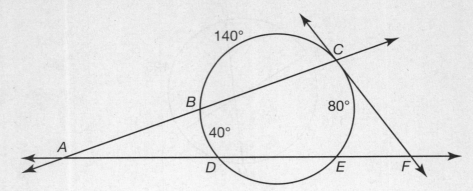

1

Find the measure of $\angle BAD$.

Angle BAD results from the intersection of two secant lines, so its measure is equal to half the difference of its intercepted arcs.

Its intercepted arcs are $\overarc{BD}$ and $\overarc{CE}$.

$m\angle BAD = \frac{1}{2}(m\overarc{CE} - m\overarc{BD})$

$m\angle BAD = \frac{1}{2}(80° - 40°)$

$m\angle BAD = \frac{1}{2}(40°)$

▶ $m\angle BAD = 20°$

2

Find the measure of $\angle CFE$.

Angle CFE results from the intersection of a secant line, $\overleftrightarrow{DE}$, and a tangent line, $\overleftrightarrow{CF}$, so its measure is equal to half the difference of its intercepted arcs.

Its intercepted arcs are $\overarc{CE}$ and $\overarc{CD}$. $\overarc{CD}$ is divided into $\overarc{CB}$ and $\overarc{BD}$.

$m\overarc{CD} = m\overarc{CB} + m\overarc{BD}$

$m\overarc{CD} = 140° + 40°$

$m\overarc{CD} = 180°$

$m\angle CFE = \frac{1}{2}(m\overarc{CD} - m\overarc{CE})$

$m\angle CFE = \frac{1}{2}(180° - 80°)$

$m\angle CFE = \frac{1}{2}(100°)$

▶ $m\angle CFE = 50°$

TRY

What is the measure of $\angle ACF$?

EXAMPLE B In the diagram below, $\overline{ST}$ is tangent to circle P at point T. Find the values of x, y, and z.

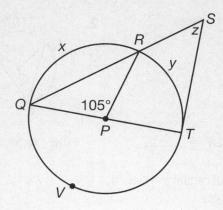

1

Find the value of x.

The measure of an arc is equal to the measure of its central angle. The central angle of $\overparen{QR}$ is $\angle QPR$.

▶ $m\angle QPR = 105°$, so $x = 105°$.

2

Find the value of y.

$\overline{QT}$ is a diameter of circle P, so $\overparen{QRT}$ is a semicircle that measures $180°$.

The measure of $\overparen{QRT}$ is equal to the sum of the measures of $\overparen{QR}$ and $\overparen{RT}$.

$m\overparen{QR} + m\overparen{RT} = m\overparen{QRT}$

$105° + y = 180°$

▶ $y = 75°$

3

Find the value of z.

Secant line SQ and tangent line ST intersect outside the circle at point S. They intercept arcs QVT and RT.

Because $\overline{QT}$ is a diameter of circle P, $\overparen{QVT}$ is a semicircle that measures $180°$.

$m\angle QST = \frac{1}{2}(m\overparen{QVT} - m\overparen{RT})$

$z = \frac{1}{2}(180 - 75)$

$z = \frac{1}{2}(105)$

▶ $z = 52.5°$

TRY

What is the measure of $\angle RQT$ in the circle?

Practice

Identify the measure of the angles in each circle O.

1.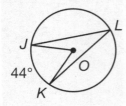

    m∠JOK = _____   m∠JLK = _____

     HINT Use what you know about central angles and inscribed angles.

2.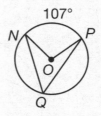

    m∠NOP = _____   m∠NQP = _____

Identify the measure of the arcs.

3.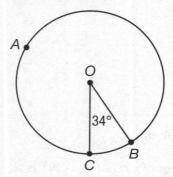

    $m\overset{\frown}{CB}$ = _____ $m\overset{\frown}{CAB}$ = _____

4.

    $m\overset{\frown}{DF}$ = _____ $m\overset{\frown}{DGF}$ = _____

    REMEMBER A full circle measures 360°.

Write *true* or *false* for each statement. If the statement is false, rewrite it so that it is true.

5. An angle whose vertex is on the circle and whose rays contain radii is called a central angle.

    _____

6. A semicircle is an arc that measures 180°.

    _____

7. A minor arc has a measure greater than 180°.

    _____

8. The measure of an angle formed by two secant lines that intersect outside a circle is half the sum of the measures of the intercepted arcs.

    _____

    _____

Find the measure of each angle or arc in circles V and E.

9.

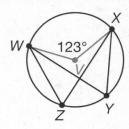

$\text{m}\widehat{WX}$ = _____

$\text{m}\angle WZX$ = _____

$\text{m}\angle WYX$ = _____

10.

$\text{m}\angle ACD$ = _____

$\text{m}\widehat{AD}$ = _____

$\text{m}\angle AED$ = _____

Choose the best answer.

11. In circle *O*, angle *TOV* measures 56°. What is the measure of the arc it intercepts, arc *TV*?

   A. 28°

   B. 56°

   C. 112°

   D. 304°

12. Points *P*, *Q*, and *R* are on circle *N*. If $\angle PQR$ measures 74°, what is the measure of the arc it intercepts, $\widehat{PR}$?

   A. 37°

   B. 74°

   C. 148°

   D. 212°

13. Segments $\overline{PR}$ and $\overline{PQ}$ are tangent to the circle below. Which expression is equivalent to the measure of $\angle QPR$?

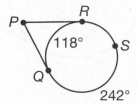

   A. $\frac{1}{2}(118°)$

   B. $\frac{1}{2}(242°)$

   C. $\frac{1}{2}(242° - 118°)$

   D. $\frac{1}{2}(242° + 118°)$

14. Chords $\overline{FG}$ and $\overline{JK}$ intersect at point *H*. Which expression is equivalent to the measure of $\angle FHJ$?

   A. $\frac{1}{2}(46°)$

   B. $\frac{1}{2}(88°)$

   C. $\frac{1}{2}(88° - 46°)$

   D. $\frac{1}{2}(88° + 46°)$

Find the value of z.

15.

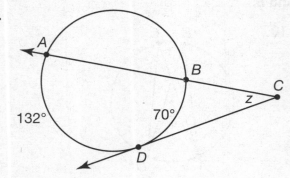

z = _____

16.

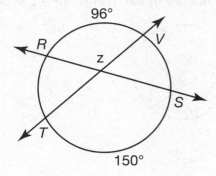

z = _____

17.

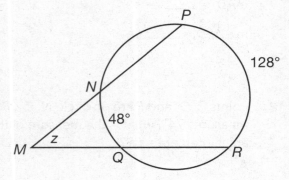

z = _____

18.

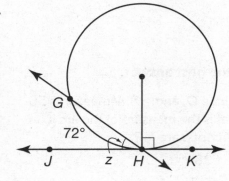

z = _____

19.

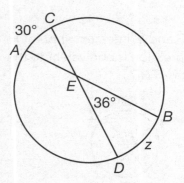

z = _____

20.

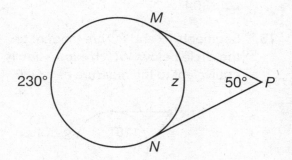

z = _____

21. (SHOW) A satellite in orbit above Earth's equator has a camera with a 35° viewing angle of Earth. What is the measure of the arc of the equator that can be viewed from the satellite? Explain how you found your answer.

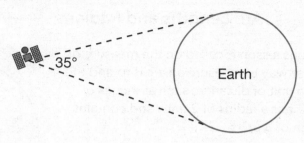

_____

_____

_____

22. (PROVE) Quadrilateral *EFGH* is said to be inscribed in the circle below because all of its vertices lie on the circle. Fill in the blanks based on this figure.

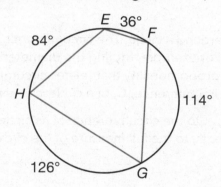

$$\text{m}\widehat{EF} + \text{m}\widehat{FG} + \text{m}\widehat{GH} + \text{m}\widehat{HE} = \underline{\quad}°$$

$\text{m}\angle E = \frac{1}{2}(\text{m}\widehat{FG} + \text{m}\underline{\quad}) = \underline{\quad}°$ 　　　$\text{m}\angle F = \frac{1}{2}(\text{m}\widehat{GH} + \text{m}\underline{\quad}) = \underline{\quad}°$

$\text{m}\angle G = \frac{1}{2}(\text{m}\underline{\quad} + \text{m}\underline{\quad}) = \underline{\quad}°$ 　　　$\text{m}\angle H = \frac{1}{2}(\text{m}\underline{\quad} + \text{m}\underline{\quad}) = \underline{\quad}°$

$\text{m}\angle E + \text{m}\angle G = \underline{\quad}°$ 　　　　　　　$\text{m}\angle F + \text{m}\angle H = \underline{\quad}°$

In a quadrilateral inscribed in a circle, opposite angles are _____.

LESSON 26 Arc Lengths and Areas of Sectors

Arc Lengths and Radians

UNDERSTAND The previous lesson focused on the measure of an arc in degrees. Another way to measure an arc is to find the length along its curve in a unit of distance, such as inches or centimeters. Blue circle O has a radius of 2 units and contains arc AB, which has a length of 3 units.

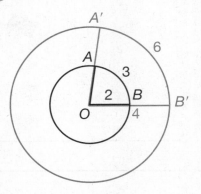

Dilating the circle by a factor of 2 produces a circle with similar arc $A'B'$. Arcs AB and $A'B'$ have the same measure because they have the same central angle, but they have different lengths. Because the scale factor of the dilation was 2, the length of the radius was doubled and the length of the arc was doubled.

For similar arcs (arcs with the same measure or the same central angle), a proportion can be set up by comparing arc length, s, and radius, r.

$$\frac{s_1}{r_1} = \frac{s_2}{r_2}$$

Circumference is the distance around a circle. The circumference of a circle is directly proportional to its diameter, d. For example, tripling the diameter of a circle also triples its circumference. The constant of proportionality that relates circumference to diameter is π. So, the formula for finding the circumference, C, of a circle is $C = \pi d$.

The ratio of the length of an arc, s, to the circumference of its circle, C, is equal to the ratio of the measure of the central angle, $t°$, to the full measure of the circle, $360°$.

$$\frac{s}{C} = \frac{t°}{360°}$$

Recall that a diameter is twice the radius, $d = 2r$, and circumference is π times diameter, $C = \pi d$, so $C = 2\pi r$. Substitute this expression for C into the above formula.

$$\frac{s}{2\pi r} = \frac{t°}{360°} \qquad \text{Solve for } \tfrac{s}{r}.$$

$$\frac{s}{r} = t° \cdot \frac{2\pi}{360°}$$

Because 2, π, and $360°$ are all constants, we can define a new variable, θ (the Greek letter theta), to measure the central angle. Let $\theta = t° \cdot \frac{2\pi}{360°}$.

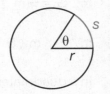

$$\frac{s}{r} = \theta \quad \longrightarrow \quad s = \theta r$$

θ represents an angle measure in **radians**. Like degrees, radians are units for measuring angles. A full circle ($360°$) contains 2π radians.

$$\theta_{circle} = t°_{circle} \cdot \frac{2\pi}{360°} = 360° \cdot \frac{2\pi}{360°} = 2\pi$$

$180°$ is equivalent to π radians, and a right angle (a $90°$ angle) contains $\frac{\pi}{2}$ radians.

⊏Connect

What is the length of $\overset{\frown}{AB}$ in circle O?

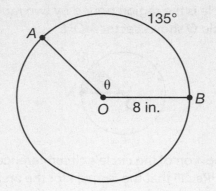

135°

1

Find the measure of angle AOB.

Angle AOB is a central angle that intercepts $\overset{\frown}{AB}$.

Since m$\overset{\frown}{AB}$ = 135°, m∠AOB = 135°.

2

Convert the measure of angle AOB to radians.

360° is equivalent to 2π radians, so:

$$\theta = 135° \cdot \frac{2\pi}{360°} = \frac{270}{360}\pi = \frac{3}{4}\pi$$

3

Find the arc length, s.

$s = \theta r$

$s = \left(\frac{3}{4}\pi\right)(8)$

$s = 6\pi$

▶ Arc AB measures 6π inches, or approximately 18.84 inches.

 CHECK

Solve the problem by using the relation $\frac{s}{C} = \frac{t°}{360°}$. Compare the calculations you did to the work above.

UNDERSTAND A **sector** of a circle is the region bound by two radii and the arc that connects them. The shaded region of circle O shows sector MON.

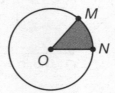

Just as the length of an arc is a portion of the circle's circumference, the area of a sector is a portion of the circle's total area. Recall that the formula for the area of a circle is $A_{circle} = \pi r^2$. If the central angle and the arc of a sector have a degree measure of $t°$, then this proportion can be used to find A_{sector}, the area of the sector:

$$\frac{A_{sector}}{A_{circle}} = \frac{t°}{360°}$$

$$\frac{A_{sector}}{\pi r^2} = \frac{t}{360}$$

$$A_{sector} = \frac{t}{360} \cdot \pi r^2$$

UNDERSTAND The area of a sector can also be found by using θ, the measure of its central angle in radians. Begin by setting up a proportion to relate $t°$ and θ. A circle contains 360°, or 2π radians.

$$\frac{t°}{360°} = \frac{\theta}{2\pi}$$

Substitute the expression on the right in the above equation into the relation for the area of a sector. Then simplify.

$$A_{sector} = \frac{\theta}{2\pi} \cdot \pi r^2$$

$$A_{sector} = \frac{1}{2}\theta r^2$$

UNDERSTAND Recall that θ represents the ratio of an arc length to the radius of its associated circle, $\theta = \frac{s}{r}$. This expression can be substituted into the formula above.

$$A_{sector} = \frac{1}{2}\theta r^2$$

$$A_{sector} = \frac{1}{2}\left(\frac{s}{r}\right) r^2$$

$$A_{sector} = \frac{1}{2}sr$$

The new formula allows the area of a sector to be calculated if the lengths of the radii and arc that enclose it are known.

⬅ Connect

A dog is leashed to the corner of a rectangular house, as shown. Approximately how much area does the dog have in which to run?

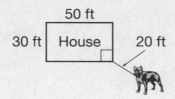

1

Sketch the area in which the dog can run.

The dog can wander up to 20 feet along either adjacent wall. Since both walls are at least 20 feet long, the dog cannot go around any other corners.

The area in which the dog can run is a sector of a circle. The length of the leash is the circle's radius.

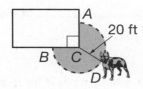

2

Find the measure of arc *BDA*.

Angle *BCA* is a 90° angle.

So, the arc of the circle that is covered by the house measures 90°.

The measure of $\overgroup{BDA}$ must, therefore, be:

$360° - 90° = 270°$

3

Find the area in which the dog can run.

$A = \dfrac{m\overgroup{BDA}}{360°} \cdot \pi r^2$

$A = \dfrac{270}{360} \cdot \pi(20)^2$

$A = \dfrac{3}{4} \cdot 400\pi$

$A = 300\pi$

$A \approx 300 \cdot 3.14 \approx 942 \text{ ft}^2$

▶ The area in which the dog can run is approximately 942 square feet.

Convert the degree measure of the central angle of the sector to radians. Then use radians to determine the area. Is the result the same?

Practice

Complete each table by converting the given measure to its equivalent measure in degrees or radians.

1.

Degrees	Radians
0°	
30°	
	$\frac{\pi}{4}$
	$\frac{\pi}{2}$

2.

Degrees	Radians
	$\frac{2\pi}{3}$
	π
270°	
360°	2π

> REMEMBER 360° = 2π rad

Write an appropriate word to complete each statement.

3. Angles and arcs can be measured in degrees or in _____.

4. The length of a(n) _____ is a fraction of the circumference of a circle.

5. A sector is a region of a circle bounded by a(n) _____ and two _____ of the circle.

Choose the best answer.

6. What is the area of sector *WZY* if the measure of ∠*WZY* is $\frac{\pi}{9}$ radians?

    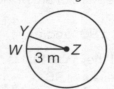

    A. $\frac{\pi}{3}$ m^2 C. 2π m^2

    B. $\frac{\pi}{2}$ m^2 D. 3π m^2

7. What is the length of $\overarc{GJ}$, in radians, if m$\overarc{GH}$ = 40° and $\overline{HJ}$ is a diameter?

    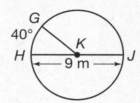

    A. π m   C. $\frac{7\pi}{9}$ m

    B. 2π m   D. 7π m

Find each indicated arc length and sector area in each circle *A*.

8.

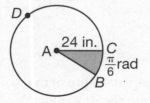

length of $\overarc{CB}$ = _____

area of shaded sector = _____

9.

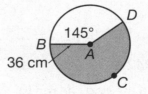

length of $\overarc{BCD}$ = _____

area of shaded sector = _____

**Circle *O* was dilated by a scale factor of $\frac{1}{3}$ and translated to the right to form circle *O'*.
Use these circles for questions 10–12.**

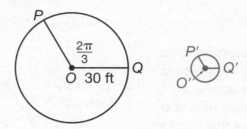

10. How does the radian measure of $\overset{\frown}{PQ}$ compare to the measure of $\overset{\frown}{P'Q'}$?

_____

11. What are the lengths of $\overset{\frown}{PQ}$ and $\overset{\frown}{P'Q'}$? How do they compare to each other?

_____

_____

12. What are the areas of sectors *POQ* and *P'O'Q'*? How do they compare to each other?

_____

_____

Solve.

13. **APPLY** A lawn sprinkler is set to spray water over a distance of 20 feet and rotate through an angle of 110°. What is the approximate area of the lawn that will be watered? Explain how you found your answer.

_____

_____

_____

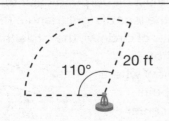

14. **COMPUTE** Line segments *OM* and *ON* are radii of circle *O*. The shaded area that is bounded by $\overline{MN}$ and $\overset{\frown}{MN}$ is called a segment of the circle. Compute the approximate area of this segment.

_____

Constructions with Circles

LESSON 27

UNDERSTAND A **point of concurrency** is a point at which three or more lines intersect. Recall that a perpendicular bisector is a line that is perpendicular to a line segment and passes through the midpoint of that segment. A triangle has three sides. The point at which the three perpendicular bisectors of those sides intersect is called the **circumcenter**. As its name suggests, the circumcenter is the center of the **circumscribed circle** that fits around the triangle.

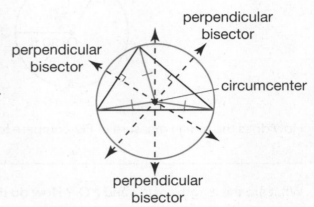

A circle is circumscribed about a triangle if all three of the triangle's vertices are on the circle. A line segment drawn from one of those vertices to the circumcenter is a radius of the circle. So, the circumcenter is equidistant from all three vertices of the triangle.

Recall that an angle bisector is a line or ray that divides an angle in half. A triangle contains three angles. The point at which the three angle bisectors of those angles intersect is the **incenter** of that triangle. As its name suggests, the incenter is the center of the **inscribed circle** that fits within the triangle.

A circle is inscribed in a triangle if every side of the triangle is tangent to the circle. The circle and the triangle intersect at exactly three points. A line segment drawn from one of those points of tangency to the incenter is a radius of the inscribed circle. So, the incenter is equidistant from all three sides of the triangle.

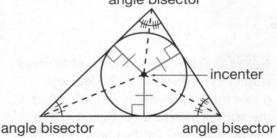

UNDERSTAND The circumcenter of a right triangle is always the midpoint of its hypotenuse. Notice that when a circle is circumscribed about a polygon, every angle in that polygon is an inscribed angle of the circumscribed circle. An inscribed right angle intercepts a semicircle, so the hypotenuse of the triangle must also be a diameter of the circumscribed circle.

In the diagram below, $\overleftrightarrow{PT}$ is tangent to circle O at point T, so $\overleftrightarrow{PT}$ must be perpendicular to radius $\overline{OT}$. Notice that these two line segments can be seen as the legs of right triangle PTO, which has $\overline{OP}$ as its hypotenuse. The midpoint of $\overline{OP}$ is the center of circle M, the circle that circumscribes $\triangle PTO$. This circle contains exterior point P, point of tangency T, and the center of the circle, O. So, if you did not know where the point of tangency was, you could find it by finding the midpoint of $\overline{PO}$ and then constructing the circle with that midpoint as its center and $\overline{PO}$ as its diameter.

⟵ Connect

Circumscribe a circle about △*FGH*.

G

F   H

1

Construct the perpendicular bisector of $\overline{FH}$.

Use a compass to draw equivalent arcs from endpoints *F* and *H*. Identify the points where these arcs intersect and connect them to form the perpendicular bisector.

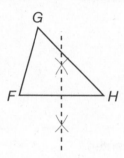

2

Find the circumcenter.

Use similar processes to construct the perpendicular bisectors of sides $\overline{FG}$ and $\overline{GH}$.

Label the circumcenter *C* at the point where the perpendicular bisectors intersect.

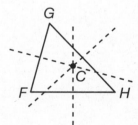

3

Draw the circumscribed circle.

Place the compass point on *C* and the pencil point on *F*. Draw a circle with radius *CF*.

 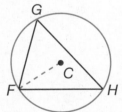

DISCUSS

Could you have measured a different distance, other than *CF*, to draw the circumscribed circle? Explain.

EXAMPLE A Inscribe a circle inside △*ABC*.

B

A   *C*

1

Construct the angle bisector of ∠*A*.

Draw an arc from angle *A* that intersects $\overline{AB}$ and $\overline{AC}$. From these intersection points, draw arcs to locate a point on the angle bisector.

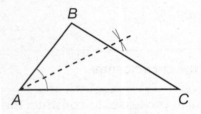

2

Find the incenter.

Use similar steps to construct the bisectors of angles *B* and *C*. Label the incenter *I* at the point where the angle bisectors intersect.

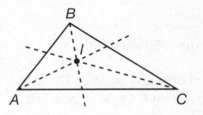

3

Find a radius of the inscribed circle.

Construct a line perpendicular to side $\overline{AC}$ passing through point I. From point I, draw an arc that intersects $\overline{AC}$. From the intersection points of the arc, draw arcs to locate a point on the perpendicular line. Label the point where the perpendicular line crosses $\overline{AC}$ as point D.

▶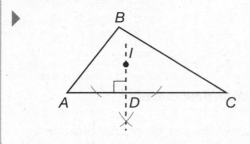

4

Draw the inscribed circle.

Place the compass point on I and the pencil point on D. Draw a circle with radius ID.

▶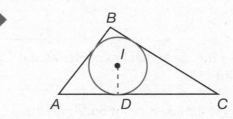

Did you need to draw all three angle bisectors to find the incenter of $\triangle ABC$?

EXAMPLE B Point *K* lies outside circle *L*. Draw two tangent lines to circle *L* from point *K*.

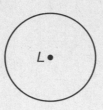

1

Draw a segment connecting point *K* to the center of the circle, point *L*.

Use a straightedge to draw $\overline{LK}$.

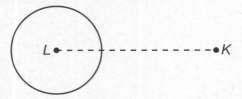

2

Find the midpoint of $\overline{LK}$.

Construct the perpendicular bisector to find the midpoint. Label the midpoint *M*.

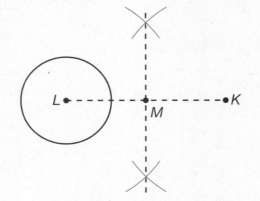

3

Draw the circle that has center *M* and radius *LM*.

Place the compass point on *M* and the pencil point on *L*. Draw a circle with radius *LM*.

Label the points where circles *M* and L intersect as *N* and *P*.

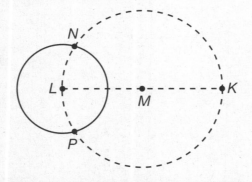

4

Draw $\overleftrightarrow{KN}$ and $\overleftrightarrow{KP}$.

Use a straightedge to draw a line connecting point K to point N and another line connecting point K and point P.

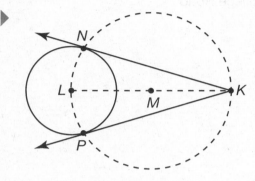

5

Check that $\overleftrightarrow{KN}$ and $\overleftrightarrow{KP}$ are tangent to circle L.

Draw in radius $\overline{LN}$. Angle LNK is an inscribed angle of circle M. Its intercepted arc is semicircle LPK, so $\angle LNK$ must be a right angle. Thus, $\overleftrightarrow{KN} \perp \overline{LN}$.

A tangent line is perpendicular to a circle at the point of tangency, so point N is the point at which $\overrightarrow{KN}$ is tangent to circle L.

Draw in radius $\overline{LP}$. Angle LPK intercepts semicircle LNK, so the same reasoning can be used to show that $\overrightarrow{KP}$ is tangent to circle L.

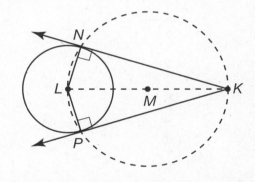

DISCUSS

Is it possible to draw a third tangent line (other than $\overleftrightarrow{KN}$ and $\overleftrightarrow{KP}$) from point K to circle L? Explain.

EXAMPLE C The diagram below shows plans for three buildings on a college campus and the three roads connecting them. The planning committee wishes to place a water fountain in the center of campus, equidistant from each of the three buildings. Add the fountain to the plans.

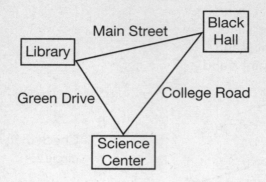

1 Examine the problem.

The fountain will lie on a point equidistant from the three buildings, each of which touches a vertex of the triangle.

The point equidistant from the three vertices of a triangle is the circumcenter.

2 Locate the circumcenter of the triangle.

Construct the perpendicular bisectors. The fountain will be located where the three perpendicular bisectors intersect one another.

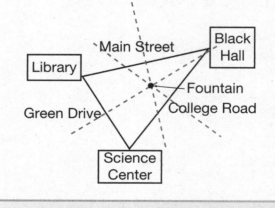

TRY

Suppose instead that the committee chose to place the fountain so that it is equidistant from the three roads. Mark this location on the diagram.

EXAMPLE D If possible, circumscribe a circle around quadrilateral *MNOP*.

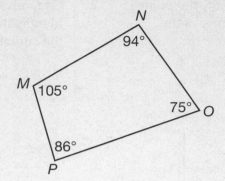

1

Determine if the figure can be circumscribed by a circle.

A quadrilateral can be circumscribed by a circle if its opposite angles are supplementary.

m∠M + m∠O = 105° + 75° = 180° ✓

m∠N + m∠P = 94° + 86° = 180° ✓

MNOP can be circumscribed by a circle.

2

Find the circumcenter of △*MNP*.

Drawing diagonal $\overline{NP}$ divides *MNOP* into two triangles. The circle that circumscribes those triangles also circumscribes the quadrilateral.

Construct the perpendicular bisectors of the sides of △*MNP* to locate its circumcenter.

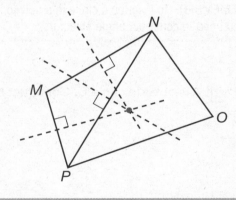

3

Draw the circumscribed circle.

Place the compass point on the circumcenter and the pencil point on *M*. Draw a circle around the figure.

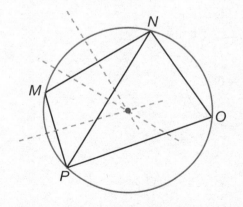

DISCUSS

Would the perpendicular bisectors of △*NOP* intersect at the same point? Could you find the center of the circumscribed circle by finding the perpendicular bisectors of the sides of *MNOP*, without dividing it into triangles?

Practice

Perform each construction.

1. Inscribe a circle in △*JKL*. Identify the point of concurrency that is the center of the circle you drew.

2. Circumscribe a circle about △*FGH*. Identify the point of concurrency that is the center of the circle you drew.

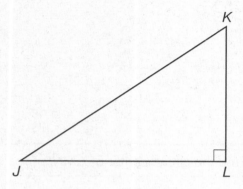

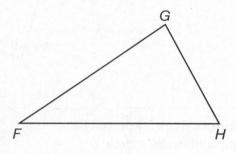

point of concurrency:

_____

point of concurrency:

_____

> REMEMBER: To inscribe a circle in a polygon, you need to construct angle bisectors.

> HINT The name of the point of concurrency is similar to the word *circumscribe*.

3. Point *A* is outside circle *C*. Construct two lines through point *A* that are tangent to circle *C*.

A•

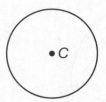
•*C*

The triangles below are equilateral and congruent. Use them for questions 4–6.

4. Construct the circumcenter of △QRS. Label it point C.

5. Construct the incenter of △XYZ. Label it point I.

6. What do you notice about the circumcenter and incenter of the two triangles?

_____

_____

Perform the necessary constructions.

7. **SHOW** Construct the circumcenter of △ABC below to show that it is located at the midpoint of the hypotenuse.

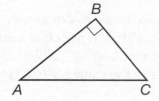

8. **DRAW** Adam is talking on the phone in a triangular park that is surrounded on all sides by roads. The noise from the cars is so loud that he is having difficulty hearing. Draw a point to show the location where he should stand if he wants to be as far as possible from any of the traffic. Explain how you know that is the correct location.

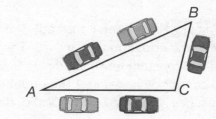

_____

_____

UNDERSTAND Recall that a circle can be defined as a collection of points that are equidistant from a given point, called the center. A circle can also be defined as a type of conic section. Recall that a conic section is a two-dimensional cross section formed by the intersection of a plane and a double cone like the one shown. When the cone is sliced horizontally, by a plane parallel to its base, the cross section is a circle.

Recall that a conic section is a curve having degree 2, so it can be represented by a quadratic equation. The general form for the equation of a conic section is $Ax^2 + By^2 + Cx + Dy + E = 0$, in which A and B cannot both equal zero. When $A = B$, as in $4x^2 + 4y^2 + 4x - 12y + 6 = 0$, the equation represents a circle. An equation of a circle has two quadratic terms, such as $4x^2$ and $4y^2$. But, because the greatest exponent of any term is 2, the equation of a circle is classified as a quadratic equation.

UNDERSTAND The center of a circle is the point that is an equal distance from all points on the circle. That distance is the radius of the circle. When a circle is graphed on the coordinate plane, knowing the center and the radius allows you to determine its equation.

The standard form of the equation of a circle with center (h, k) and radius r is:

$$(x - h)^2 + (y - k)^2 = r^2$$

For example, the circle on the coordinate plane with its center at $(2, -3)$ and a radius of 5 units has the equation $(x - 2)^2 + (y + 3)^2 = 25$.

Every point (x, y) on a circle is a solution to the equation of that circle. The equation of a circle or other conic section allows the figure to be examined on the coordinate plane.

UNDERSTAND The center and radius of a circle can be determined, given its equation. Consider the equation $x^2 + y^2 = 9$. The length of the radius is equal to the principal square root of the constant term. So, if $r^2 = 9$, then $r = 3$. (The radius r cannot equal -3 because a length cannot be negative.) The equation can be rewritten to make the values of h, k, and r obvious: $(x - 0)^2 + (y - 0)^2 = 3^2$. So, the center is $(0, 0)$.

When the equation is given in general form or some other form, it is necessary to convert it into standard form in order to determine the center and radius. This can be done by completing the square for the terms containing x and the terms containing y.

⊱Connect

The circle on the coordinate plane on the right has center (h, k) and radius r. Use this circle to derive the equation of a circle.

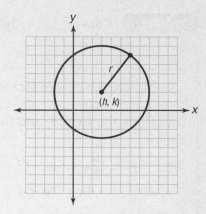

1

Find the endpoints of the radius.

One endpoint of the radius is the center (h, k). Label the other endpoint, which is on the circle, (x, y). Notice that (x, y) could stand for any point on the circle.

2

Using the radius as the hypotenuse, draw a right triangle.

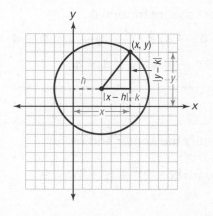

3

Find expressions for the lengths of the legs of the triangle.

Notice that the vertex of the right angle of the triangle is the point (x, k). The length of the vertical leg of the triangle is the distance from point (x, y) to this point, (x, k). Use the distance formula to find this length.

$$l_1 = \sqrt{(x - x)^2 + (y - k)^2}$$
$$l_1 = \sqrt{(0)^2 + (y - k)^2}$$
$$l_1 = \sqrt{(y - k)^2}$$
$$l_1 = |y - k|$$

The length of the horizontal leg of the triangle is the distance from point (x, k) to the center, (h, k).

$$l_1 = \sqrt{(x - h)^2 + (k - k)^2}$$
$$l_1 = |x - h|$$

4

Apply the Pythagorean Theorem

Substitute $|x - h|$ and $|y - k|$ for the leg lengths and r for the hypotenuse length.

$$a^2 + b^2 = c^2$$
$$|x - h|^2 + |y - k|^2 = r^2$$

Since those expressions are squared, the absolute value symbols can be dropped.

▶ $(x - h)^2 + (y - k)^2 = r^2$

Identify the center and radius of the circle represented by $(x - 4)^2 + (y + 3)^2 = 4$.

EXAMPLE A Convert $3x^2 + 3y^2 - 12x + 6y - 12 = 0$ to standard form. Then graph the circle.

1

Complete the square for the *x* terms.

Divide out the GCF, 3, and then group the *x* terms.

$3x^2 + 3y^2 - 12x + 6y - 12 = 0$

$x^2 + y^2 - 4x + 2y - 4 = 0$

$(x^2 - 4x) + y^2 + 2y - 4 = 0$

Compare $x^2 - 4x$ to $ax^2 + bx + c$.

$a = 1$ and $b = -4$, so $\left(\frac{b}{2a}\right)^2 = \left(\frac{4}{2(1)}\right)^2 = 4$.

Add 4 to both sides. Then factor the perfect square trinomial.

$(x^2 - 4x + 4) + y^2 + 2y - 4 = 0 + 4$

$(x - 2)^2 + y^2 + 2y - 4 = 4$

2

Complete the square for the *y* terms.

Group the *y* terms, and move all constant terms to the right side of the equation.

$(x - 2)^2 + (y^2 + 2y) - 4 = 4$

$(x - 2)^2 + (y^2 + 2y) = 8$

For the *y*-terms, $a = 1$ and $b = 2$, so $\left(\frac{b}{2a}\right)^2 = \left(\frac{2}{2(1)}\right)^2 = 1$. Add 1 to both sides. Then factor the trinomial.

$(x - 2)^2 + (y^2 + 2y + 1) = 8 + 1$

$(x - 2)^2 + (y + 1)^2 = 9$

3

Identify the center and radius.

Compare $(x - 2)^2 + (y + 1)^2 = 9$ to $(x - h)^2 + (y - k)^2 = r^2$.

$r^2 = 9$

$r = 3$

The radius of the circle is 3.

$x - h = x - 2 \qquad y - k = y + 1$

$-h = -2 \qquad\qquad -k = 1$

$h = 2 \qquad\qquad\quad k = -1$

The center of the circle is $(2, -1)$.

4

Graph the circle.

Plot the center $(2, -1)$. Then, count 3 units right, left, up, and down to find points on the circle—$(5, -1)$, $(-1, -1)$, $(2, 2)$, and $(2, -4)$. Connect the four points with a smooth curve.

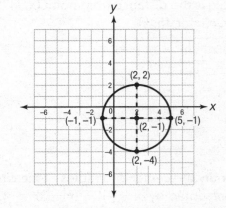

CHECK

Substitute points on the circle into the general form of the equation to verify that the graph is correct.

EXAMPLE B A circle is graphed below. Write the equation for the circle in standard form.

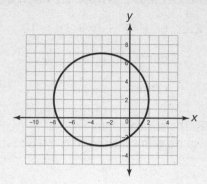

1

Identify the radius of the circle.

Points $(-3, 7)$ and $(-3, -3)$ appear to lie on opposite ends of the circle. Calculate the distance between those points.

$d = \sqrt{(-3 - (-3))^2 + (-3 - 7)^2}$

$d = \sqrt{(0)^2 + (-10)^2}$

$d = \sqrt{100}$

$d = 10$

This can be verified by using two other points, such as $(-8, 3)$ and $(2, 3)$.

$d = \sqrt{(2 - (-8))^2 + (3 - 3)^2} = 10$

If $d = 10$ units, then $r = \frac{10}{2} = 5$ units.

2

Identify the center of the circle.

The center of the circle is the midpoint of the diameters. Find the average of the coordinates of the endpoints of a diameter, $(-3, 7)$ and $(-3, -3)$:

$\left(\dfrac{x_1 + x_2}{2}, \dfrac{y_1 + y_2}{2}\right) = \left(\dfrac{-3 + (-3)}{2}, \dfrac{7 + (-3)}{2}\right)$

$= (-3, 2)$

3

Substitute the values you found into the standard form of the equation.

The center is $(-3, 2)$. The radius is 5.

$(x - h)^2 + (y - k)^2 = r^2$

$(x - (-3))^2 + (y - 2)^2 = 5^2$

▶ The equation of the circle in standard form is $(x + 3)^2 + (y - 2)^2 = 25$.

Write the general form of the equation for this circle.

Practice

Identify the center and radius of the circle described by each equation.

1. $(x - 8)^2 + (y - 1)^2 = 81$

center: (_____, _____)

radius: _____

2. $(x + 4)^2 + (y + 1)^2 = 10$

center: (_____, _____)

radius: _____

3. $(x - 6)^2 + \left(y + \frac{4}{3}\right)^2 = \frac{64}{9}$

center: (_____, _____)

radius: _____

> **REMEMBER** The standard form $(x - h)^2 + (y - k)^2 = r^2$ describes a circle with center (h, k) and radius r.

Convert each equation of a circle from general form to standard form by completing the square. Then identify the circle's center and radius.

4. $x^2 + y^2 - 8x + 4y - 16 = 0$

standard form: _____

center: (_____, _____)

radius: _____

5. $4x^2 + 4y^2 - 8y = 0$

standard form: _____

center: (_____, _____)

radius: _____

 HINT Remove a factor of 4 before completing the square.

Write an appropriate word or phrase to complete each sentence.

6. A conic section is a figure formed by the intersection of a plane and a(n) _____.

7. A conic section is a curve having an equation of degree _____.

8. The general form for the equation of a circular conic section is $Ax^2 + By^2 + Cx + Dy + E = 0$, where _____ = _____.

Graph the circle that is represented by each equation.

9. $(x + 1)^2 + (y - 1)^2 = 9$

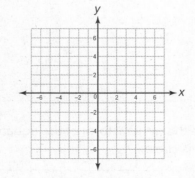

10. $x^2 + y^2 - 4x - 8y + 16 = 0$

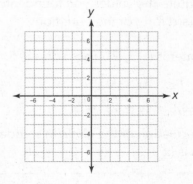

Write an equation to represent each circle in standard form. Then write the equation in the general form for a conic section.

11.

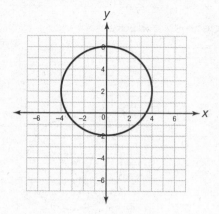

_____

_____

12.

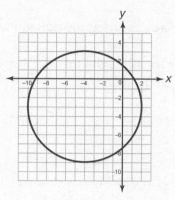

_____

_____

Solve.

13. A circle has a diameter with endpoints at $(-3, -10.25)$ and $(-3, 1.75)$. What is the equation of the circle in standard form?

_____

14. **WRITE** Point $(-7, 0)$ is on a circle with center $(-8, -4)$. Write the equation of the circle.

_____

15. **JUSTIFY** The grid shows a map of an acoustic music festival. Each unit on the grid represents $\frac{1}{10}$ mile. The volunteer coordinator gives each volunteer a walkie-talkie with a range of $\frac{1}{2}$ mile. Will the coordinator be able to communicate from her kiosk with all sites shown on the map? Justify your answer.

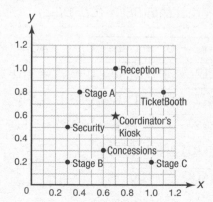

Using Coordinates to Prove Theorems about Circles

Representing figures as algebraic equations can help you prove geometric theorems.

EXAMPLE A Demonstrate the intersecting chords theorem by proving that $(AE)(BE) = (CE)(DE)$.

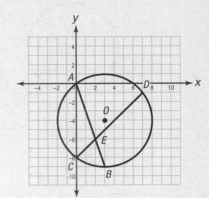

1

Write an equation for each chord.

The endpoints of $\overline{AB}$ appear to be $A(0, 0)$ and $B(3, -9)$. Find the slope of $\overline{AB}$.

$$m_{\overline{AB}} = \frac{y_2 - y_1}{x_2 - x_1} = \frac{-9 - 0}{3 - 0} = \frac{-9}{3} = -3$$

The y-intercept for $\overleftrightarrow{AB}$ is $(0, 0)$. So, the equation of the line is $y = -3x + 0$.

The endpoints of $\overline{CD}$ appear to be $C(0, -8)$ and $D(7, -1)$. Find the slope of $\overline{CD}$.

$$m_{\overline{CD}} = \frac{-1 - (-8)}{7 - 0} = \frac{7}{7} = 1$$

The y-intercept for $\overleftrightarrow{CD}$ is $(0, -8)$. So, the equation of the line is $y = x - 8$.

2

Find the point of intersection.

The point of intersection is the solution to the system containing $\overleftrightarrow{AB}$ and $\overleftrightarrow{CD}$.

$$\begin{cases} y = -3x \\ y = x - 8 \end{cases}$$

Substitute $-3x$ for y in $y = x - 8$.

$$-3x = x - 8$$
$$-4x = -8$$
$$x = 2$$

Substitute 2 for x in either equation.

$$y = -3x = -3(2) = -6$$

Point E is $(2, -6)$.

3

Show that $(AE)(BE) = (CE)(DE)$.

$$AE = \sqrt{(2 - 0)^2 + (-6 - 0)^2} = \sqrt{40}$$
$$BE = \sqrt{(2 - 3)^2 + (-6 - (-9))^2} = \sqrt{10}$$
$$CE = \sqrt{(2 - 0)^2 + (-6 - (-8))^2} = \sqrt{8}$$
$$DE = \sqrt{(2 - 7)^2 + (-6 - (-1))^2} = \sqrt{50}$$
$$(\sqrt{40})(\sqrt{10}) \overset{?}{=} (\sqrt{8})(\sqrt{50})$$
$$\sqrt{400} = \sqrt{400} \checkmark$$

TRY

Show that $A(0, 0)$, $B(3, -9)$, $C(0, -8)$, and $D(7, -1)$ lie on the circle whose center is $(3, -4)$ and whose radius is 5 units long.

EXAMPLE B The equation of circle P is $(x - 1)^2 + y^2 = 2$. The equation of line RS is $y = x + 1$. Prove that $\overleftrightarrow{RS}$ is tangent to circle P. Then prove that the tangent line is perpendicular to the radius of the circle.

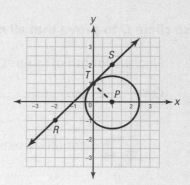

1

Prove that $\overleftrightarrow{RS}$ is tangent to circle P.

A tangent line intersects a circle at exactly one point. So, if $\overleftrightarrow{RS}$ is tangent to circle P, then there will be only one solution to the system containing the equations of the line and the circle.

$$\begin{cases} (x - 1)^2 + y^2 = 2 \\ y = x + 1 \end{cases}$$

Substitute $x + 1$ for y in the equation of the circle and solve for x.

$$(x - 1)^2 + y^2 = 2$$
$$(x - 1)^2 + (x + 1)^2 = 2$$
$$x^2 - 2x + 1 + x^2 + 2x + 1 - 2 = 0$$
$$2x^2 = 0$$
$$x^2 = 0$$
$$x = 0$$

Substitute 0 for x in the linear equation.

$$y = x + 1 = 0 + 1 = 1$$

▶ There is only one real solution, $(0, 1)$, so $\overleftrightarrow{RS}$ intersects circle P at this one point only. So, $\overleftrightarrow{RS}$ must be tangent to circle P.

2

Prove that radius $\overline{PT}$ is perpendicular to $\overline{RS}$.

Perpendicular lines have slopes that are opposite reciprocals of each other.

The equation for $\overleftrightarrow{RS}$ is $y = x + 1$, so, $m_{\overline{RS}} = 1$.

Find the slope of radius PT.

Point T was found to be $(0, 1)$. Point P is the center of circle P. The equation of circle P is $(x - 1)^2 + y^2 = 2$, so the center, (h, k), of the circle is $(1, 0)$.

$$m_{\overline{PT}} = \frac{1 - 0}{0 - 1} = \frac{1}{-1} = -1$$
$$m_{\overline{RS}} \cdot m_{\overline{PT}} = 1 \cdot -1 = -1$$

▶ The slopes of $\overleftrightarrow{RS}$ and $\overleftrightarrow{PT}$ are opposite reciprocals, so $\overleftrightarrow{PT} \perp \overleftrightarrow{RS}$.

Demonstrate the Secant-Tangent Theorem by proving that $(SV)(SW) = (ST)^2$.

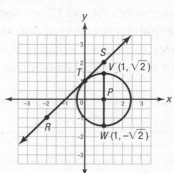

Practice

Use circle *O* to prove that all radii of a circle have the same length.

1. Find the length of radius *OA*.

    OA = _____ = _____

     HINT Since $\overline{OA}$ is a vertical segment, $OA = |y_2 - y_1|$.

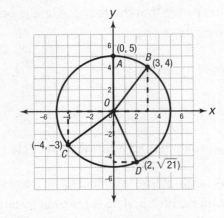

2. Find the lengths of other radii.

    OB = _____ = _____

    OC = _____ = _____

    OD = _____ = _____

3. Will all radii of the circle have the same length? Explain how you know.

    _____

    _____

Prove or disprove.

4. The line $y = x - 1$ is tangent to the circle $x^2 + (y - 3)^2 = 8$ at the point (2, 1). Prove the tangent line is perpendicular to the radius at the point of tangency.

    _____

    _____

    _____

    REMEMBER Perpendicular lines have slopes that are opposite reciprocals.

5. Prove or disprove that the point $(1, \sqrt{3})$ lies on the circle centered at the origin and containing the point (3, 0).

    _____

    _____

    _____

    _____

6. Line segments *PR* and *PT* are secants drawn from point *P*. Prove that the product of one secant segment and its external segment is equal to the product of the other secant segment and its external segment.

    _____

    _____

    _____

Prove or disprove.

7. **PROVE** Prove that the diameter of circle *J* is twice the length of its radius.

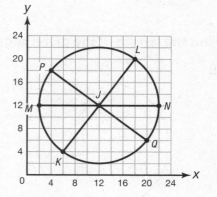

Use the distance formula (or another formula) to find each length. Show your work.

MN = _____ = _____

MJ = _____ = _____

KL = _____ = _____

KJ = _____ = _____

PQ = _____ = _____

PJ = _____ = _____

So, each diameter is _____ the length of each radius.

8. **JUSTIFY** In circle *P*, chord $\overline{CD}$ intersects chord $\overline{AB}$ at point *E*.

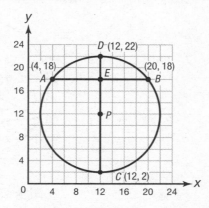

Show that because the diameter intersects the chord and is perpendicular to the chord, it bisects the chord. Justify each step by completing the two-column proof.

Statements	Reasons
1. $\overline{AB}$ and $\overline{CD}$ intersect at point *E*.	Given
2. $\overline{CD}$ is a diameter of circle *P*.	$\overline{CD}$ is a chord that passes through _____.
3. $\overline{AB} \perp \overline{CD}$	$\overline{AB}$ is a horizontal segment and _____
4. AE = EB	AE = |12 − _____| = _____ EB = _____
5. $\overline{CD}$ bisects $\overline{AB}$.	$\overline{CD}$ divides $\overline{AB}$ into two segments of equal lengths. Definition of _____.

UNIT

5 Review

Find the length of the given segment for each circle.

1.
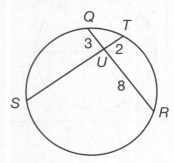

SU = _____

2. $\overline{LP}$ is tangent to the circle.
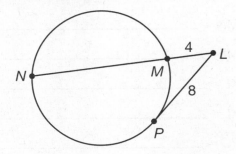

NM = _____

Find the measure of the given angles and arcs in each circle Q.

3.
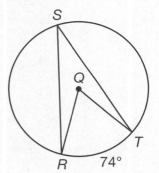

∠RQT = _____

∠RST = _____

4.
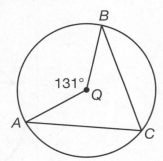

∠ACB = _____

$\overarc{AB}$ = _____

Find the measure of the given angle.

5.
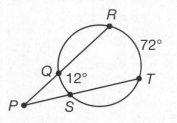

∠RPT = _____

6.
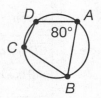

∠BCD = _____

Choose the best answer.

7. Which equation represents the circle graphed below?

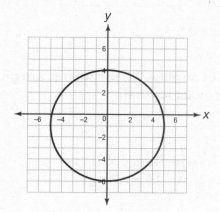

- **A.** $x^2 + (y - 1)^2 = 5$
- **B.** $(x - 1)^2 + y^2 = 5$
- **C.** $x^2 + (y - 1)^2 = 25$
- **D.** $x^2 + (y + 1)^2 = 25$

8. Radius $\overline{KH}$ is perpendicular to $\overline{FG}$.

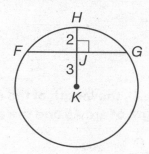

What is the length of $\overline{JG}$?

- **A.** $\sqrt{6}$
- **B.** 4
- **C.** $\sqrt{22}$
- **D.** 8

9. Point C is the center of circle C. What is the length of the radius of circle C?

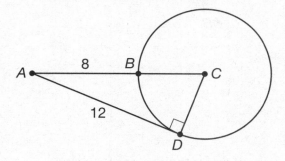

- **A.** 5 units
- **B.** 6 units
- **C.** 9 units
- **D.** 18 units

10. $\overline{SR}$ is a diameter of the circle. What is the measure of $\angle STR$?

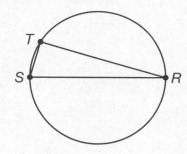

- **A.** 45°
- **B.** 90°
- **C.** 120°
- **D.** 180°

Identify the center and radius of the circle described by each equation.

11. $(x - 8)^2 + (y + 10)^2 = \frac{49}{16}$

center: (_____, _____)

radius: _____

12. $2x^2 + 2y^2 - 12x - 16y = 0$

center: (_____, _____)

radius: _____

In each circle O, the length of the radius and the measure of angle AOB, in radians, are given. Find the length of arc AB and the area of sector AOB. Give exact answers.

13.

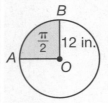

Length of $\overarc{AB}$ = _____

Area of sector AOB = _____

14.

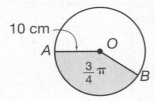

Length of $\overarc{AB}$ = _____

Area of sector AOB = _____

Construct the figures.

15. Construct two lines passing through point B and tangent to circle A.

• B

16. Inscribe a circle in △DEF. Identify the point of concurrency that is the center of the circle you drew.

point of concurrency: _____

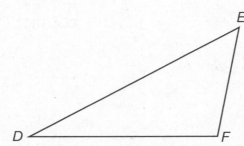

Line segment *MN* is a chord of circle *O*, and $\overline{PQ}$ is a diameter. Use the diagram below and questions 17 and 18 to show that the diameter is the longest chord in the circle.

17. Draw radii $\overline{OM}$ and $\overline{ON}$ to form $\triangle OMN$. Then use the distance formula (or another formula) to find the lengths of two sides of the triangle.

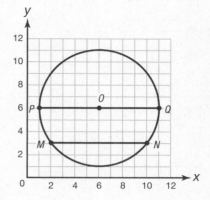

MN = _____

OM = _____

Without performing any calculations, what must be the length of $\overline{ON}$? Why?

ON = _____ because _____

18. Write an equality or inequality symbol (=, ≤, or ≥) to compare *MN* to the sum *OM* + *ON*.

MN _____ OM + ON

Complete the expression for diameter $\overline{PQ}$ and find its length.

PQ = OP + _____ = 5 + _____ = _____

Write equality or inequality symbols to compare $\overline{OP}$ to $\overline{OM}$ and $\overline{OQ}$ to $\overline{ON}$.

OP _____ OM   OQ _____ ON

Substitute *OP* for *OM* and *OQ* for *ON*.

MN _____ OM + ON → MN ≤ _____ + _____

Substitute *PQ* for *OP* + *OQ*.

MN _____ PQ

Prove.

19. Fill in the blanks below to prove that a 90° inscribed angle intercepts a semicircle.

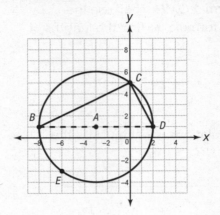

The slope of the line containing $\overline{BC}$ is _____.

The slope of the line containing $\overline{CD}$ is _____.

The product of those slopes is: _____ · _____ = _____.

So, $\overline{BC}$ is _____ to $\overline{CD}$ because the slopes of _____ lines are opposite reciprocals. Therefore, angle *ABC* measures _____ degrees.

Point *A* is the _____ of circle *A*. $\overline{BD}$ passes through point *A*, so it is a _____ of circle *A*.

The endpoints of arc *BED* are the endpoints of a diameter, so arc *BED* is a _____.

So, 90° inscribed angle *BCD* intercepts a _____.

20. Nika says that a circle with a radius of 6 units is similar to a circle with a radius of 2 units. Plot a circle with radius 6 units on the coordinate plane. Then perform a dilation and explain why your dilation shows that Nika is correct.

_____

_____

_____

_____

_____

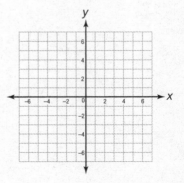

Solve.

21. A visitors' kiosk will be built at a state park so that it is equidistant from three attractions: the geyser, the waterfalls, and the hot springs. Draw a point to show the location where the kiosk will be built.

Hot Springs
•

•   •
Geyser   Waterfalls

22. PROVE Prove that the point $(3, \sqrt{7})$ lies on the circle centered at the origin and containing the point $(0, 4)$.

_____

_____

_____

23. DESIGN A jewelry designer has made the following sketch for a necklace made of pearls and diamonds.

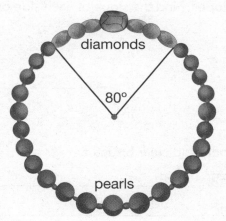

When it is arranged in a circle, the necklace has a radius of 7 cm. Find the length of the section made up of pearls and the length of the section made up of diamonds. Round your answers to the nearest tenth.

_____

PROVE IT

MATERIALS:
pencil
compass

For this activity, you will work individually or in pairs to prove several statements to be true.

Equilateral triangle ABC has vertices $A(\sqrt{3}, -3)$, $B(4\sqrt{3}, 0)$, and $C(\sqrt{3}, 3)$. Prove that the circumcenter of the triangle is the center of the circle that circumscribes the triangle.

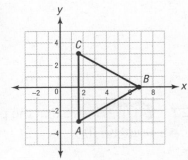

1 The circumcenter is the concurrent point of the perpendicular bisectors of the three sides of the triangle. The perpendicular bisector of a segment passes through the midpoint of the segment. Find the midpoint of each side of the triangle.

$M_{\overline{AB}} = ($ _____ , _____ $)$

$M_{\overline{BC}} = ($ _____ , _____ $)$

$M_{\overline{AC}} = ($ _____ , _____ $)$

2 The perpendicular bisector of a segment is perpendicular to the segment. Perpendicular lines have opposite reciprocal slopes. Find the slope of each side of the triangle and its opposite reciprocal.

$m_{\overline{AB}} =$ _____ $m_{\overline{AB}} \perp =$ _____

$m_{\overline{BC}} =$ _____ $m_{\overline{BC}} \perp =$ _____

$m_{\overline{AC}} =$ _____ $m_{\overline{AC}} \perp =$ _____

3 Find the equation of each perpendicular bisector.

perpendicular bisector of $\overline{AB}$: _____

perpendicular bisector of $\overline{BC}$: _____

perpendicular bisector of $\overline{AC}$: _____

4 The circumcenter of $\triangle ABC$ is the point $(2\sqrt{3}, 0)$. Show that this point lies on all three perpendicular bisectors.

_____   _____   _____

_____   _____   _____

_____   _____   _____

Duplicating this page is prohibited by law. © 2015 Triumph Learning, LLC

5 Find the radius of the circumscribed circle by finding the distance between the center and one of the vertices. Then write the equation of the circumscribed circle.

$r_c =$ _____ $(x -$ _____$)^2 + (y -$ _____$)^2 =$ _____

6 Prove that all three vertices are on the circumscribed circle.

_____   _____   _____

_____   _____   _____

_____   _____   _____

_____   _____   _____

7 Because the triangle is equilateral, the circumcenter is also the incenter. Find the length of the radius of the inscribed circle. Then write the equation of the circumscribed circle.

$r_i =$ _____ $(x -$ _____$)^2 + (y -$ _____$)^2 =$ _____

8 Find the equations for the lines that contain the sides of the triangle.

$\overleftrightarrow{AB}$: _____

$\overleftrightarrow{BC}$: _____

$\overleftrightarrow{AC}$: _____

9 How could you prove that the three sides of the triangle are tangent to the inscribed circle?

_____

_____

_____

_____

_____

_____

10 Find the following. Round answers to the nearest tenth, as needed.

$m\angle A =$ _____ ° $m\angle A =$ _____ rad

$m\widehat{BC} =$ _____ ° $m\widehat{BC} =$ _____ rad

$m\widehat{BAC} =$ _____ ° $m\widehat{BAC} =$ _____ rad

length of $\widehat{BC} =$ _____   length of $\widehat{BCA} =$ _____

Statistics and Probability

Interpreting Categorical and Quantitative Data

Summarize, represent, and interpret data on two categorial and quantitative variables.

Interpret linear models.

Grade 7 Geometry

Solve real-life and mathematical problems involving angle measure, area, surface area, and volume.

Grade 8 Geometry

Solve real-world and mathematical problems involving volume of cylinders, cones, and spheres.

Grade 7 Statistics and Probability

Investigate chance processes and develop, use, and evaluate probability models.

Statistics and Probability

Conditional Probability and the Rules of Probability

Understand independence and conditional probability and use them to interpret data.

Use the rules of probability to compute probabilities of compound events in a uniform probability model.

Using Probability to Make Decisions

Use probability to evaluate outcomes of decisions.

Algebra

Arithmetic with Polynomials and Rational Expressions

Use polynomial identities to solve problems.

Statistics and Probability

Interpreting Categorical and Quantitative Data

Summarize, represent, and interpret data on a single count or measurement variable.

Making Inferences and Justifying Conclusions

Understand and evaluate random processes underlying statistical experiments.

Make inferences and justify conclusions from sample surveys, experiments, and observational studies.

Using Probability to Make Decisions

Use probability to evaluate outcomes of decisions.

Unit 6
Applications of Probability

Sets, Subsets, and Sample Spaces

UNDERSTAND A **set** is a collection of elements, such as objects or numbers. Imagine that you have a bag containing four cards with a number printed on each card. The numbers on the cards are listed below.

4   7   8   9

You can indicate a set by listing its elements in braces. For example, the set of numbers on the cards is {4, 7, 8, 9}, which we can refer to as set A. So, $A = \{4, 7, 8, 9\}$.

If every element in a set also belongs to another set, then the first set is a **subset** of the second set. For example, if set $B = \{4, 7\}$, then set B is a subset of set A because every element of set B is also an element of set A.

A set containing all possible elements is called the **universal set**, or parent set, denoted by the letter U. For sets A and B, the universal set might be the digits 0–9. A set containing no elements is called the empty set, or null set, and is indicated by the symbol $\varnothing$. The empty set is a subset of every set.

A set can have a **complement**, which includes all of the elements in the universal set that are not included in that set. The complement of subset B is denoted as $\overline{B}$, ~B, B^c, or B'.

$\overline{B} = \{0, 1, 2, 3, 5, 6, 8, 9\}$

UNDERSTAND Consider the following sets:

$C = \{7, 8\}$ $D = \{7, 11\}$

The **intersection** of sets, shown by the symbol ∩, consists only of the elements that the two sets have in common. You can think of the symbol ∩ as meaning "and." The intersection of C and D contains elements that are in set C and also in set D.

$C \cap D = \{7\}$

The **union** of sets, shown by the symbol ∪, consists of all the elements contained in either or both sets. You can think of the symbol ∪ as meaning "or." The union of C and D contains elements that are either in set C or in set D or in both sets.

$C \cup D = \{7, 8, 11\}$

UNDERSTAND You can use what you know about sets to understand and describe **probabilities**. The **sample space** for a probability experiment is the set of all the possible **outcomes** for the experiment. So, the sample space for tossing a standard number cube is {1, 2, 3, 4, 5, 6}. An **event** in a probability experiment is a subset of the sample space. When a number cube is tossed, you can define any number of events, such as tossing a 2—in which case, the subset is {2}—or tossing an even number—in which case, the subset is {2, 4, 6}.

⊏ Connect

A large bag holds marbles of the following colors: blue (B), green (G), orange (O), and pink (P). A small bag holds marbles of the following colors: red (R), green (G), yellow (Y), and orange (O). Define the universal set of marble colors. Define a subset of the universal set. Find the complement of the set of colors in the small bag. Find the union and intersection of the sets of colors in the two bags.

1

Define the universal set.

The universal set is the set of all marble colors.

$U = \{B, G, O, P, R, Y\}$

2

Define a subset of the universal set.

You can define many subsets of the universal set. For now, let the colors in the large bag be set L.

$L = \{B, G, O, P\}$

Set L is a subset of the universal set U.

3

Find the complement of the set of colors in the small bag.

Let the colors in the small bag be set S.

$S = \{R, G, Y, O\}$.

The complement of set S includes the colors that appear in the universal set (set U) but not in set S.

$\overline{S} = \{B, P\}$

4

Find the union of sets L and S.

The union of the sets contains the elements in set L or set S, or both.

$L \cup S = \{B, G, O, P, R, Y\}$
In this case, $L \cup S = U$.

5

Find the intersection of the sets.

The intersection of the sets contains only the elements that appear in both set L and set S.

In this case, $L \cap S = \{G, O\}$.

TRY

If $M = \{B, P\}$, what is $S \cap M$?

Venn Diagrams

UNDERSTAND Suppose a universal set consists of all the single-digit whole numbers.

$$U = \{0, 1, 2, 3, 4, 5, 6, 7, 8, 9\}$$

Many subsets can be selected from this set. For example, the set of all even numbers, set E, and the set of all odd numbers, O, would be:

$$E = \{0, 2, 4, 6, 8\} \qquad O = \{1, 3, 5, 7, 9\}$$

Another way to represent these sets would be to use a Venn diagram. In the Venn diagram below, the large rectangle represents the universal set, U. Subsets E and O are represented as circles inside the larger rectangle. The circles do not overlap. This means that while all of the numbers are part of the universal set, none of the numbers are common to both subsets. This is because no number is both even and odd. From observing the diagram, you can see the following:

- $E \cup O = \{0, 1, 2, 3, 4, 5, 6, 7, 8, 9\} = U$

- $E \cap O = \varnothing$

- $\overline{E} = \{1, 3, 5, 7, 9\} = O$

- $\overline{O} = \{0, 2, 4, 6, 8\} = E$

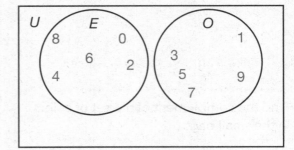

Consider the subset of single-digit whole numbers that are also prime numbers. This set could be represented as $P = \{2, 3, 5, 7\}$. If a circle for set P is added to the Venn diagram, it will overlap with the circle for E (since 2 is prime) and with the circle for O (since 3, 5, and 7 are prime). This diagram allows us to visualize the following:

- $E \cap P = \{2\}$

- $O \cap P = \{3, 5, 7\}$

- $\overline{P} = \{0, 1, 4, 6, 8, 9\}$

- $E - P = E \cap \overline{P} = \{0, 4, 6, 8\}$

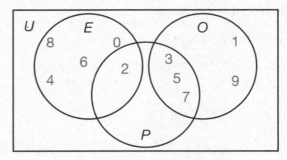

As shown above, there is often more than one way to describe data by using set notation. For example, to represent the values that are in set E but not in set P, use a set difference, $E - P$, or an intersection with a complement, $E \cap \overline{P}$.

It is important to consider what Venn diagrams do and do not show. For example, $\overline{P}$, the complement of set P, shows the single-digit numbers that are not prime, but that does not mean that it shows only the composite numbers. (0 and 1 are neither prime nor composite.) However, it can be used to show that 2 is the only even prime number, especially if additional whole numbers are added.

⊏ Connect

Three student journalists predicted which intramural soccer teams would make it to the semifinals of a regional tournament.

Make a Venn diagram to represent these sets of predictions.

Xavier	Yuriko	Zachary
Dolphins	Eagles	Dolphins
Eagles	Panthers	Eagles
Hawks	Sharks	Foxes
Wolves	Tigers	Tigers

1 Identify the universal set and the subsets.

The universal set will be every team in the league. This includes every team in the table, and possibly others.

The subsets are set X (Xavier's choices), set Y (Yuriko's choices), and set Z (Zachary's choices).

X = {Dolphins, Eagles, Hawks, Wolves}

Y = {Eagles, Panthers, Sharks, Tigers}

Z = {Dolphins, Eagles, Foxes, Tigers}

2 Plan the Venn diagram.

Before drawing the circles, decide if and how they will intersect.

$X \cap Y$ = {Eagles}

$Y \cap Z$ = {Eagles, Tigers}

$X \cap Z$ = {Dolphins, Eagles}

$X \cap Y \cap Z$ = {Eagles}

Each set overlaps the others and one element is in all three sets.

3 Fill in the Venn diagram.

Draw a rectangle to represent the universal set. Place $X \cap Y \cap Z$ (Eagles) first.

Then, place the other elements from the intersections (Dolphins, Tigers).

Then, place the remaining elements from each set.

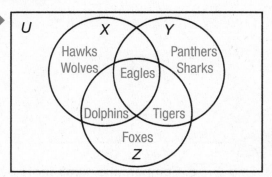

Any teams that were not in X, Y, or Z would be written in the rectangle, but outside the circles.

MODEL

What does the empty region in the Venn diagram represent?

EXAMPLE A The table shows all of the boys in Homeroom 201. Consider this to be the universal set.

Amal	Benji	Cheng	Dugan	Eric	Frank
Gus	Hal	Jorge	Karl	Leo	Max

Amal, Cheng, Frank, Gus, Jorge, and Karl are all in the art club. Consider this set A.

Benji, Cheng, Jorge, Karl, and Max are all in the environmental club. Consider this set E.

Determine $\overline{A \cup E}$, the complement of the union of sets A and E. What does that set show about the students' involvement in clubs?

1

List the universal set.

U = {Amal, Benji, Cheng, Dugan, Eric, Frank, Gus, Hal, Jorge, Karl, Leo, Max}

2

Find the union of sets A and E.

A = {Amal, Cheng, Frank, Gus, Jorge, Karl}

E = {Benji, Cheng, Jorge, Karl, Max}

The union of the sets includes every boy in Homeroom 201 who is in either club.

So, $A \cup E$ = {Amal, Benji, Cheng, Frank, Gus, Jorge, Karl, Max}

3

Find the complement of $A \cup E$.

The complement includes all of the elements of set U that are not in the union of sets A and E. So, it shows which students are not in either club.

List the elements of the universal set and cross out elements of $A \cup E$.

{~~Amal, Benji, Cheng,~~ Dugan, Eric, ~~Frank, Gus,~~ Hal, ~~Jorge, Karl,~~ Leo, ~~Max~~}

▶ $\overline{A \cup E}$ = {Dugan, Eric, Hal, Leo}, so, there are 4 boys in Homeroom 201 who are not in the art club or the environmental club.

TRY

Find $\overline{A \cap E}$. Compare the number of boys in the complement of the intersection of the sets to the number of boys in the complement of the union of the sets.

EXAMPLE B Julia and Theo are playing a game in which they toss a six-sided number cube. If the cube lands on an even number, Julia gets a point. If the cube lands on a number less than 4, Theo gets a point. Create a Venn diagram to represent all the possible outcomes of a toss and who, if anyone, will get a point if it lands on that number.

1

List the universal set, or all the possible outcomes of tossing the cube.

$U = \{1, 2, 3, 4, 5, 6\}$

2

Find the outcomes that result in a point for Julia or a point for Theo.

Julia earns a point if an even number is tossed.

$J = \{2, 4, 6\}$

Theo earns a point if a number less than 4 is tossed.

$T = \{1, 2, 3\}$

The intersection of the sets shows the numbers for which both Julia and Theo would earn a point.

$J \cap T = \{2\}$

3

Draw the Venn diagram.

There is an intersection between the sets, so draw a rectangle with two intersecting circles inside.

Write 2 in the area where the circles overlap to show the intersection of the sets.

In the non-overlapping part of the circle for set J, write the remaining numbers from set J. Do the same for set T.

The number 5 does not earn a point for either player, so it is not written inside the circles. Since it is still part of the universal set, write it inside the rectangle but outside the circles.

 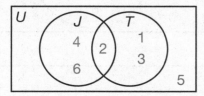

DISCUSS

Shade the Venn diagram to show $J \cap T$. Then shade the diagram in another color to show $J \cup T$. How are those shadings alike? How are they different?

Practice

Use the information below for questions 1–3.

$U = \{1, 3, 5, 6, 8, 10\}$ $A = \{3, 5, 10\}$ $B = \{3, 5, 6, 8\}$

1. Find $A \cup B$.

_____

2. Find $A \cap B$.

_____

3. Find $\overline{B}$.

_____

> REMEMBER $\overline{B}$ means the complement of B.

Write the sample space for each situation.

4. the result of tossing a fair coin _____

5. the suit of a card chosen from a deck of standard playing cards

_____

6. the coin you receive as change for a cash purchase _____

> REMEMBER A sample space is the set of all possible outcomes.

Use set notation (e.g., $\cup$, $\cap$, $\sim$) to describe the shaded portion of each Venn diagram.

7.
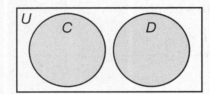

_____

8.
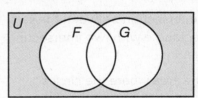

_____

9.
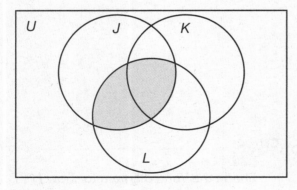

_____

10.
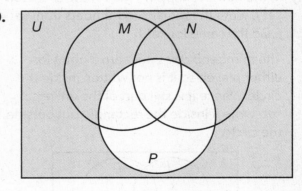

_____

The Venn diagram shows the arts electives that members of a girls' swim team are taking this year in school: Creative Writing (*C*), Fine Arts (*F*), and Music Appreciation (*M*). Let the entire diagram represent *U*, the universal set. Use the diagram for questions 11–13.

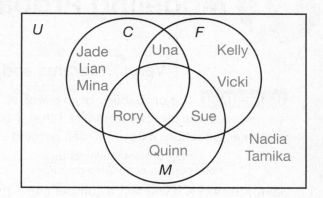

11. Find $C \cup F$. What does it represent?

_____

12. Find $C \cap F$. What does it represent?

_____

13. Find $\overline{M \cup C}$. What does it represent?

_____

14. **DRAW** Lorenzo and Maggie are spinning a spinner with 8 equal-size sections, numbered 1 to 8. If the spinner lands on a composite number (a number with more than 2 factors), Lorenzo gets a point. If the spinner lands on a number less than 4, Maggie gets a point. Draw a Venn diagram to show set *L*, the winning outcomes for Lorenzo, and set *M*, the winning outcomes for Maggie.

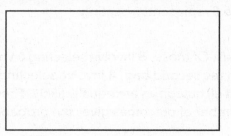

Do sets *L* and *M* intersect? Explain why.

_____

15. **CREATE** A universal set consisting of elements that are plane figures is divided into two subsets, *A* and *B*. $A \cup B$ = {circle, pentagon, rectangle, triangle}, and $A \cap B$ = {triangle}. Create three possible sets, *U*, *A*, and *B*, that fit the description. Are the sets you chose the only possible sets? Explain.

_____

_____

_____

LESSON 31 Modeling Probability

Venn Diagrams and Geometric Probability

UNDERSTAND The probability of an event, *A*, occurring is represented as *P(A)*. Probability is expressed as a number from 0 to 1 that shows how likely the event is to occur. It can be written as a fraction, a decimal, or a percent and is given by the following ratio:

$$P(A) = \frac{\text{number of favorable outcomes}}{\text{total number of possible outcomes}}$$

So, for example, if you toss a number cube, there are 6 possible outcomes: {1, 2, 3, 4, 5, 6}. Suppose you want to know the probability of tossing an even number. In that case, there are 3 favorable outcomes: {2, 4, 6}.

$$P(\text{even}) = \frac{3}{6} = \frac{1}{2} \text{ or } 0.5 \text{ or } 50\%$$

UNDERSTAND **Joint probability** is the probability that two events will occur at the same time or one right after the other. For example, suppose you have two bags, each containing four cards lettered A, C, E, and G. Suppose you want to determine the probability of selecting vowels (A or E) from both bags. Placing the possible outcomes in a Venn diagram allows you to analyze them. Circle *F* represents selecting a vowel from the first bag. Circle *S* represents selecting a vowel from the second bag.

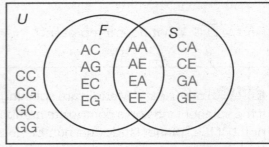

There are 16 possible outcomes. Of those, 8 involve selecting a vowel from the first bag, 8 involve selecting a vowel from the second bag, 4 involve selecting two vowels, and 4 involve selecting no vowels. Note that all outcomes are equally likely. The number of outcomes in a region divided by the total number of outcomes gives the probability for the event that the region represents.

There are 4 outcomes in the intersection of the sets, so the probability that you will select a vowel from both bags is $\frac{4}{16} = \frac{1}{4}$.

UNDERSTAND For problems involving **geometric probability**, instead of counting the number of outcomes in a region, you find the total length, area, or volume of a region. For example, consider a target with a radius of 24 inches and a bull's-eye of radius 2 inches. The probability of hitting the bull's-eye when the target is hit is equal to the ratio of the area of the bull's-eye to the area of the target.

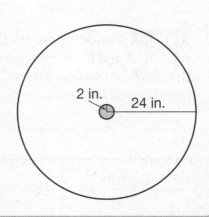

$$P(\text{bull's-eye}) = \frac{\pi(2)^2}{\pi(24)^2} = \frac{4\pi}{576\pi} = \frac{1}{144} \approx 0.0069$$

The geometric probability of hitting the bull's-eye is about 0.69%.

⊏ Connect

Lila is spinning a spinner with sectors numbered 1 to 8 and recording the results. Event A is spinning an odd number. Event B is spinning a number greater than 2. The Venn diagram shows the possible outcomes for this experiment.

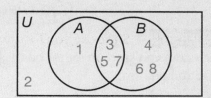

Create a second Venn diagram to show the probabilities of the following:

$A - B$, $B - A$, $A \cap B$, and $\overline{A \cup B}$.

1

Find $P(A - B)$ and $P(B - A)$.

There are 8 possible outcomes:

1, 2, 3, 4, 5, 6, 7, and 8.

The region of circle A that does not overlap with circle B contains only one outcome: 1. So, $P(A - B) = \frac{1}{8} = 0.125$.

The region of circle B that does not overlap with circle A contains three outcomes: 4, 6, and 8. So, $P(B - A) = \frac{3}{8} = 0.375$.

2

Determine $P(A \cap B)$.

The region where circles A and B overlap shows their intersection.

There are three outcomes, 3, 5, and 7, in that region. So, $P(A \cap B) = \frac{3}{8} = 0.375$

3

Determine $P(\overline{A \cup B})$ and write the probabilities in a Venn diagram.

All of the outcomes inside circles A and B show the union of events A and B.

So, its complement is the one outcome, 2, that is outside the circles.

▶ $P(\overline{A \cup B}) = \frac{1}{8} = 0.125$

4

Draw the Venn diagram of probabilities.

Write the probabilities in the corresponding regions.

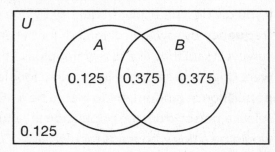

CHECK

Add together all four probabilities. What is the sum? Why?

Tree Diagrams and Two-Way Tables

UNDERSTAND Suppose you toss two fair coins—a nickel and a quarter—at the same time. Each coin can land on either heads (H) or tails (T). So for each individual coin toss, the probabilities are:

$$P(H) = \frac{1}{2} \qquad P(T) = \frac{1}{2}$$

However, the probability of both coins landing on heads, $P(HH)$, is not $\frac{1}{2}$. Drawing a **tree diagram** to represent all the possible outcomes can help you see this. The last column of the tree diagram below shows that there are 4 possible outcomes: {HH, HT, TH, TT}. All outcomes are equally likely, so the probability of each outcome is $\frac{1}{4}$. That means $P(HH) = \frac{1}{4}$.

UNDERSTAND Probabilities can also help you understand data that are collected by surveying a representative **sample** of people drawn from a larger **population**. If you want to compare two categorical variables such as gender and reading habits, you can construct a **two-way frequency table** like the one below. The table shows **joint frequencies** and **marginal frequencies**.

	Reads for Pleasure	Reads Only for School	Total
Boys	20	30	50
Girls	30	20	50
Total	50	50	100

Joint frequencies are in the body of the table.

Marginal frequencies are in the "Total" row and "Total" column.

If you divide a particular frequency by one of the totals, you can determine its **relative frequency** by row, by column, or for the entire table. For example, $\frac{20}{50}$, or 40%, of all the boys surveyed said they like to read for pleasure, and $\frac{20}{100}$, or 20%, of all the people surveyed above were boys who said they like to read for pleasure. This means that if you select a boy from the population at random, there would be a 40% chance that he reads for pleasure, and if you select a person from the population at random, there would be a 20% chance that that person would be a boy who reads for pleasure

⊏ Connect

The table shows the results of a survey of students in grades 9, 10, 11, and 12 that asked them if they preferred rock music or rap music.

What is the chance that a student chosen from the school at random is a 10th-grade student who prefers rap music to rock music?

	Rock	Rap
9th Grade	15	35
10th Grade	26	24
11th Grade	25	25
12th Grade	32	18

1

Extend the table.

The table above shows only joint frequencies. Add the numbers in the columns and rows to find the marginal frequencies.

	Rock	Rap	Total
9th Grade	15	35	50
10th Grade	26	24	50
11th Grade	25	25	50
12th Grade	32	18	50
Total	98	102	200

2

Find the cell (joint frequency) and total (marginal frequency) that you need.

Look at the cell in the table that lies in the 10th-grade row and the rap column. That cell contains the value 24.

The question asks for the probability of choosing a 10th grader who prefers rap from among all the students at the school. So, use the total for the entire table, 200.

3

Calculate the probability.

$$P(\text{10th grader who prefers rap}) = \frac{\text{number of 10th graders who prefer rap}}{\text{total number of students}} = \frac{24}{200} = 0.12$$

▶ If a student is selected from the school at random, there is a 12% chance that the student will be a 10th-grade student who prefers rap.

TRY

What is the chance that a student chosen from the school at random prefers rock music?

EXAMPLE A Miguel has a chest with three drawers. One drawer contains T-shirts, another contains shorts, and a third contains pairs of socks. Miguel will choose an outfit by reaching into each drawer and choosing one item without looking. The tree diagram shows the possible combinations of a T-shirt, shorts, and a pair of socks that he could select.

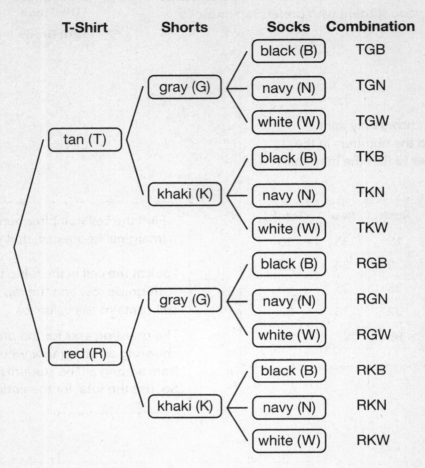

T-Shirt	Shorts	Socks	Combination

If each outfit has an equal probability of being chosen, what is the probability that Miguel will select a red T-shirt, khaki shorts, and white socks?

1

Identify the sample space.

The 12 different combinations of T-shirts, shorts, and socks make up the sample space. So, there are 12 possible outcomes.

2

Find the probability.

The outcome RKW shows selecting a red T-shirt, khaki shorts, and white socks. That outcome appears once in the sample space, so there is one favorable outcome.

▶ $P(RKW) = \dfrac{\text{favorable outcomes}}{\text{total possible outcomes}} = \dfrac{1}{12}$

TRY

What is the probability that Miguel will select gray shorts as part of his outfit?

Problem Solving

READ

The spinner shown is for a carnival game. It has a radius of 3 feet and is divided into unequal sectors. The sector marked "Grand Prize" has a central angle of 36°. What is the probability of winning the grand prize on a given spin?

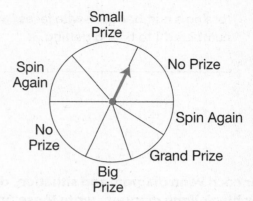

PLAN

To find geometric probability, find $P = \dfrac{\text{particular area}}{\text{total area}}$. The particular area is the area of the

_____. The total area is the area of the _____.

SOLVE

First, find the total area.

$$A_{\text{total}} = \pi(\underline{\hspace{1cm}})^2 = \underline{\hspace{1.5cm}}\pi \text{ in.}^2$$

Next, find the particular area.

The central angle of the sector is _____°.

$$A_{\text{particular}} = \underline{\hspace{1.5cm}}\pi \cdot \dfrac{\overline{\hspace{1cm}}}{360°} = \underline{\hspace{1.5cm}} \text{ in.}^2$$

Finally, find the probability.

$$P(\text{Grand Prize}) = \dfrac{\overline{\hspace{2.5cm}}}{\underline{\hspace{1.5cm}}} = \underline{\hspace{2.5cm}}$$

Expressed as a percent, the probability of winning the grand prize is about _____%.

CHECK

In actuality, the probability does not depend on the radius or area of the circle.

$$P(\text{Grand Prize}) = \dfrac{\overline{\hspace{1cm}}}{360°} \cdot \dfrac{\pi r^2}{\pi r^2} = \dfrac{\overline{\hspace{1cm}}}{360°} = \underline{\hspace{1cm}}$$

Is this value equal to the probability found above? _____

▶ The probability that a given spin will win the grand prize is _____.

Practice

Identify the probability for each simple event.

1. tossing a number cube with faces numbered 1 to 6, and getting 3.

_____

2. Drawing a spade from a standard 52-card deck

_____

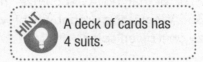

HINT

A deck of cards has 4 suits.

For each Venn diagram and situation, determine $P(A - B)$, $P(B - A)$, $P(A \cap B)$ and $P(\overline{A \cup B})$. In the blank Venn diagram, write those probabilities in the appropriate sections.

3. Two puppies were born. Event A represents a female puppy being born first. Event B represents a female puppy being born second.

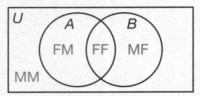

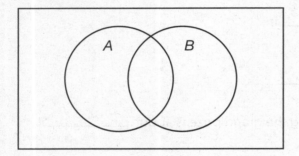

4. Two spinners each have sections numbered 1–3. Event A represents getting an odd number on the first spinner. Event B represents getting an odd number on the second spinner.

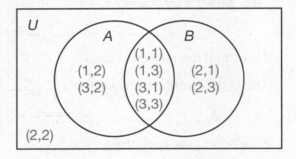

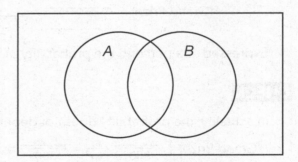

HINT

(1, 2) shows spinning a 1 on the first spinner and a 2 on the second spinner.

Use the information below for questions 5 and 6.

A bag contains six marbles. Four of the marbles are striped: one red/black, one red/green, one blue/gray, and one blue/white. Two of the marbles are solid colors: one solid white and one solid green. Curtis will reach into the bag and pick a marble without looking. Event *R* is picking a marble that is at least partially red. Event *B* is picking a marble that is at least partially blue.

5. Create a Venn diagram to show all the possible outcomes of one pick.

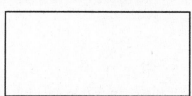

6. Determine each probability

$P(R) = $ _____

$P(B) = $ _____

$P(R \cap B) = $ _____

$P(\overline{R \cup B}) = $ _____

The tree diagram represents tossing a fair coin 3 times. Use the tree diagram for questions 7–9.

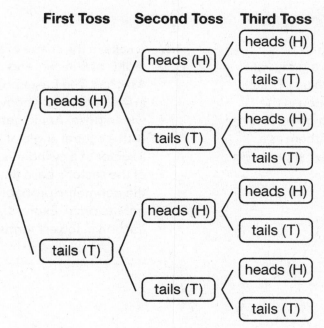

First Toss   Second Toss   Third Toss   Outcome

7. List all the possible outcomes on the tree diagram.

8. Each outcome is equally likely. What is the probability of tossing 3 tails?

_____

9. What is the probability of tossing heads on at least 2 tosses?

_____

Use the table below for questions 10–12.

The table shows the results of a survey of people in different age groups. The survey asked each person if he or she was for or against a proposal to build a new high school in town.

Age	For	Against	No Opinion
18 to 35	20	34	6
35 to 65	25	32	3
65 and over	18	27	15

10. Extend the table to show the marginal frequencies.

11. What is the chance that a person over the age of 65 has no opinion about the proposal? _____

12. What is the chance that an adult selected at random is for the proposal? _____

Calculate the probabilities.

13. The target shown has a radius of 1 meter. The bull's-eye has a radius of 5 centimeters. The point value of each section of the target is written in the section. Find the following geometric probabilities, and express them as a percent. (Hint: Your answers should add up to 100%)

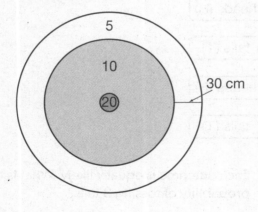

P(5 points) = _____

P(10 points) = _____

P(20 points) = _____

14. A cake in the shape of a cylinder has a radius of 6 inches and a height of 4 inches. The baker put a plastic figure in the cake, and whoever finds the figure wins a prize. Annie gets a slice of cake with a central angle of 20°. The area of a sector of a cylinder is equal to the area of the sector's base times its height. Find the geometric probability that Annie will get the prize. Express your answer as a fraction in lowest terms.

_____

Use this information for questions 15 and 16.

Fifty students were asked which television genre they like best. Five boys said drama, eight boys said sitcom, and twelve boys said reality. Eight girls said drama, ten said sitcom, and seven said reality.

15. Use the grid below to create a two-way frequency table for these data.

				Total
Boys				
Girls				
Total				

16. EXPLAIN What is the probability that a student who likes sitcoms best is a girl? Explain how determined your answer.

_____

_____

_____

Solve.

17. MODEL A pirate has forgotten exactly where he buried his gold coin, but knows that it is somewhere within a 20-foot-by-30-foot rectangular area on the beach. He only has time to dig a 5-foot-by-5-foot square hole before high tide comes in. Sketch a model of the problem and determine the geometric probability that the pirate will find the gold coin.

_____

UNDERSTAND The **factorial** of an integer n is the product of all positive integers less than or equal to n. The factorial of a number n is written as $n!$.

$$n! = n \cdot (n-1) \cdot (n-2) \cdot (n-3)...\cdot 2 \cdot 1 \qquad 5! = 5 \cdot 4 \cdot 3 \cdot 2 \cdot 1 = 120$$

Since factorials are made up of integer factors, you can divide factorials by cancelling common factors. You can simplify $\frac{9!}{7!}$ without calculating either factorial.

$$\frac{9!}{7!} = \frac{9 \cdot 8 \cdot \cancel{7} \cdot \cancel{6} \cdot \cancel{5} \cdot \cancel{4} \cdot \cancel{3} \cdot \cancel{2} \cdot \cancel{1}}{\cancel{7} \cdot \cancel{6} \cdot \cancel{5} \cdot \cancel{4} \cdot \cancel{3} \cdot \cancel{2} \cdot \cancel{1}} = 9 \cdot 8 = 72$$

UNDERSTAND A **permutation** is an arrangement of items or events in a particular order. A different order of the same items or events is a different permutation. A password, such as ABC123, is an example of a permutation. If you enter in the characters of a password in an incorrect order, such as A1B2C3, the password will not be accepted.

You can use factorials to find the number of possible permutations in a given situation. For example, in how many different orders can 4 students line up against a wall? When choosing a student for the first spot, you have 4 options. Once the first spot is filled there are 3 options remaining for the second spot, then 2 for the next spot, and then 1 for the last spot. The total is $4 \cdot 3 \cdot 2 \cdot 1$, or $4!$.

The formula for finding the number of permutations of n objects taken r at a time is:

$$_nP_r = \frac{n!}{(n-r)!}$$

Suppose that a club with 20 members wants to select a president and secretary. The students could select John and Anne, or Anne and David. Also, selecting John for president and Anne for secretary is not the same as selecting Anne for president and John for secretary. There are 20 possible presidents. Once the president is chosen, there are 19 possibilities for secretary. In mathematical language, this is represented by $_{20}P_2$.

$$_{20}P_2 = \frac{20!}{(20-2)!} = \frac{20!}{18!} = \frac{20 \cdot 19 \cdot \cancel{18!}}{\cancel{18!}} = 20 \cdot 19 = 380$$

UNDERSTAND A **combination** is an arrangement of items or events in which the order does not matter. The formula for finding the number of combinations of n objects taken r at a time is:

$$_nC_r = \frac{n!}{r!(n-r)!}$$

Suppose a dinner entrée is served with 2 sides from a menu of 5 choices. All of the food comes together, so order is not important. Fries and a salad is the same as a salad and fries. This combination may be expressed as "5 choose 2" and is represented by $_5C_2$

$$_5C_2 = \frac{5!}{2!(5-2)!} = \frac{5 \cdot 4 \cdot \cancel{3!}}{2!(\cancel{3!})} = \frac{5 \cdot 4}{2 \cdot 1} = \frac{20}{2} = 10$$

⟞ Connect

Given the letters A, B, C, and D, determine the number of possible sequences of two letters if the order matters and the letters cannot be reused. Use a table and a formula and then compare the results.

1

Make a table and count the number of possibilities.

List the first choices in the top row and the second choices in the first column. Fill in the possible sequences. Remember that letters cannot be used twice.

	A	B	C	D
A		BA	CA	DA
B	AB		CB	DB
C	AC	BC		DC
D	AD	BD	CD	

Counting the boxes, there are 12 possible sequences.

2

Determine which formula to use.

It is given that the order of the letters matters, so AB is not the same sequence as BA. This means we are counting permutations.

The formula for the number of permutations of n objects taken r at a time is $_nP_r = \dfrac{n!}{(n-r)!}$.

3

Use the formula and compare the results.

There are 4 letters and we are choosing 2, so find $_4P_2$.

$$_4P_2 = \frac{4!}{(4-2)!} = \frac{4!}{2!} = \frac{4 \cdot 3 \cdot 2!}{2!} = 4 \cdot 3 = 12$$

▶ Using both the table and the formula, we find that there are 12 possible sequences of two letters.

TRY

Suppose that the order of the letters does not matter. Look at the table again. How many possible combinations are there? Compare this to the result from the formula for $_nC_r$.

EXAMPLE A Ingrid will choose a group of 3 marbles at random from a bag. The bag contains one marble of each of the following colors: blue, green, yellow, red, orange, purple, black, and gray. How many different groups of 3 marbles can Ingrid choose?

1

Determine if the groups are permutations or combinations.

Imagine if Ingrid chooses a blue marble, then a red, then a purple. Compare this to choosing purple then blue then red. In the end, Ingrid has the same group of marbles in both scenarios: blue, red, and purple. Thus, the groups of marbles are combinations.

2

Set up a formula to find the number of combinations.

The formula for finding the number of combinations of n objects taken r at a time is $_nC_r = \frac{n!}{r!(n-r)!}$.

There are a total of 8 marbles, and Ingrid is choosing a group of 3. Therefore, we must find $_8C_3$.

3

Evaluate the formula.

$$_8C_3 = \frac{8!}{3!(8-3)!}$$

$$= \frac{8!}{(3!)(5!)}$$

$$= \frac{8 \cdot 7 \cdot 6 \cdot 5!}{(3!)(5!)}$$

$$= \frac{8 \cdot 7 \cdot 6}{3 \cdot 2 \cdot 1}$$

$$= 56$$

▶ There are 56 ways for Ingrid to choose a combination of 3 marbles from the bag.

DISCUSS

What is the probability that Ingrid will choose a group having a black marble, a green marble, and a gray marble?

Problem Solving

READ

The Pythagoras High School basketball team has twelve players. Six of those players are seniors. Two seniors will be chosen as team captains. How many different ways can the team choose two captains?

PLAN

The captains are equal in rank, so choosing Terry and Sam is the same as choosing Sam and Terry. The order in which the captains are chosen _____ matter.

Therefore, we must use the formula for _____, which is

$$_n\text{_____}_r = \text{_____}.$$

How many students on the team are eligible to be a captain? _____

How many captains will be chosen? _____

So, find _____C_____.

SOLVE

Substitute _____ for n and _____ for r in the formula and evaluate.

$$\text{\_\_\_}C\text{\_\_\_\_} = \text{_____} = \text{_____}$$

CHECK

Let the letters A, B, C, D, E, and F represent the six seniors on the team.

Would AB and BA represent different possible outcomes or the same outcome?

_____

List every possible group of captains.

AB, AC, AD, AE, _____

How many groups are on the list? _____

▶ The team can choose from _____ possible combinations of team captains.

Practice

Determine whether order matters for each situation. If order matters, write *permutation*. If order does not matter, write *combination*.

1. choosing 4 students from a class of 18 to pass out supplies _____

2. the numbers and letters on a license plate _____

3. buying ingredients for a salad _____

4. choosing the first, second, and third place winners of a contest _____

Evaluate each expression.

5. $4!$

6. $\frac{7!}{3!}$

7. $\frac{10!}{8!}$

_____   _____   _____

Choose the best answer.

8. There are 9 books on a shelf. If books are chosen at random, how many different groups of 3 books could be chosen?

    A.   27
    B.   84
    C.   504
    D. 60,480

9. To access a Web site, users must choose a 4-digit numerical PIN (Personal Identification Number) in which a digit may not be used more than once. How many unique PINs are possible?

    A.   36
    B.   126
    C.   5,040
    D. 15,120

Evaluate each combination or permutation.

10. $_9P_4 = $ _____

11. $_{100}P_3 = $ _____

12. $_7C_6 = $ _____

13. $_{50}C_2 = $ _____

Solve.

14. Debra must read 6 books over the summer for next year's English class. In how many different orders can she read the 6 books? Express your answer as a factorial and as a number.

_____

15. For a jury trial, 5 people out of a panel of 11 people will be chosen as jurors. How many different groups of 5 jurors are possible?

_____

16. Eighteen gymnasts are competing for the gold, silver, and bronze medals. How many ways can the medals be awarded among the gymnasts?

_____

17. **DERIVE** Suppose that Alan, Brianna, and Cris are starting a band. One will play drums, one will play guitar, and one will sing. How many different configurations can the band have?

_____

Write out a formula to solve this problem:

$$ {}_3P_3 = \frac{\boxed{}!}{(\boxed{} - \boxed{})!} = \frac{\boxed{}!}{(\boxed{})!} $$

Suppose a bag contains 5 marbles, one of each color: red, orange, yellow, green, and blue.

How many different groups of 5 marbles could you draw from the bag? _____

Write out a formula to solve this problem:

$$ {}_5C_5 = \frac{\boxed{}!}{\boxed{}!(\boxed{} - \boxed{})!} = \frac{\boxed{}!}{\boxed{}!(\boxed{})!} = \frac{\boxed{}}{\boxed{}!} $$

Based on these formulas, what does 0! equal? 0! = _____

18. **EXTEND** From her class of 12 students, Mrs. Albanez will select one player and one alternate at random for the math team. How many possibilities are there for Mrs. Albanez to select a player and an alternate? _____

What is the probability that she will choose the student with the highest grade as the player and the student with the second-highest grade as the alternate? Give your answer as a percent rounded to the nearest hundredth. _____

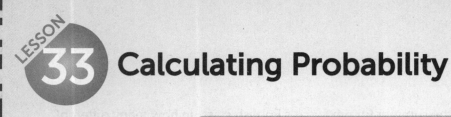

Calculating Probability

LESSON 33

Independent and Dependent Events

UNDERSTAND Sometimes, two or more events happen together. This is called a **compound event**. There are two types of compound events.

Independent events are events in which the outcome of one event does not affect the outcome of other events. For example, the outcome of tossing one coin does not affect the outcome of a second coin toss.

For **dependent events**, the outcome of one event affects the outcome of other events. An example is picking a marble from a bag containing marbles of different colors and then picking a second marble from the bag without replacing the first one. Whatever marble was picked first affects the probabilities of the second pick.

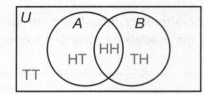

UNDERSTAND The probability that two events *A* and *B* will occur at the same time can be represented as the intersection of sets *A* and *B*. Suppose two fair coins are tossed. Let's say that event *A* is the first coin landing on heads, and event *B* is the second coin landing on heads. This Venn diagram represents the possible outcomes and shows that $A \cap B = \{HH\}$.

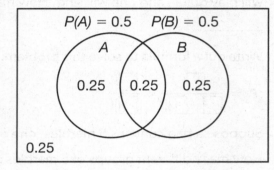

A second Venn diagram can be created to represent the probabilities associated with tossing these two coins, as shown.

> **Multiplication Rule for Independent Events:** The probability of the intersection of two subsets composed of independent events is equal to the product of their probabilities:
>
> $P(A \cap B) = P(A)P(B)$

Substitute the probabilities into the formula to show that events *A* and *B* are independent.

$P(A \cap B) = P(A)P(B)$

$0.25 \overset{?}{=} (0.5)(0.5)$

$0.25 = 0.25 \checkmark$

If two events are independent, you can multiply their probabilities to find the probability that both will occur. This formula can also be used to determine if events are independent. If the probability of the events happening together or one after the other is equal to the product of their probabilities, the events must be independent.

←€ Connect

Holden will select marbles from two bags without looking. First, he will choose a marble from a bag that has 1 red marble and 2 blue marbles in it. Next, he will choose a marble from a different bag that has 4 red marbles, 2 blue marbles, and 2 green marbles in it. What is the probability that he will select a blue marble followed by a red marble?

1

Determine the probabilities for each pick.

The first bag has 1 red marble and 2 blue marbles, so the probabilities for the first pick are:

$$P(\text{red}) = \frac{1}{1+2} = \frac{1}{3}$$

$$P(\text{blue}) = \frac{2}{1+2} = \frac{2}{3}$$

The second bag has 4 red marbles, 2 blue marbles, and 2 green marbles, so the probabilities for the second pick are:

$$P(\text{red}) = \frac{4}{4+2+2} = \frac{4}{8} = \frac{1}{2}$$

$$P(\text{blue}) = \frac{2}{4+2+2} = \frac{2}{8} = \frac{1}{4}$$

$$P(\text{green}) = \frac{2}{4+2+2} = \frac{2}{8} = \frac{1}{4}$$

2

Create a tree diagram, writing probabilities on the appropriate branches.

The first branch shows the first pick. The second branch shows the second pick.

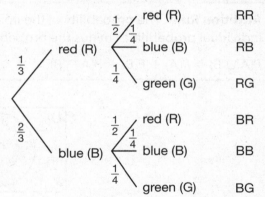

3

Determine the probability of choosing a blue marble followed by a red marble (BR).

The marbles are from different bags. The marble chosen from one bag does not affect the marble chosen from the other bag. So, the events are independent. Multiply the probabilities.

▶ $P(\text{BR}) = P(\text{blue first}) \cdot P(\text{red second})$

$= \frac{2}{3} \cdot \frac{1}{2} = \frac{2}{6} = \frac{1}{3}$

DISCUSS

The tree diagram shows a sample space with 6 possible outcomes. Why isn't $P(\text{BR})$ equal to $\frac{1}{6}$?

The Addition Rule

UNDERSTAND If two events cannot happen together, they are **mutually exclusive events**. The probability of either of two mutually exclusive events occurring is equal to the sum of their individual probabilities. For example, suppose you toss a standard number cube. The result could be a 4, and the result could be a 5, but the result cannot be both a 4 and a 5 at the same time, as shown by the Venn diagram below. They are mutually exclusive events. So, the probability of tossing a 4 or a 5 is:

$$P(4 \text{ or } 5) = P(4) + P(5) = \frac{1}{6} + \frac{1}{6} = \frac{2}{6} = \frac{1}{3}$$

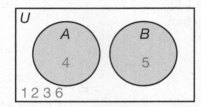

Events that are not mutually exclusive may have outcomes in common. For example, suppose you toss a number cube. Consider the event of a toss resulting in an odd number and the event of a toss resulting in a number greater than 4. Those events overlap, because 5 is a member of both sets, as shown by the Venn diagram below. So, to find the probability of tossing an odd number or a number greater than 4, apply the Addition Rule.

> **Addition Rule:** The probability of the union of two subsets is equal to the sum of their individual probabilities minus the probability of the intersection of the subsets.
>
> $$P(A \cup B) = P(A) + P(B) - P(A \cap B)$$

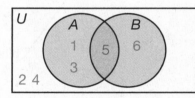

$$P(\text{odd or} >4) = P(\text{odd}) + P(>4) - P(\text{odd and} >4) = \frac{3}{6} + \frac{2}{6} - \frac{1}{6} = \frac{5}{6} - \frac{1}{6} = \frac{4}{6} = \frac{2}{3}$$

Consider the events as sums of the probabilities of mutually exclusive events.

$$P(\text{odd}) = P(1 \text{ or } 3 \text{ or } 5) = P(1) + P(3) + P(5)$$

$$P(>4) = P(5 \text{ or } 6) = P(5) + P(6)$$

$$P(\text{odd and} >4) = P(5)$$

$$P(\text{odd}) + P(>4) - P(\text{odd and} >4) = P(1) + P(3) + P(5) + P(5) + P(6) - P(5)$$

$$P(\text{odd}) + P(>4) - P(\text{odd and} >4) = P(1) + P(3) + P(5) + P(6) = P(\text{odd or} >4)$$

⌐€ Connect

The two-way frequency table shows the results of a survey of 11th-grade and 12th-grade students at Brookdale High School. Students were asked if they had a job last summer.

	Had Summer Job (S)	No Summer Job (N)
11th Grade (E)	18	22
12th Grade (T)	30	10

Use the Addition Rule to find $P(S \cup T)$. What does this probability represent?

1

Write the Addition Rule, using sets S and T.

$P(S \cup T) = P(S) + P(T) - P(S \cap T)$

2

Find the probabilities for the sets and their intersection.

The total number of students surveyed was: $18 + 22 + 30 + 10 = 80$

Consider the S column and the T row.

$P(S) = \dfrac{18 + 30}{80} = \dfrac{48}{80} = 0.6$

$P(T) = \dfrac{30 + 10}{80} = \dfrac{40}{80} = 0.5$

$P(S \cap T) = \dfrac{30}{80} = 0.375$

This could be represented in a Venn diagram as follows:

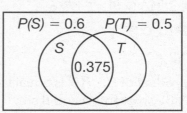

3

Substitute the probabilities into the Addition Rule.

$P(S \cup T) = P(S) + P(T) - P(S \cap T)$

▶ $P(S \cup T) = 0.6 + 0.5 - 0.375 = 0.725$

This means that if you chose a student at random from a list of 11th- and 12th-grade students, you would have a 72.5% chance of selecting a student who is either a 12th-grade student or who had a summer job (or both).

TRY

Use the Addition Rule to find $P(N \cup E)$.

EXAMPLE A This Venn diagram shows the probabilities for events A and B, their intersection, and the complement of their union. Are events A and B independent events?

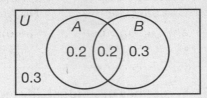

1

Choose a rule to use to determine if events A and B are independent.

If A and B are independent events, then $P(A)P(B) = P(A \cap B)$.

2

Identify or determine the necessary probabilities.

The overlap shows the intersection of A and B.

So, $P(A \cap B) = 0.2$.

$P(A)$ and $P(B)$ refer to the whole circles, including the intersection.

Add together the probabilities within circle A.

$P(A) = 0.2 + 0.2 = 0.4$

Add together the probabilities within circle B.

$P(B) = 0.2 + 0.3 = 0.5$

3

Apply the Multiplication Rule for Independent Events.

$P(A)P(B) \overset{?}{=} P(A \cap B)$

$(0.5)(0.4) \overset{?}{=} 0.2$

$0.2 = 0.2$ ✓

▶ The product of $P(A)P(B)$ is equal to $P(A \cap B)$, so events A and B are independent events.

 TRY

Events C and D in the Venn diagram are independent events. Write the missing probabilities in the blanks of the Venn diagram.

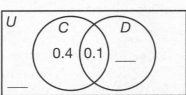

EXAMPLE B An optional workshop to improve players' basketball skills was held for varsity players in the county. One month after the workshop, the organization that conducted it collected data about players who did and did not attend the workshop to see if any had improved their field goal percentages during games. The data are recorded in the table. Determine if attending the workshop and improving field goal percentages are independent events.

	Attended	Did Not Attend	Total
Improved	44	6	50
Did Not Improve	18	32	50
Total	62	38	100

1

Find the probability that a local player chosen at random attended the workshop and showed improvement.

$$P(\text{attended} \cap \text{improved}) = \frac{\text{athletes who attended and improved}}{\text{total number of athletes}} = \frac{44}{100} = 0.44$$

2

Find the probabilities for the marginal frequencies.

Find the probability that a local player attended the workshop.

$$P(\text{attended}) = \frac{\text{athletes who attended}}{\text{total number of athletes}} = \frac{62}{100} = 0.62$$

Find the probability that a local player improved.

$$P(\text{improved}) = \frac{\text{athletes who improved}}{\text{total number of athletes}} = \frac{50}{100} = 0.5$$

3

Use the Multiplication Rule to determine if the events are independent or not.

$P(\text{attended})P(\text{improved}) \stackrel{?}{=} P(\text{attended} \cap \text{improved})$

$(0.62)(0.5) \stackrel{?}{=} 0.44$

$0.31 \neq 0.44$

▶ Attending the workshop and improving field goal percentage are not independent events.

DISCUSS

Does it make sense that whether or not a player improved would depend on attending the workshop?

Practice

For questions 1–4, events *A* and *B* (and *C*, if given) are independent events. Their probabilities are given below. Find the probability requested.

1. $P(A) = \frac{1}{2}$, $P(B) = \frac{1}{2}$

   $P(A \cap B) = $ _____

2. $P(A) = 0.7$, $P(B) = 0.3$

   $P(A \cap B) = $ _____

3. $P(A) = 0.3$, $P(B) = 0.2$

   $P(A \cap B) = $ _____

4. $P(A) = \frac{3}{4}$, $P(B) = \frac{1}{3}$, $P(C) = \frac{1}{2}$

   $P(A \cap B \cap C) = $ _____

For questions 5 and 6, events *A* and *B* are overlapping events. Their probabilities are given below. Find the probability asked for.

5. $P(A) = 0.3$, $P(B) = 0.2$, $P(A \cap B) = 0.1$

   $P(A \cup B) = $ _____

6. $P(A) = \frac{1}{2}$, $P(B) = \frac{2}{3}$, $P(A \cap B) = \frac{1}{3}$

   $P(A \cup B) = $ _____

> REMEMBER ∪ is the union of the sets, and ∩ is the intersection of the sets.

Find *P*(*A* ∪ *B*) given the probabilities in the Venn diagrams.

7. $P(A) = 0.6$ $P(B) = 0.5$

   A   0.25   B

   $P(A \cup B) = $ _____

8.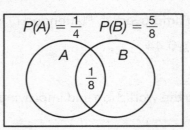

   $P(A) = \frac{1}{4}$ $P(B) = \frac{5}{8}$

   A $\frac{1}{8}$ B

   $P(A \cup B) = $ _____

Use the tree diagram and the information below for questions 9–13.

Mei-lin has two bags of colored tiles. She will select one tile from the first bag and then select one tile from the second bag. The tree diagram shows the probability for each possible outcome.

	First Bag	Second Bag	Outcome

$\frac{1}{4}$ — blue (B)

$\frac{1}{6}$ / $\frac{1}{2}$ blue (B)   BB

green (G)   BG

$\frac{1}{3}$ yellow (Y)   BY

$\frac{3}{4}$ — yellow (Y)

$\frac{1}{6}$ / $\frac{1}{2}$ blue (B)   YB

green (G)   YG

$\frac{1}{3}$ yellow (Y)   YY

9. What is the sample space for the experiment? _____

10. Are all of the outcomes equally likely? How do you know?

_____

11. What is the probability of selecting a blue tile first and a green tile second? _____

12. What is the probability of selecting two yellow tiles? _____

13. One outcome above has a probability of $\frac{1}{12}$. Which outcome is it? _____

Determine whether or not events C and D are independent events.

14.

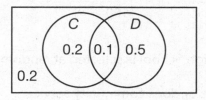

0.2 | 0.1 | 0.5

0.2

$P(C) =$ _____ $P(D) =$ _____

$P(C)P(D) \stackrel{?}{=} P(C \cap D)$

_____

Events C and D _____ independent.

15.

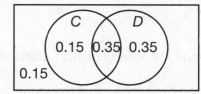

0.15 | 0.35 | 0.35

0.15

$P(C) =$ _____ $P(D) =$ _____

$P(C)P(D) \stackrel{?}{=} P(C \cap D)$

_____

Events C and D _____ independent.

Use the diagram below for questions 16–19.

A carnival game has players throw table tennis balls into buckets sitting on a platform. If a ball lands in the big bucket (*B*), they win 2 tokens. If a ball lands in the small bucket (*S*), they win 5 tokens. Give your answers as percents rounded to the nearest tenth.

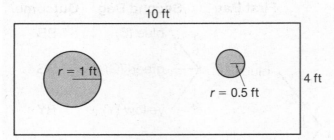

16. Find the probability of winning exactly two tokens on a single throw. _____

17. Find the probability of winning five tokens on a single throw. _____

18. Are the events *B* and *S* mutually exclusive?

_____

19. Find the probability of winning any tokens on a single throw. _____

Use the two-way frequency table and information below for questions 20 and 21.

The two-way frequency table shows the results of a survey of 11th-grade and 12th-grade students at Hamilton High School. Students were asked if they do community service.

	Does Community Service (C)	No Community Service (N)	Total
11th Grade (E)	24	12	36
12th Grade (T)	16	8	24
Total	40	20	60

20. Suppose an 11th-grade or 12th-grade student at Hamilton High School is selected at random.

What is the probability that the student is either in 11th grade or does community service (or both)?

_____

What is the probability that the student is either in 12th grade or does community service (or both)?

_____

21. **SHOW** Are the events "does community service" and "11th grade" independent? Explain your reasoning.

_____

_____

_____

22. **CREATE** Shelley will spin three spinners. The first spinner has two congruent sectors, one red and one blue. The second spinner has four congruent sectors: one red, two blue, and one yellow. The third spinner has nine congruent sectors, three of which are red and the rest of which are blue. Create a tree diagram to represent all the possible outcomes for this experiment. Label the probabilities on each branch. Then determine the probability of spinning blue on all three spinners.

_____

_____

UNDERSTAND A **conditional probability** is the probability that an event will occur given that one or more events have occurred. You can write the conditional probability of event A happening assuming event B has occurred as $P(A \mid B)$. This is read as the probability of "A given B." The conditional probability $P(A \mid B)$ is equal to the joint probability for A and B divided by the marginal probability of B.

$$P(A \mid B) = \frac{P(A \cap B)}{P(B)}$$

UNDERSTAND Conditional probability is not the same thing as compound probability. Suppose you toss two coins—two independent events. The sample space is {HH, HT, TH, TT}. The compound probability that both coins will land on heads is:

$$P\text{ (heads first} \cap \text{heads second)} = P\text{(heads first)} \cdot P\text{(heads second)} = \frac{1}{2} \cdot \frac{1}{2} = \frac{1}{4}$$

Suppose you already tossed the first coin and you already know that it landed on heads. The probability of both coins landing on heads is now different. Given that the first coin toss resulted in heads, there are only two possible outcomes now, {HH, HT}. So, the probability of getting {HH} is now $\frac{1}{2}$.

$$P\text{(heads second} \mid \text{heads first)} = \frac{P\text{(heads second} \cap \text{heads first)}}{P\text{(heads first)}} = \frac{\frac{1}{2} \cdot \frac{1}{2}}{\frac{1}{2}} = \frac{\frac{1}{4}}{\frac{1}{2}} = \frac{1}{2}$$

Notice that the probability of P(heads second | heads first) is the same as P(heads second). If events A and B are independent, then $P(A$ given $B) = P(A)$ and $P(B$ given $A) = P(B)$. Remember that for independent events $P(A \cap B) = P(B \cap A) = P(A)P(B)$.

$$P(A \mid B) = \frac{P(A \cap B)}{P(B)} = \frac{P(A)P(B)}{P(B)} = P(A) \qquad P(B \mid A) = \frac{P(B \cap A)}{P(A)} = \frac{P(B)P(A)}{P(A)} = P(B)$$

UNDERSTAND You can use conditional probability to find a compound probability.

> **Multiplication Rule:** The probability of the intersection of two subsets is equal to the product of the probability of one event and the conditional probability of the other event given the first event.
>
> $$P(A \text{ and } B) = P(A) \cdot P(B \mid A) = P(B) \cdot P(A \mid B)$$

Imagine drawing two marbles without replacement from a bag with 5 red marbles and 4 blue marbles. The probability of drawing a red marble on the first draw is $P\text{(red first)} = \frac{5}{9}$. The probability of drawing a second red marble, after the first was drawn, is $P\text{(red second} \mid \text{red first)} = \frac{4}{8} = \frac{1}{2}$. Use the Multiplication Rule to find the probability of drawing a red marble on both draws.

$$P\text{(red first and red second)} = P\text{(red first)} \cdot P\text{(red second} \mid \text{red first)} = \frac{5}{9} \cdot \frac{1}{2} = \frac{5}{18}$$

⊆ Connect

Students responding to a poll were asked whether they were for or against or had no opinion about a proposal to increase funding for the school's football program.

What is the probability that a randomly selected student at the school would be for the proposal given that the student was a girl?

	For (F)	Against (A)	No Opinion (N)	Total
Boys (B)	40	5	10	55
Girls (G)	10	30	5	45
Total	50	35	15	100

1

Determine which parts of the table must be considered.

The question asks for $P(F \mid G)$. It is given that the student is a girl, so look in the Girls (G) row. Find the cell that represents For (F) in that row.

2

Determine $P(F \mid G)$.

$$P(F \mid G) = \frac{P(F \cap G)}{P(G)}$$

$$= \frac{\frac{10}{100}}{\frac{45}{100}}$$

$$= \frac{10}{100} \cdot \frac{100}{45}$$

$$= \frac{10}{45} = \frac{2}{9} = 0.222\ldots$$

▶ Given that the student randomly selected is a girl, the probability that she is for the proposal is about 22%.

What is the probability that a randomly selected student at the school would be a boy, given that the student was for the proposal?

1

Determine which parts of the table must be considered.

The condition is that the person selected was for the proposal. So, we only need to consider the For (F) column. The total in that column is 50. Find the cell that represents Boys (B) in that column. The value in that cell is 40.

2

Determine $P(B \mid F)$.

The marginal frequency shows that 50 people are for the proposal. 40 of those people are boys, so

$$P(B \mid F) = \frac{40}{50} = 0.8$$

▶ Given that the student randomly selected is for the proposal, the probability that the student is a boy is 80%.

⇨ **TRY**

What is the probability that a randomly selected student at the school would have no opinion about the proposal, given that the student was a boy?

EXAMPLE A This Venn diagram shows the intersection of two sets. Set *A* shows the number of 10th-grade students surveyed, and set *B* shows the number of high school students surveyed who have computers at home. Show which parts of the Venn diagram can be used to calculate $P(A \mid B)$. Then find that probability and explain what it represents in the problem.

U A 20   15 B 45   10

1

Determine which parts of the table must be considered.

$P(A \mid B)$ means the probability of *A* given *B*.

Since *B* is given, only values within the circle for *B* may be considered. Regions outside *B* must be ignored. The region "*A* given *B*" refers to the parts of region *A* that are also part of region *B*, in other words, the overlap or intersection.

The Venn diagram below shows which parts must be considered.

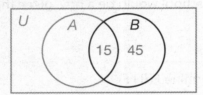

2

Determine $P(A \mid B)$ and explain what it represents.

Divide the joint frequency for *A* and *B* by the marginal probability of *B*.

$$P(A \mid B) = \frac{P(A \cap B)}{P(B)}$$

$$= \frac{15}{15 + 45}$$

$$= \frac{15}{60}$$

$$= \frac{1}{4}$$

▶ Given that a student selected at random has a computer at home, the probability that the student is in 10th grade is $\frac{1}{4}$.

DISCUSS

Is $P(B \mid A) = P(A \mid B)$ for this situation? Why or why not?

EXAMPLE B Brenna asked 100 shoppers at a clothing store if they bought a coat that day and if they bought a shirt that day. The results of the survey are shown on the right.

Are the events buying a coat and buying a shirt independent events?

	Bought a Coat	No Coat
Bought a Shirt	3	12
No Shirt	17	68

1

Make a plan.

Let C = bought a coat.

Let S = bought a shirt.

If $P(C \mid S) = P(C)$, then C and S are independent events.

Find the marginal frequencies for the table by extending it, as shown below.

	Bought a Coat	No Coat	Total
Bought a Shirt	3	12	15
No Shirt	17	68	85
Total	20	80	100

2

Find $P(C \mid S)$.

Find the probability of buying a coat and a shirt.

$P(C \cap S) = \frac{3}{100} = 0.03$

Find the probability of buying a shirt.

$P(S) = \frac{15}{100} = 0.15$

Find the probability of buying a coat, given that you bought a coat.

$P(C \mid S) = \frac{P(C \cap S)}{P(S)}$

$= \frac{0.03}{0.15}$

$= 0.2$

3

Find $P(C)$ and compare.

Find the probability of buying a coat.

$P(C) = \frac{20}{100} = 0.2$

▶ $P(C \mid S) = 0.2$ and $P(C) = 0.2$ also. So, buying a coat and buying a shirt are independent events.

DISCUSS

Could you also show that events C and S are independent by proving that $P(S \mid C) = P(S)$? Explain and show your work.

EXAMPLE C Antoine made 24 cheese sandwiches for a family picnic. For each sandwich, he used one kind of bread and one kind of cheese. The tree diagram shows the probability of choosing each sandwich combination.

Suppose Antoine's cousin is the first person to choose a sandwich. He chooses a sandwich with wheat bread but does not pay attention to what cheese is inside. What is the probability that the cousin chooses a sandwich with cheddar cheese?

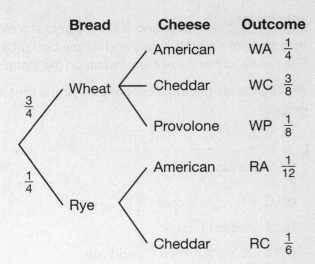

Bread	Cheese	Outcome	
	American	WA	$\frac{1}{4}$
Wheat	Cheddar	WC	$\frac{3}{8}$
	Provolone	WP	$\frac{1}{8}$
	American	RA	$\frac{1}{12}$
Rye			
	Cheddar	RC	$\frac{1}{6}$

1 Determine what probability to find.

Let W represents the set of sandwiches made with wheat bread.

Let C represent the set of sandwiches made with cheddar.

The question asks for $P(C \mid W)$.

2 Calculate $P(C \mid W)$.

The tree diagram shows that
$P(C \cap W) = \frac{3}{8}$ and $P(W) = \frac{3}{4}$.

$P(C \mid W) = \dfrac{P(C \cap W)}{P(W)}$

$= \dfrac{\frac{3}{8}}{\frac{3}{4}}$

$= \dfrac{3}{8} \cdot \dfrac{4}{3}$

$= \dfrac{12}{24}$

$= \dfrac{1}{2}$

▶ Given that Antoine's cousin chose a sandwich with wheat bread, the probability that the sandwich had cheddar cheese is $\frac{1}{2}$.

TRY

If Antoine's cousin had chosen a sandwich with rye bread instead, would the probability of choosing a sandwich with cheddar cheese have been the same or different? If different, identify the new probability.

Problem Solving

A total of 90 students (30 students each in grades 10, 11, and 12) at Davis High School were asked if they own smartphones. Of those surveyed, 8 students in 10th grade, 12 students in 11th grade, and 13 students in 12th grade own smartphones. Is owning a smartphone independent of grade level?

PLAN

Create a _____ table to show the survey results.

If smartphone owners make up set S and students in particular grades make up sets G_{10}, G_{11} and G_{12}, determine if $P(S \mid G) = P(S)$.

SOLVE

The problem states that the total number of students surveyed in each grade was 30. Write that as the total for each grade-level row. Fill in the rest of the table.

	Smartphone (S)	No Smartphone (N)	Total
10th Grade (G_{10})	8		
11th Grade (G_{11})			
12th Grade (G_{12})			
Total			90

Determine if $P(S \mid G_{10}) = P(S)$.

$P(S \cap G_{10}) = \dfrac{8}{90} = $ _____

$P(G_{10}) = \dfrac{\boxed{}}{90} = $ _____

$P(S \mid G_{10}) = \dfrac{P(S \cap G_{10})}{P(G_{10})} = \dfrac{\boxed{}}{\boxed{}} = $ _____

$P(S) = \dfrac{\boxed{}}{90} = $ _____

Does $P(S \mid G_{10}) = P(S)$? _____

CHECK

Verify that the $P(S \mid G_{11}) \neq P(S)$ and $P(S \mid G_{12}) \neq P(S)$.

$P(S \mid G_{11}) = $ _____ $P(S \mid G_{12}) = $ _____

▶ So, owning a smartphone _____ independent of grade level.

Practice

For questions 1 and 2, a white number cube and a red number cube, each with faces numbered 1 to 6, are tossed at the same time.

1. What is the probability of both cubes landing on 4 if you know that the white cube landed on 4?
   _____

2. What is the probability of both cubes landing on even numbers if you know that the white cube landed on 4? _____

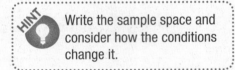

REMEMBER $P(A \mid B) = \dfrac{P(A \cap B)}{P(B)}$

For questions 3 and 4, a quarter, a nickel, and a penny are all tossed at the same time.

3. What is the probability of all 3 coins landing on heads if you know that the quarter and the nickel landed on heads? _____

4. What is the probability of all 3 coins landing on heads if all you know is that the quarter landed on heads? _____

HINT Write the sample space and consider how the conditions change it.

For questions 5–7, a bag contains 3 green marbles and 7 yellow marbles. Parker will draw a marble at random and then draw a second marble without replacing the first marble.

5. Are the events of drawing the first marble and the second marble dependent or independent? Explain.

   _____

   _____

6. Use the general Multiplication Rule to find the probability of drawing a green marble followed by a yellow marble. _____

7. Find P(yellow first and yellow second). _____

Choose the best answer.

8. The Venn diagram shows the number of possible outcomes in sets A and B and their intersection. What is $P(B \mid A)$ for this Venn diagram?

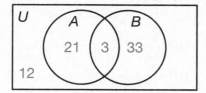

   A. $\frac{1}{12}$

   B. $\frac{1}{11}$

   C. $\frac{1}{8}$

   D. $\frac{1}{7}$

9. The Venn diagram shows the number of possible outcomes in sets M and N and their intersection. What is $P(N \mid M)$ for this Venn diagram?

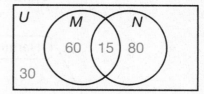

   A. 0.1875

   B. 0.2

   C. 0.25

   D. 0.5

10. The two-way frequency table below shows the quiz scores of students in the same biology class and whether or not each student studied for the quiz.

	Score ≥ 90	Score < 90
Studied	12	3
Did Not Study	1	14

What is the probability that a randomly selected student from the class had a score less than 90, given that the student did not study for the quiz?

   A. $\frac{7}{15}$ **C.** $\frac{4}{5}$

   B. $\frac{17}{30}$ **D.** $\frac{14}{15}$

11. The two-way frequency table below shows the number of boys and girls who are working on the school play and whether they are performers or stage-crew members.

	Performer	Stage Crew
Boys	14	18
Girls	21	7

What is the chance that a randomly selected student working on the school play is a boy, given that the student is a member of the stage crew?

   A. 30%   **C.** 72%

   B. 56.25%   **D.** 78.26%

Use the information and tree diagram below for questions 12 and 13.

There were 50 boxed lunches prepared for a school meeting. Each boxed lunch contains either a ham sandwich or a turkey sandwich and either an apple, a banana, or a pear. Alice is the first to choose a boxed lunch. She chooses a box marked "ham sandwich," but she does not pay attention to which type of fruit is inside.

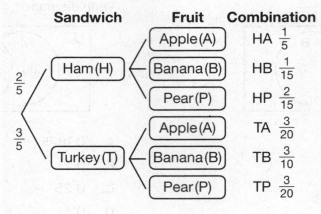

| Sandwich | Fruit | Combination |

12. Given that she chose a ham sandwich, what is the probability that she chose a boxed lunch with

    an apple? _____

    with a banana? _____

    with a pear? _____

13. Compare $P(A \mid T)$ to $P(P \mid T)$.

    _____

    _____

Choose the best answer.

14. Events A and B are dependent events. Which of the following is true?

    A. $P(A \mid B) = P(A)$

    B. $P(A \mid B) = \dfrac{P(A \cap B)}{P(A)}$

    C. $P(A \text{ and } B) = P(A) \cdot P(B \mid A)$

    D. $P(A \text{ and } B) = P(A) \cdot P(B)$

15. A bag contains 2 blue, 5 yellow, and 1 black tile. What is the probability of drawing a blue tile followed by a black tile if the first tile drawn is **not** replaced?

    A. $\dfrac{1}{32}$

    B. $\dfrac{1}{28}$

    C. $\dfrac{1}{12}$

    D. $\dfrac{1}{8}$

Use the two-way frequency table and information below for questions 16–19.

A poll asked voters of different ages if they were for or against a proposal to build a new public library.

Ages	For	Against	No Opinion	Total
18–39	30	42	3	75
40–59	80	55	5	140
60 and over	120	13	2	135
Total	230	110	10	350

16. What is the chance that a voter has no opinion on the proposal, given that the voter is younger than 40 years old?

_____

17. What is the probability that a voter is for the proposal, given that he or she is 60 or over?

_____

18. What is the probability that a voter who is against the proposal is age 40–59?

_____

19. Is a voter's opinion about the proposed new library independent of age? How do you know?

_____

_____

Use the information below for questions 20 and 21.

A total of 60 students in grades 10, 11, and 12 were surveyed and asked whether or not they play on a sports team. Of those surveyed, 20 out of 30 tenth-grade students play on a team, 8 out of 12 eleventh-grade students play on a team, and 12 out of 18 twelfth-grade students play on a team.

20. **CREATE** Enter the above information in the two-way frequency table. List the joint and marginal frequencies.

	Play on Team(s)	No Team	Total
10th Grade			
11th Grade			
12th Grade			
Total			

21. **JUSTIFY** Is participation in team sports independent of grade level? Justify your answer.

_____

_____

_____

_____

LESSON 35 Using Probability to Make Decisions

UNDERSTAND In a fair game, each player is equally likely to win. In a fair selection process, each person is equally likely to be chosen. Fairness can be determined by examining probabilities and by comparing the probabilities of winning or being selected for each player. When not playing against others, fairness can be determined by comparing your probability of winning to your probability of losing. For example, flipping a coin is a fair way to decide between two things since the probability of getting heads is equal to the probability of getting tails.

You can also use probabilities to evaluate effectiveness, to decide on problem-solving strategies, or to make an educated decision about a problem. Inventors and companies test their products for effectiveness by gathering and analyzing data in order to make informed decisions. The quality of a test can be evaluated by looking at the relative number of **false positive** and **false negative** results.

UNDERSTAND If a game or process is fair, this does not mean that, in any given number of trials, the results, or **experimental probability**, will directly match the **theoretical probability**. For example, it is possible (though very unlikely) to flip a coin and get heads 10 times in a row. However, if the experiment is repeated many times, there will be roughly the same number of heads as tails. In general, the larger the number of **trials**, the closer the experimental probability will be to the theoretical probability.

A **simulation** is a representative re-creation of a situation or an event. This can sometimes be done by using probabilities. For example, imagine you are in a group of 5 people and one of you will be chosen at random to win a prize. Each person in the group has the same probability of being chosen, $\frac{1}{5}$. You could create a simulation using a spinner that is divided into 5 equal sections, where each section represents a group member. Each time you spin the spinner, the trial will simulate a result. Another way to simulate the situation would be to assign each person a number from 1 to 5 and roll a number cube. If the number cube lands on 6, you would disregard that trial and roll again.

For situations that are not easily simulated using coins, dice, or spinners, you can use random numbers to create simulations. The Random Digits Math Tool on p. 343 has columns of single digits from 0 to 9 arranged in no particular order. You can also use your calculator to generate random numbers. These digits can be used to simulate most situations involving chance behavior. Here are some rules for using random digits for a simulation.

1) Assign numbers to the possible outcomes based on their probabilities. For example, to simulate flipping a coin, assign even numbers to heads and odd numbers to tails.

2) Determine how many digits you will select at a time. For example, to simulate choosing one out of one hundred people, you would need to read every two digits as a number, such as 99 or 05. (The hundredth person could be 00.)

3) Determine which values you will ignore. These are values that are larger than your biggest value or numbers that do not make sense. For example, to simulate rolling a number cube, ignore the digits 7, 8, 9, and 0.

⚡ Connect

Mark and Jorge are playing a game in which they roll two number cubes and add the result. If the sum is odd, Mark gets a point. If the sum is even, Jorge gets a point. Evaluate the game to determine if it is fair. Then, use column 1 of the Random Digits Math Tool on p. 343 to simulate a game with six rolls and see who wins.

1

Make a table to find all of the possible sums.

Count the squares with an odd sum.

+	1	2	3	4	5	6
1	2	3	4	5	6	7
2	3	4	5	6	7	8
3	4	5	6	7	8	9
4	5	6	7	8	9	10
5	6	7	8	9	10	11
6	7	8	9	10	11	12

2

Determine if the game is fair.

Find the probability of getting an odd or an even sum.

There are 18 odd sums out of 36.

$P(\text{odd}) = \frac{18}{36} = \frac{1}{2}$

There are 18 even sums out of 36.

$P(\text{even}) = \frac{18}{36} = \frac{1}{2}$

$P(\text{odd}) = P(\text{even})$

▶ Since both players have the same probability of winning a point on any given roll, the game is fair.

3

Use random numbers to simulate a game with six rolls.

Each turn consist of rolling two number cubes with numbers from 1 to 6. So, each digit will represent a single roll and the digits 0, 7, 8, and 9 will be ignored. Here are the first 20 numbers from column 1 of the Random Digits Math Tool.

6, 0, 2, 9, 3, 1, 6, 5, 8, 2, 3, 7, 0, 1, 4, 3, 6, 7, 9, 2

First, cross out the excluded numbers.

6, Ø, 2, 9̸, 3, 1, 6, 5, 8̸, 2, 3, 7̸, Ø, 1, 4, 3, 6, 7̸, 9̸, 2

Then, take the remaining numbers in pairs and find their sums. Stop when you have 6 sums.

$6 + 2 = 8$ $3 + 1 = 4$ $6 + 5 = 11$ $2 + 3 = 5$ $1 + 4 = 5$ $3 + 6 = 9$

The random numbers generated 2 even sums and 4 odd sums.

▶ Jorge wins 2 points and Mark wins 4 points, so Mark wins the game in this simulation.

TRY ▷

Simulate another game with six rolls using row 18 of the Random Digits Math Tool. Are the results the same or different? Why?

EXAMPLE A Celiac disease is a disorder of the digestive system that causes discomfort and other symptoms when a person eats certain grains. A doctor is developing a blood test for determining if a patient has celiac disease. The doctor gave the test to 1,000 volunteers, and then confirmed the results via endoscopy. The results are shown in the table below.

Correct Positive	194	Correct Negative	776
False Positive	2	False Negative	28

Evaluate the data and determine whether the new test is reliable. Compare it to a test currently used, which has a false negative rate of about 3.5% and a false positive rate of about 0.5%.

1 Find the probability for a correct result and a false result.

The total number of patients is 1,000.

The total number of correct results is 194 + 776 = 970.

$P(\text{correct}) = \frac{970}{1000} = 97\%$

The total number of false results is 2 + 28 = 30.

$P(\text{false}) = \frac{30}{1000} = 3\%$

2 Find the probability for a false positive and a false negative.

The total number of patients is 1,000.

There were 2 false positive results.

$P(\text{false positive}) = \frac{2}{1000} = 0.2\%$

There were 28 false negative results.

$P(\text{false}) = \frac{28}{1000} = 2.8\%$

3 Compare the results to the current test and evaluate the new test.

The probability of a false positive, 0.2%, is less than the current test's false positive rate of 0.5%.

The probability of a false negative, 2.8%, is also less than the current test's false negative rate of 3.5%.

The overall accuracy rate of 97% is very high.

▶ The new test is generally reliable.

TRY

Another blood test for celiac disease was tested on 500 patients already known to have the disease. The results are shown in the table. Evaluate the data and determine whether the test is reliable.

Positive	412
Negative	88

EXAMPLE B A certain professional basketball player has a free throw average of 0.839. Use a calculator to generate random integers from 0 to 999 to simulate free throws. Generate 20 trials and find the experimental probability of making a basket. Then, compare it to the average.

1

Set the parameters of the simulation.

The player's average is 0.839, meaning that he makes free throws an average of 83.9% of the time, or 839 times out of 1,000. We are generating integers from 0 to 999, with a range of 1,000 numbers. The first 839 numbers, that is, numbers from 0 to 838, will be considered making the basket and any number from 839 to 999 will be considered a miss.

2

Prepare your calculator.

Choose a seed (a list of random numbers) by pressing 0 and then STO▸. From the home screen, press MATH and scroll to the right to access the **PRB** menu. Choose **1:rand** from the menu.

The screen should display 0 ⇒ rand. Press ENTER.

3

Generate random integers.

Press MATH and access the **PRB** menu again. Choose **5:randInt(** from the menu. Enter in the smallest number, 0, followed by a comma and then the largest number, 999, and a closing parenthesis.

The screen should display randint(0,999).

Each time you press ENTER, a random number will be generated. Let's say we get the following 20 numbers.

943, 900, 146, 514, 405, 733, 43, 339, 995, 200, 798, 951, 220, 369, 7, 935, 108, 6, 548, 855

4

Interpret the results of the simulation and compare probabilities.

Underline all of the numbers in the list that are between 0 and 838.

943, 900, <u>146</u>, <u>514</u>, <u>405</u>, <u>733</u>, <u>43</u>, <u>339</u>, 995, <u>200</u>, <u>798</u>, 951, <u>220</u>, <u>369</u>, <u>7</u>, 935, <u>108</u>, <u>6</u>, <u>548</u>, 855

In all, there were 14 goals and 6 misses out of 20 trials.

$P(\text{goal}) = \frac{16}{20} = 0.8$

▶ The experimental probability of 0.8 is close to but below the actual probability of 0.839. This is because we only did 20 trials in our simulation. If we generated more trials, the experimental results would most likely more closely match the actual average.

DISCUSS

Another player had a career free throw average of 0.8857. Would she beat the player described above in a shoot-off of 10 free throws?

Practice

Fill in the correct word or words to complete each sentence.

1.   A game is _____ if each player is equally likely to win.

2.   As the number of _____ increases, the experimental probability gets closer to the _____ probability.

3.   You can use random numbers to create a _____ for an event involving chance.

Solve.

4.   Orit and Amy are playing a game in which they roll two number cubes and multiply the results. If the product is even, Orit gets a point. If the product is odd, Amy gets a point. Is the game fair? If not, who has an advantage? Explain.

_____

_____

_____

5.   Harold will take a 10-question true/false quiz. In order to pass the quiz, he must get at least 7 questions right. Harold wants to know if random guessing is a good strategy for taking the quiz. How could you design a simulation to show the possible results of random guessing?

_____

_____

Carry out your simulation. Give the results and determine whether the guessing strategy is effective. Use both the theoretical and experimental probabilities in your explanation.

_____

_____

6.   There are 10 minutes remaining in a baseball game. The team is losing by 1 run, and the coach is trying to decide whether or not to put in his designated hitter. Out of 12 games this season where they were down by a single run and the hitter was put in, they won 5 and lost 7 games. Out of 8 games this season where they were down by a single run and the hitter was not put in, they won 3 and lost 5 games. Should the coach put in the designated hitter? Use probabilities to explain your answer.

_____

_____

_____

Solve.

7. A coin was flipped 10 times, then 100 times, then 1,000 times. The results are displayed in the table.

Total Flips	Heads	Tails
10	7	3
100	41	59
1,000	512	488

Is the coin most likely a fair coin or a weighted coin? Explain.

_____

_____

8. **SIMULATE** A certain baseball player had a batting average of 0.321. Begin with row 15 of the Random Digits Math Tool to simulate 10 at bats. Calculate the experimental probability of her getting a hit and compare it to the real batting average. Show your work.

9. **ANALYZE** Toxoplasmosis is an infection by a parasite in cats. A veterinarian is developing a test for the parasite. He administers the test to 100 cats whose infection status is known. The results of the tests are listed in the table below. Evaluate the test.

Correct Positive	63	Correct Negative	20
False Positive	8	False Negative	9

_____

_____

_____

Use the information below for questions 1–3.

$U = \{25, 30, 35, 40, 60, 70, 80\}$ $A = \{25, 40, 60, 70, 80\}$ $B = \{30, 40\}$

1. Find $A \cup B$.

_____

2. Find $A \cap B$.

_____

3. Find $\overline{A}$.

_____

Use set notation (e.g., ∪, ∩, ~) to describe the shaded portion of each Venn diagram.

4.

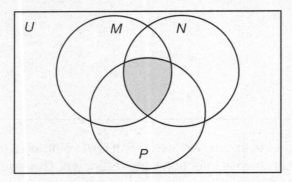

5.

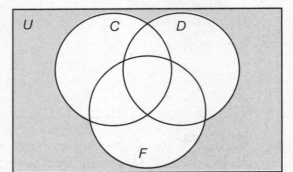

_____

Choose the best answer.

6. Event *B* is independent of event *A* if which of the following is true?

  A. $P(B \mid A) = P(A)$

  B. $P(B \mid A) = P(B)$

  C. $P(B \mid A) = P(A)P(B)$

  D. $P(B \mid A) = \dfrac{P(A \cap B)}{P(B)}$

7. Event *B* is independent of event *A* if which of the following is true?

  A. $P(A \cap B) = P(A)$

  B. $P(A \cap B) = P(B)$

  C. $P(A \cap B) = P(A)P(B)$

  D. $P(A \cap B) = \dfrac{P(A \cap B)}{P(B)}$

Each Venn diagram shows the probabilities for events Y and Z, their intersection, and the complement of their union. Determine whether or not events Y and Z are independent events. Fill in the blanks to show your work.

8.

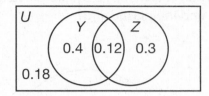

$P(Y) =$ _____

$P(Z) =$ _____

$P(Y)P(Z) \overset{?}{=} P(Y \cap Z)$

_____

Events Y and Z _____ independent.

9.

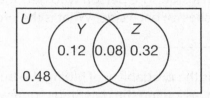

$P(Y) =$ _____

$P(Z) =$ _____

$P(Y)P(Z) \overset{?}{=} P(Y \cap Z)$

_____

Events Y and Z _____ independent.

Solve.

10. The spinner shown has a radius of 2 feet and is divided into unequal sections. The sector marked "30 tokens" has a central angle of 20°. The sector marked "25 tokens" has a central angle of 25°. What is the probability of winning at least 25 tokens on a given spin? Give your answer as a percent.

_____

Choose the best answer.

11. Events A and B are dependent events. Which of the following is equal to $P(A \text{ and } B)$?

A. $P(A) \cdot P(B \mid A)$

B. $P(A \mid B) \cdot P(B \mid A)$

C. $P(A)P(B)$

D. $\dfrac{P(A \cap B)}{P(B)}$

12. A bag contains 8 white tiles and 4 green tiles. Jenna will draw a tile and then, without replacing the first tile, draw a second tile. What is the probability that she will draw 2 white tiles?

A. $\dfrac{8}{33}$

B. $\dfrac{14}{33}$

C. $\dfrac{4}{9}$

D. $\dfrac{1}{2}$

Solve

13. A rectangular sheet cake for a party measures 1 foot by 2 feet by 3 inches and has a plastic ring hidden inside. The person who gets the ring wins a prize. Jordan cuts herself a square piece that is 3 inches on each side. What is the probability that she will find the plastic ring?

    _____

14. What is the probability of hitting the bull's-eye on the target shown, assuming the dart lands somewhere on the target? The target has a radius of 1 meter, and the bull's-eye has a radius of 10 centimeters.

    _____

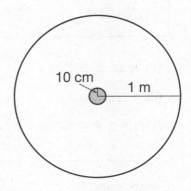

Use the information below for questions 15–17.

Sixty voters were asked which mayoral candidate they plan to vote for. Five Democrats said Walker, twelve Democrats said Wilson, and eight Democrats were undecided. Ten Republicans said Walker, four Republicans said Wilson, and eleven Republicans were undecided. Of voters who said they belonged to other political parties, one said Walker, one said Wilson, and eight were undecided.

15. Use the grid below to create a two-way frequency table for these data.

	Walker	Wilson	Undecided	Total
Democrats				
Republicans				
Other Party				
Total				

16. What is the probability that a randomly selected voter would say that he or she plans to vote for Walker?

    _____

17. What is the probability that a randomly selected voter would say that he or she plans to vote for Walker given that the voter is a Republican?

    _____

Calculate the combinations or permutations.

18. Han will play 7 pieces at his piano recital. In how many different orders can he play all 7 pieces? _____

19. Out of a group of 18 club members, 5 will be chosen for an advisory committee. How many committees are possible? _____

20. There are 10 members of the key club. They must elect a president, vice president, treasurer, and secretary. In how many different ways can they fill the positions? _____

Examine the situation.

21. A tetrahedron is a solid with four triangular faces. Cleo and Marvin are playing a game in which they roll a pair of tetrahedrons, each with the faces labeled 1, 2, 3, and 4. If the product of the numbers rolled is greater than 7, Cleo gets a point. Otherwise, Marvin gets a point. Explain why the game is not fair. Then, find a way that the game can be changed to make it fair.

_____

_____

_____

Use the two-way frequency table and information below for question 22.

Physical education teachers surveyed students to find out in which activity 10th-grade students most wanted to participate.

	Yoga (Y)	Baseball (BB)
Boys (B)	15	35
Girls (G)	40	10

22. If you chose a 10th-grade girl at random from the school, would you expect that the student would be more likely to want to do yoga or play baseball? Make a prediction just by looking at the table. Explain your thinking.

_____

Now, use conditional probabilities to show how accurate your prediction was.

_____

_____

Find P(A ∪ B) given the probabilities in the Venn diagrams.

23.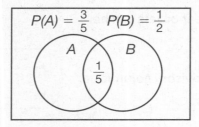

$P(A) = \frac{3}{5}$ $P(B) = \frac{1}{2}$

$P(A \cup B) = $ _____

24.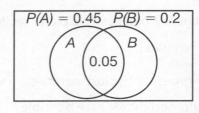

$P(A) = 0.45$ $P(B) = 0.2$

$P(A \cup B) = $ _____

Use the two-way frequency table and information below for questions 25 and 26.

Freshmen and sophomores had to sign up for either chorus or band as their music elective. The table shows which activity the freshmen and sophomores chose.

	Chorus (*C*)	Band (*B*)
Freshmen (*F*)	40	60
Sophomore (*S*)	72	28

25. What is the value of $P(C \cup F)$? What does this probability represent?

_____

_____

26. What is the value of $P(B \cup S)$? What does this probability represent?

_____

_____

Solve.

27. A new test for a genetic mutation was given to 1,000 subjects. This mutation occurs in about 4.2% of the population. The results of the test are shown in the table.

Positive result (mutation is present)	81
Negative result (mutation is absent)	919

Compare the experimental probability and the actual probability of a positive result. Is the test reliable? Explain.

_____

_____

_____

Use the two-way frequency table and information below for questions 28–30.

The table shows the number of sophomores, juniors, and seniors at Bennett High School who play one or more instruments and the number who play no instrument.

	Plays Instrument(s) (I)	No Instrument (N)	Total
Sophomore (SO)	16	24	40
Junior (J)	20	30	50
Senior (SE)	10	15	25
Total	46	69	115

28. What is the probability that a randomly selected student is a junior given that the student does not play an instrument? _____

29. Is "playing an instrument" independent of "year in school"? Use the Multiplication Rule to show that your answer is correct.

_____

_____

_____

30. **DEMONSTRATE** Demonstrate how you could also have used conditional probabilities to show that your answer to question 29 is correct.

_____

_____

_____

31. **SIMULATE** Shawn will take a 10-question multiple-choice quiz. Each question has 4 answer choices, and he must answer 6 questions correctly to pass the quiz. Shawn wants to know if guessing is a good strategy for taking the quiz. Using probability, determine how many he is likely to guess correctly and if guessing is a good strategy.

_____

_____

Use a row of the Random Digits Math Tool to create a simulation. Explain how many digits you will take at a time, what they will represent, and which, if any, will be excluded.

_____

_____

Now, carry out your simulation and give the results.

_____

What Do You Think?

For this activity, you will work in pairs or individually to survey your classmates. You will then use what you have learned about probability to analyze the data you have collected.

1. Think of a survey question you would like to ask your classmates. For example, you might want to ask your classmates which kind of movie or clothing or school lunch option they like best. Offer your classmates THREE choices for their answers. Write your question below:

   Which do you like best—_____, _____, or _____?

2. When your teacher tells you it is time, walk around and survey your classmates. Record the name of each student and their response in the appropriate column below.

Boys	Girls

   Why do you think it may be helpful to record each student's name along with his or her response?

   _____

3. Organize your data in a two-way frequency table using the grid below. Record the data for boys and girls in separate rows.

				Total
Boys (B)				
Girls (G)				
Total				

4. Use the table to answer these questions.

If you put the names of everyone present in class today in a hat and picked one, what would be the probability of selecting...

- a girl's name? _____

- the name of a student who said they liked _____ best? (Fill in a category.) _____

- either a boy's name or the name of a student who said they liked _____ best? _____

5. Look at the table. Suppose you randomly choose a girl in your class. What predictions can you make about what she is likely to like best and unlikely to like best.

_____

Use conditional probabilities to determine if your answer is correct or incorrect.

_____

_____

6. Suppose you randomly choose a boy in your class. What predictions can you make about what he is likely to like best and unlikely to like best.

_____

Use conditional probabilities to determine if your answer is correct or incorrect.

_____

_____

7. Based on your results, can you say that the categories you chose are independent of gender? Explain why or why not. Show work to back up your statement.

_____

What does this indicate about the relationship, if any, between your question and gender?

_____

Glossary

Addition Rule probability rule that states that the probability of the union of two events is equal to the sum of the probabilities of both of those events minus the probability of their intersection, or $P(A \cup B) = P(A) + P(B) - P(A \cap B)$ (Lesson 33)

angle a figure formed by two rays with the same endpoint (Lesson 1)

angle bisector a line or ray that divides an angle in half (Lesson 8)

angle of depression the angle formed by a horizontal line and the line of sight to an object below that line (Lesson 14)

angle of elevation the angle formed by a horizontal line and the line of sight to an object above that line (Lesson 14)

Angle-Angle Similarity (AA∼) Postulate mathematical law stating that if two angles of one triangle are congruent to two angles of another triangle, then the triangles are similar (Lesson 11)

Angle-Side-Angle (ASA) Theorem mathematical theorem stating that if two angles and the included side of one triangle are congruent to two angles and the included side of another triangle, then the triangles are congruent (Lesson 6)

apothem in a regular polygon, the shortest distance from the center of the polygon to its side (Lessons 14, 16)

arc an unbroken part of a circle (Lesson 25)

center of dilation a fixed point from which all points in a figure or graph are dilated, either moving away from or toward that point (Lesson 10)

center of rotation the point about which a figure is turned during a rotation (Lesson 4)

central angle an angle whose vertex is the center of a circle and whose rays contain radii of the circle (Lesson 25)

chord a line segment with endpoints on a circle (Lesson 24)

circle the set of all points in a plane that are equidistant from a point called the center (Lessons 4 , 16, 24)

circumcenter the point of concurrency of the three perpendicular bisectors of a triangle (Lesson 27)

circumference the distance around a circle (Lessons 16, 26)

circumscribed circle a circle that encompasses a polygon and passes through every vertex of that polygon (Lesson 27)

collinear line segments two or more line segments that lie on the same line (Lesson 2)

combination an arrangement in which the order of elements does not matter (Lesson 32)

complement (of a set) the set of all the elements in a universal set that are not include in a given subset (Lesson 30)

complementary angles two angles whose measures sum to 90° (Lesson 13)

compound event an event that consists of two or more simple events (Lesson 33)

concentric circles circles that lie in the same plane and have the same center (Lesson 25)

conditional probability the probability that an event will occur given that one or more events have occurred (Lesson 34)

cone a three-dimensional figure formed by a circular base and a curved surface rising to single point, called an apex (Lesson 17)

congruent equal in measure; having the same size and shape (Lesson 1)

construct to create or draw a geometric figure with tools such as a straightedge and compass; measuring of lengths or angles is not permitted (Lesson 8)

cosine (cos) the function that, for a given acute angle in a right triangle, yields the ratio of the adjacent leg to the hypotenuse (Lesson 12)

cross section a two-dimensional shape formed in a plane by slicing that plane through a three-dimensional object (Lesson 17)

cylinder a three-dimensional figure with two congruent, parallel circular bases (Lesson 17)

dependent events events in which the outcome of one event affects the outcome of the other event(s) (Lesson 33)

diameter a line segment that passes through the center of a circle and has both endpoints on that circle (Lessons 16, 24)

dilation a transformation that moves the points of a figure or graph either toward or away from a center of dilation, usually enlarging or reducing the figure (Lesson 10)

directrix a fixed line used to define a parabola; each point on a parabola is equidistant from a fixed line (the directrix) and a fixed point (the focus) (Lesson 22)

event a subset of the set of all possible outcomes (Lesson 30)

experimental probability the statistical results of an experiment or simulation; the ratio of the number of times an event occurs to the number of trials (Lesson 35)

factorial the product of all positive integers less than or equal to a given integer (Lesson 32)

false negative an incorrect result of a test that presents as failure when the test was actually a success (Lesson 35)

false positive an incorrect result of a test that presents as success when the test actually failed (Lesson 35)

focus a fixed point used to define a conic section; each point on a parabola is equidistant from a fixed point (the focus) and a fixed line (the directrix) (Lesson 22)

function a relation in which every input maps to exactly one output (Lesson 13)

geometric probability a probability involving the distribution of length, area, or volume for a geometric object under certain conditions (Lesson 31)

horizontal translation a slide of a figure in the right or left direction (Lesson 2)

hypotenuse the longest side of a right triangle; the side opposite the right angle (Lesson 12)

image the figure or graph resulting from a transformation (Lesson 1)

incenter the point of concurrency of the three angle bisectors of a triangle (Lesson 27)

independent events events in which the outcome of one event does not affect the outcome of the other event(s) (Lesson 33)

input the first value in an ordered pair for a function; the value that is entered into a function in order to produce the related output (Lesson 13)

inscribed angle an angle whose vertex is on the circle and whose rays contain chords of the circle (Lesson 25)

inscribed circle a circle that lies completely within a polygon and that is tangent to every side of the polygon (Lesson 27)

intercepted arc an arc on a circle whose points lie between the rays of a given angle (Lesson 25)

intersection (of sets) the set of all elements that are common to all of the given sets; denoted as ∩ (Lesson 30)

joint frequency a frequency in the body of a two-way frequency table (Lesson 31)

joint probability the probability that two events will occur at the same time (Lesson 31)

Law of Cosines mathematical law stating that, for a triangle with side lengths a, b, and c and angle C opposite side c, $c^2 = a^2 + b^2 - 2ab\cos C$ (Lesson 15)

Law of Sines mathematical law stating that $\frac{a}{\sin A} = \frac{b}{\sin B} = \frac{c}{\sin C}$, where a, b, and c are the lengths of the sides of a triangle and A, B, and C are their opposite angles (Lesson 15)

leg a side of a right triangle opposite one of the acute angles (Lesson 12)

line of reflection the line over which a figure or graph is flipped to produce a mirror image (Lesson 3)

line of symmetry a line over which a graph or figure can be reflected such that it maps back onto itself (Lesson 5)

line segment the part of a line that falls between two points on the line, which are the endpoints of the segment (Lessons 1, 2)

line symmetry characteristic of a graph or figure that can be reflected over a line to produce an identical figure or graph; also called *reflectional symmetry* (Lesson 5)

major arc an arc having a measure greater than 180° (Lesson 25)

marginal frequency an entry in the "Total" row or "Total" column of a two-way frequency table (Lesson 31)

midpoint the center point of a line segment, which divides the line segment into two segments of equal length (Lesson 21)

minor arc an arc having a measure less than 180° (Lesson 25)

Multiplication Rule probability rule that states that the probability of two events is equal to the product of the probability of one event times the conditional probability of the other event, given the first event occurred, or $P(A \cap B) = P(A) \cdot P(B \mid A)$ (Lesson 34)

Multiplication Rule for Independent Events probability rule that states that the probability of the intersection of two subsets composed of independent events is equal to the product of their probabilities, or $P(A \cap B) = P(A)P(B)$ (Lesson 33)

mutually exclusive events two events that cannot happen at the same time (Lesson 33)

outcome the result of performing a probability experiment (Lesson 30)

output the second value in an ordered pair for a function; the value that is produced when a function is evaluated for a given input (Lesson 13)

parabola the set of points equidistant from a point called the focus and a line called the directrix; a conic section resulting from the intersection of a cone and a plane that intersects its base (Lesson 22)

parallel line segments two or more line segments that lie on parallel lines (Lesson 2)

parallel lines lines that lie in the same plane but never intersect (Lesson 19)

partition to divide (Lesson 21)

permutation one of the ways a set of objects can be arranged when the order of the objects matters (Lesson 32)

perpendicular meeting at a right angle (Lesson 3)

perpendicular bisector a line that is perpendicular to a segment and that passes through the segment's midpoint (Lesson 8)

perpendicular lines lines that intersect to form right angles (Lesson 19)

point of concurrency a point at which three or more lines intersect (Lesson 27)

polyhedron a three-dimensional figure bounded by polygons, called faces (Lesson 17)

population the entire set of cases or individuals being studied or considered (Lesson 31)

preimage an original figure or graph that is transformed to form an image (Lesson 1)

prism a polyhedron with two congruent, parallel faces connected by parallelograms (Lesson 17)

probability the measure of the likelihood that an event will occur (Lesson 30)

pyramid a three-dimensional figure with one base that is a polygon and triangular faces that meet at a point, called an apex (Lesson 17)

Pythagorean Theorem mathematical theorem stating that for any right triangle with legs of length a and b and hypotenuse of length c, $a^2 + b^2 = c^2$ (Lesson 20)

radian (rad) a unit of angular measure; a circle measures 2π radians (Lesson 26)

radius a line segment with one endpoint at the center of a circle or sphere and the other endpoint on the circle or sphere (Lessons 16, 24)

reflection a transformation that flips a figure or graph over a line (Lesson 3)

reflectional symmetry see *line symmetry* (Lesson 5)

regular polygon a polygon in which all sides are congruent and all angles are congruent (Lesson 5, 10)

relative frequency the ratio of a frequency for a category to the total frequencies in a row, column, or table (Lesson 31)

rigid motion any transformation that preserves segment length and angle measure (Lesson 1)

rotation a transformation that turns a figure or graph around a point (Lesson 4)

rotational symmetry characteristic of a graph or figure that can be rotated by a measure of less than 360° to produce an identical figure or graph (Lesson 5)

sample a subset of a larger set called the population (Lesson 31)

sample space the set of all of the possible outcomes for an experiment (Lesson 30)

scale factor the ratio of the distances from the center of dilation to an image point and to its preimage point (Lesson 10)

secant line a line in the plane of a circle that intersects the circle at two points (Lesson 24)

sector a region of a circle that is bounded by two radii and their intercepted arc (Lesson 26)

semicircle half of a circle; an arc that measures 180° (Lesson 25)

set a collection of elements, which can be numbers, objects, letters, or figures, that have some characteristic in common (Lesson 30)

Side-Angle-Side (SAS) Postulate mathematical law stating that if two sides and the included angle of one triangle are congruent to two sides and the included angle of another triangle, then the triangles are congruent (Lesson 6)

Side-Angle-Side Similarity (SAS∼) Theorem mathematical theorem stating that if two sides of one triangle have lengths that are proportional to two sides of another triangle and the included angles of those sides are congruent, then the triangles are similar (Lesson 11)

Side-Side-Side (SSS) Postulate mathematical law stating that if three sides of one triangle are congruent to three sides of another triangle, then the triangles are congruent (Lesson 6)

Side-Side-Side Similarity (SSS∼) Theorem mathematical theorem stating that if three sides of one triangle have lengths that are proportional to three sides of another triangle, then the triangles are similar (Lesson 11)

similar having the same shape or extent (Lesson 10)

simulation a representative re-creation of a situation or an event (Lesson 35)

sine (sin) the function that, for a given acute angle in a right triangle, yields the ratio of the opposite leg to the hypotenuse (Lesson 12)

sphere the set of all points in space equidistant from a given point, called the center (Lesson 17)

subset a set in which every element is also contained in a larger set (Lesson 30)

tangent (tan) the function that, for a given acute angle in a right triangle, yields the ratio of the opposite leg to the adjacent leg (Lesson 12)

tangent line a line in the plane of a circle that intersects the circle at exactly one point (Lesson 24)

theoretical probability the likeliness of an event happening based on all possible outcomes (Lesson 35)

transformation an operation that changes a figure or graph according to a rule (Lesson 1)

translation a transformation that moves all of the points on a graph or figure the same distance in the same direction (Lesson 2)

tree diagram a representation in which lines branch out from a single stem or root, showing all the possible outcomes of an event (Lesson 31)

trial each unique time an experiment or simulation is performed (Lesson 35)

trigonometric ratio a constant ratio comparing two sides of a right triangle based on an acute angle of that triangle (Lesson 12)

two-way frequency table a table that displays frequencies in two different categories (Lesson 31)

union the set of all elements that are contained in two or more of the given sets; denoted as ∪ (Lesson 30)

universal set the set containing all possible elements (Lesson 30)

vertex (of a parabola) the turning point (maximum or minimum point) of a parabola (Lesson 22)

vertical translation a slide of a graph or figure up or down (Lesson 2)

volume the amount of space occupied by a three-dimensional figure (Lesson 18)

Formula Sheet

Circumference
$C = \pi d = 2\pi r \qquad \pi \approx 3.14$

Arc Length
$s = \theta r \qquad 360° = 2\pi \text{ rad}$

Volume
Rectangular Prism/Cylinder: $\quad V = Bh$
Pyramid/Cone: $\qquad\qquad V = \frac{1}{3}Bh$
Sphere: $\qquad\qquad\quad V = \frac{4}{3}\pi r^3$

Area
Rectangle/Parallelogram: $\quad A = bh$
Triangle: $\qquad\qquad\quad A = \frac{1}{2}bh$
Circle: $\qquad\qquad\qquad A = \pi r^2$
Sector: $\qquad\qquad\quad A = \frac{1}{2}\theta r^2 = \frac{1}{2}sr$

Trigonometric Relationships
$\sin \theta = \dfrac{\text{opp}}{\text{hyp}} \qquad \cos \theta = \dfrac{\text{adj}}{\text{hyp}} \qquad \tan \theta = \dfrac{\text{opp}}{\text{adj}}$
$\sin \theta = \cos(90° - \theta)$
$\cos \theta = \sin(90° - \theta)$
$\tan \theta = \dfrac{\sin \theta}{\cos \theta}$
Law of Sines: $\quad \dfrac{a}{\sin A} = \dfrac{b}{\sin B} = \dfrac{c}{\sin C}$
Law of Cosines: $\quad c^2 = a^2 + b^2 - 2ab\cos C$

Probability
$P(A\|B) = \dfrac{P(A \cap B)}{P(B)}$
$P(A \cup B) = P(A) + P(B) - P(A \cap B)$
$P(A \cap B) = P(A)P(B\|A)$

Combinations and Permutations
Combination: $\quad {}_nC_r = \dfrac{n!}{r!\,(n-r)!}$
Permutation: $\quad {}_nP_r = \dfrac{n!}{(n-r)!}$

Distance Formula

$$d = \sqrt{(x_2 - x_1)^2 + (y_2 - y_1)^2}$$

Midpoint Formula

$$\left(\frac{x_1 + x_2}{2}, \frac{y_1 + y_2}{2}\right)$$

Partition Formula

$$(x_1 + k(x_2 - x_1), y + k(y_2 - y_1))$$

Transformations

Line Reflections: $r_{x\text{-}axis}(x, y) = (x, -y)$

$\qquad\qquad\qquad r_{y\text{-}axis}(x, y) = (-x, y)$

$\qquad\qquad\qquad r_{y = x}(x, y) = (y, x)$

Rotations: $\qquad R_{90°}(x, y) = (-y, x)$

$\qquad\qquad\qquad R_{180°}(x, y) = (-x, -y)$

$\qquad\qquad\qquad R_{270°}(x, y) = (y, -x)$

Translations: $\quad T(x, y) = (x + a, y + b)$

Dilations: $\qquad D_k(x, y) = (kx, ky)$

Conic Sections

Parabola: $\quad y - k = \dfrac{1}{4p}(x - h)^2$

$\qquad\qquad\quad x - h = \dfrac{1}{4p}(y - k)^2$

Circle: $\qquad (x - h)^2 + (y - k)^2 = r^2$

Common Conversions

12 inches = 1 foot	100 centimeters = 1 meter
3 feet = 1 yard	1,000 meters = 1 kilometer
5,280 feet = 1 mile	2.54 centimeters = 1 inch
8 ounces = 1 cup	2 pints = 1 quart
2 cups = 1 pint	4 quarts = 1 gallon
60 seconds = 1 minute	7 days = 1 week
60 minutes = 1 hour	52 weeks ≈ 1 year
24 hours = 1 day	365 days ≈ 1 year

Math Tool: Coordinate Planes

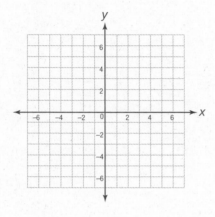

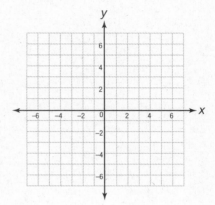

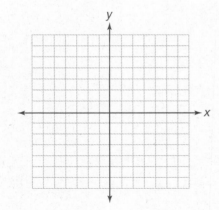

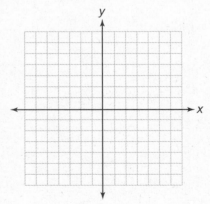

Math Tool: Coordinate Planes

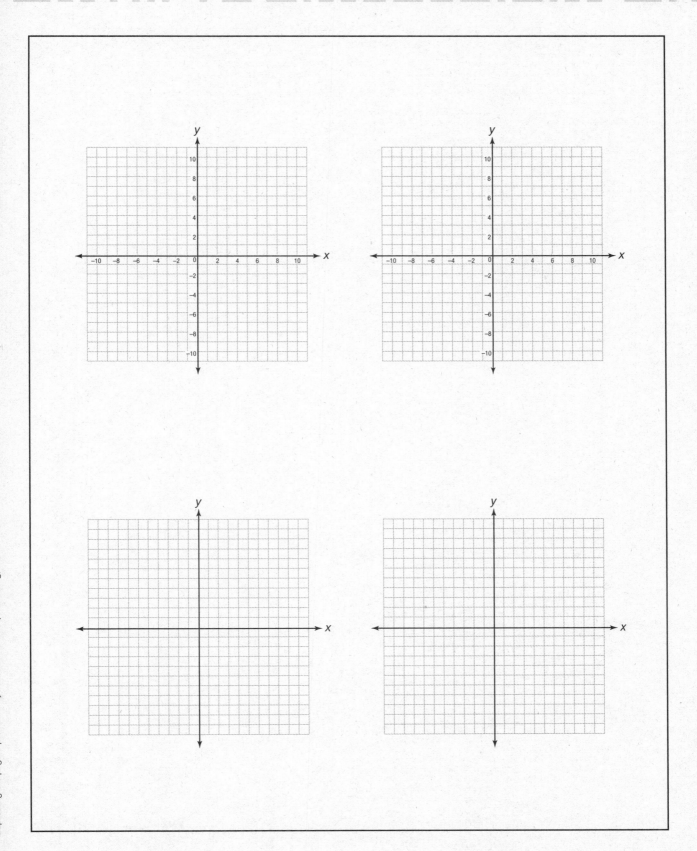

Math Tool: Coordinate Plane

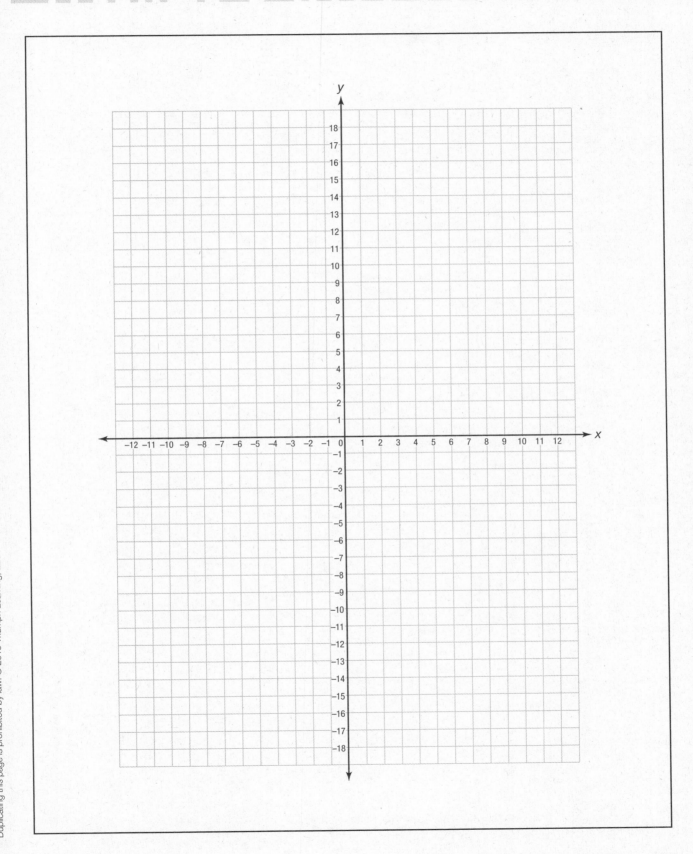

Math Tool: Coordinate Plane

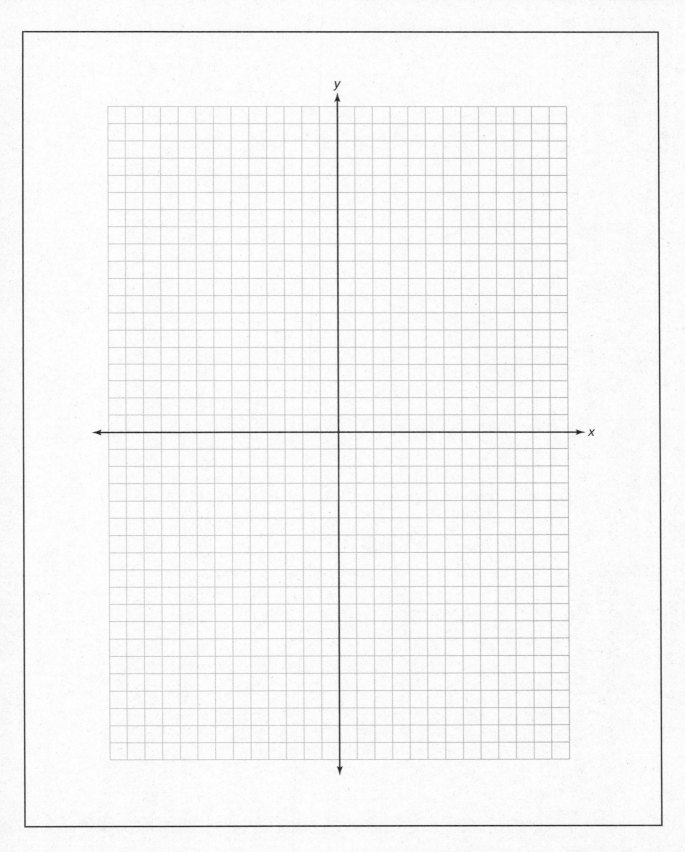

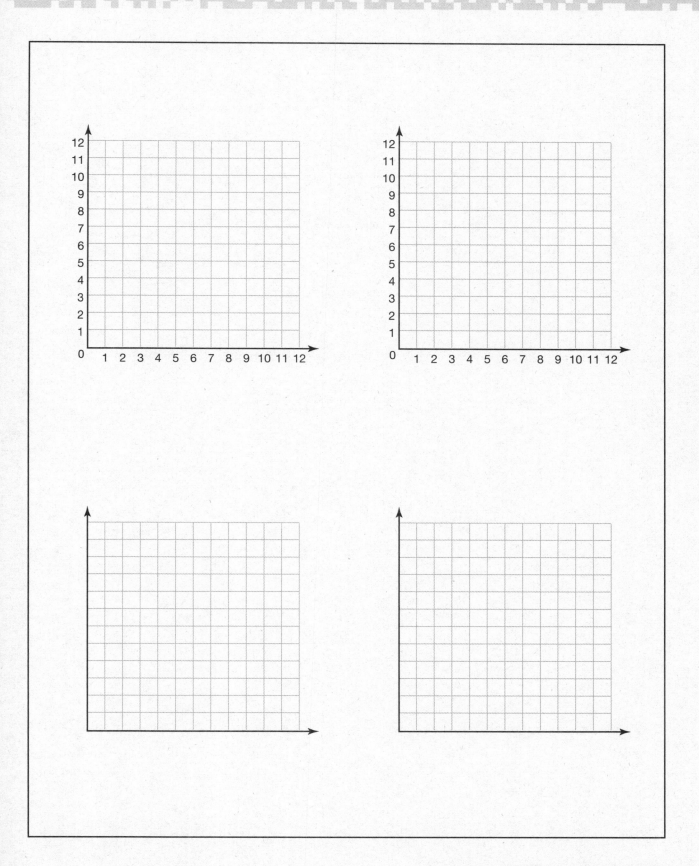

Math Tool: Grid Paper

Math Tool: Circular Thinking

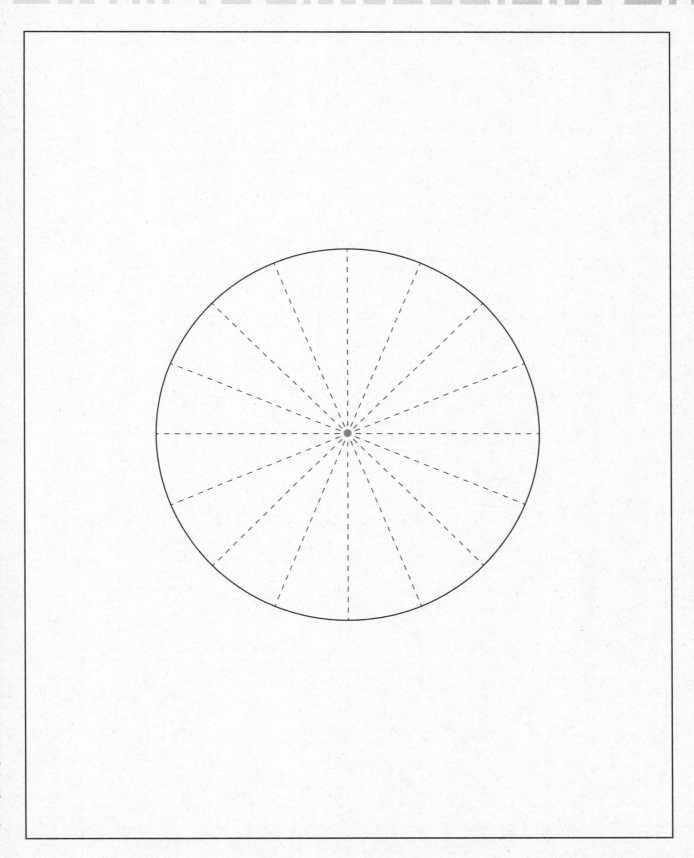

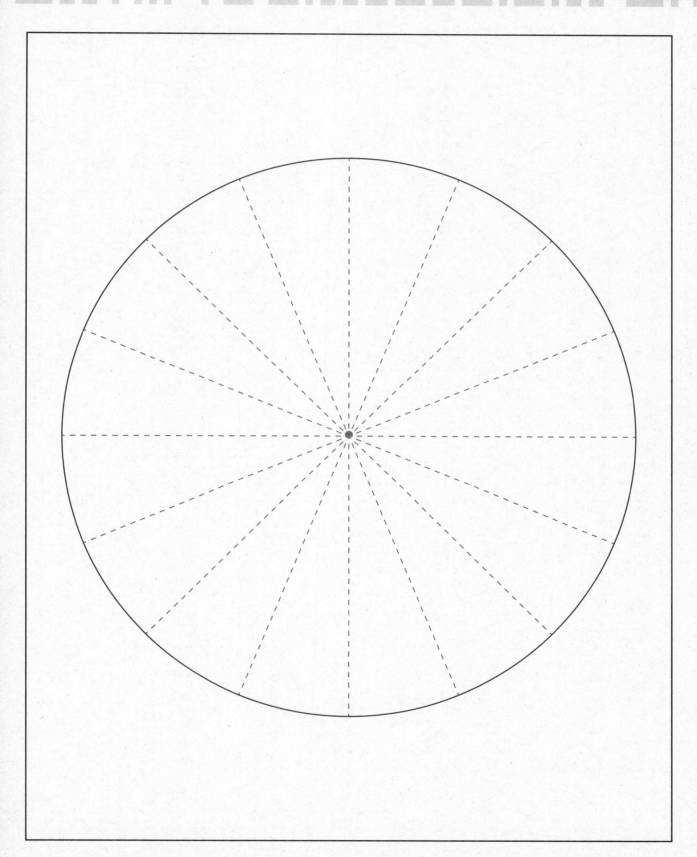

Math Tool: Random Digits

	1	2	3	4	5	6	7	8	9	10
1	6	4	8	5	4	7	2	3	5	7
2	0	9	7	3	1	3	5	7	2	8
3	2	1	9	7	6	3	9	8	2	7
4	9	4	5	9	5	7	2	8	5	3
5	3	7	2	4	8	0	5	9	5	8
6	1	2	2	2	7	1	0	7	0	1
7	6	3	1	1	9	1	7	8	7	9
8	5	8	6	8	3	3	9	0	6	5
9	8	5	0	0	0	5	9	8	0	8
10	2	8	4	6	5	1	2	9	7	3
11	3	0	8	8	0	4	1	7	7	5
12	7	4	3	9	2	1	2	8	7	9
13	0	6	6	7	6	6	6	1	5	3
14	1	2	7	2	4	3	4	0	4	5
15	4	7	9	3	7	9	1	2	9	6
16	3	7	1	5	9	4	0	7	4	4
17	6	2	0	4	2	7	9	2	5	4
18	7	1	5	0	6	0	6	4	2	8
19	9	4	0	1	3	3	6	4	7	2
20	2	8	6	5	5	6	9	1	9	8
21	5	7	5	7	4	6	1	8	6	0
22	7	5	7	9	1	2	4	9	2	4
23	3	3	9	3	2	1	0	8	6	7
24	3	8	3	6	0	3	5	9	0	1
25	1	9	2	3	8	7	2	1	8	3
26	8	3	4	5	9	0	7	9	9	4
27	5	7	1	0	5	0	3	2	7	9
28	9	9	0	2	4	3	2	7	2	2
29	0	2	8	1	3	3	9	0	1	1
30	5	0	5	2	6	8	8	9	0	1
31	7	5	3	1	6	9	1	6	8	2
32	4	0	1	8	0	4	0	8	4	5
33	8	1	1	3	5	7	5	4	6	6
34	9	6	5	6	8	5	3	8	3	0
35	6	4	6	7	1	8	0	7	2	1
36	5	5	7	4	6	1	7	2	8	2
37	4	7	9	4	4	6	7	2	7	7
38	3	9	8	6	9	3	3	5	1	6
39	2	3	1	9	9	4	6	9	9	3
40	9	2	2	1	0	7	0	4	3	9

Math Tool: Venn Diagrams

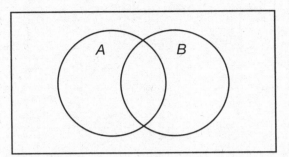

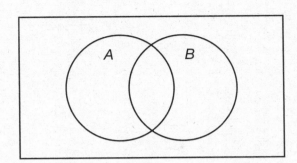

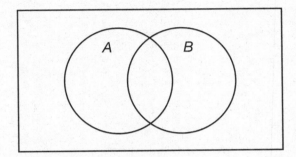

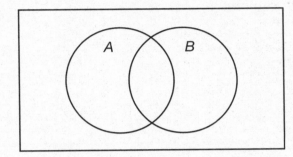

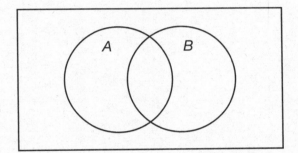

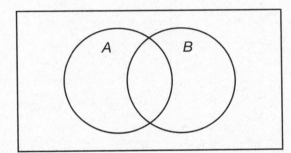

Notes

Notes

Notes

Notes